Science and
Human Destiny

Science and Human Destiny

Norman F. Dessel
San Diego State University

Richard B. Nehrich, Jr.
Naval Electronics Laboratory Center
San Diego

Glenn I. Voran
Naval Ordinance Test Station
China Lake

McGRAW-HILL BOOK COMPANY

New York / St. Louis / San Francisco
Düsseldorf / Johannesburg / Kuala Lumpur
London / Mexico / Montreal
New Delhi / Panama / Rio de Janeiro
Singapore / Sydney / Toronto

Science and Human Destiny

Copyright © 1973 by McGraw-Hill, Inc.
All rights reserved.
Printed in the United States of America.
No part of this publication may be reproduced,
stored in a retrieval system,
or transmitted, in any form or by any means, electronic,
mechanical, photocopying, recording, or otherwise,
without the prior written permission of the publisher.

1234567890KPKP79876543

This book was set in Optima by Progressive Typographers.
The editors were Jack L. Farnsworth and J. W. Maisel;
the designer was J. Paul Kirouac;
and the production supervisor was John A. Sabella.
The drawings were done by Textart Service, Inc.
The printer and binder was Kingsport Press, Inc.

Library of Congress Cataloging in Publication Data

Dessel, Norman F
  Science and human destiny.

   Includes bibliographies.
   1. Science—History.   2. Science—Social aspects.
3. Technology—Social aspects. I. Nehrich, Richard B.,
joint author. II. Voran, Glenn I., 1909–   joint
author. III. Title.
Q125.D36   500   72-7400
ISBN 0-07-016580-7

Contents

Preface

In recent years science has become so much a part of the daily lives of people that none can afford to ignore its ideas and methods. Science texts for non-science college students have recently shown increasing concern for the portrayal of science as a human activity set in a cultural-historical framework. Older, more traditional texts in the physical sciences have been heavily committed to communicating the discipline of science to the non-science student. Often this approach has placed little emphasis on the relationship of science to other human activities and the flow of history.

This text presents science as a human activity. It consists essentially of two parts, the first of which deals with the historical development of models and paradigms of science. In this first part a good deal of traditional material is included. The authors have organized this material in a logical pattern of development to help the reader along to an understanding of the few major concepts that underlie all science.

The purpose of the first part is to prepare the student to understand and appreciate more fully the second part. The latter chapters of the text assume some grasp of the great principles of science. Their purpose is to examine in depth the recent and current place of man in the universe. The authors believe that at least a nodding acquaintance with the principles of life science is required in this examination, since nature makes no distinction between life and physical sciences. Mention of these life principles is not, however, a main thrust of the text.

The text applies the principles of science to current problems of the ecosystem and their ramifications in human affairs. The authors' intent is to establish the relevance of science to human culture and the potential use of science as a tool for the solution of human problems.

The teacher may use the text as a core of readings, perhaps in conjunction with laboratory work, for an intensive academic-year study, or he may wish to develop rather closely the theme of the text, with its associated laboratory perhaps, as a one-semester course. Optional scheduling for either of these approaches has been included in the teachers manual. The teacher need not be overly concerned if students have some difficulty with the mathematical developments of Chaps. 4 through 8. These chapters have been written to provide the basis for a rather challenging development. Their main ideas, however, are all that is necessary for subsequent work, and these can be developed with considerably less rigor. In any case, the ideas developed in the first part are essential for real understanding of the second part.

Technology is discussed as a highly relevant subject, both historically and functionally. The authors have chosen not to refer to technology as applied science, preferring rather to show the clear distinction between science and technology while at the same time illuminating their dependence upon one another.

This course has been taught in experimental classes in physical science at San Diego State College with encouraging results. It was taught to sections with and without laboratory. In both cases the students were non-science majors completing pattern requirements in general education.

The authors are indebted to Bradford Bayne and his staff at McGraw-Hill Book Company and to their review staff for their many valuable assists in the writing and publication of the text. In addition they wish to thank all who contributed to this book for their generous services and authorizations.

Norman F. Dessel
Richard B. Nehrich, Jr.
Glenn I. Voran

Science and Human Destiny

Temple of Nefertiti, Luxor, Egypt. Note the incredible detail of the pictograms (hieroglyphics) and the difference in their individual sizes. Obviously these characters were suitable for short inscriptions of the type seen here but would have been extremely cumbersome for any voluminous text. Through the centuries, the glyphs were modified to simpler forms that could be drawn rapidly on papyrus. (Courtesy of the Egyptian State Tourist Administration.)

Chapter 1
The Dawn of Reason

It might at first seem that society down through the ages has been shaped largely by chance. It is our purpose in this chapter to show that this is not true. The society of man has been shaped according to definite forces within his environment. We call the study of these complex forces *human ecology*.

We shall see how his needs drove man to refine his relationships with his surroundings, and how his curiosities brought richness and further curiosity to his tradition. The entire stream of early human consciousness is related to the whole of human experience.

This chapter may seem at first to be merely a recounting of some phases of human history, but far more than this is intended. It should serve to establish a foundation upon which the whole of human tradition can be understood, leading to a more perfect understanding of human ecology in the twentieth century.

Nobody knows how far back man really goes. This question has long been the subject of study and research. During prehistory man was organized into small tribes. These small groups, much like present-day troops of baboons, must have wandered about through the land tearing a living from a balance of available food, water, and shelter. From this picture alone we can go far toward guessing where early man probably lived.

Other tribes undoubtedly represented competition for early man, so that confrontation between tribes must have led to struggles for survival and continued dispersion of the species. Once a region was stripped of food, the tribe would have to move on. Some of the more primitive tribes of American Indians, moving along with herds of bison or antelope, are examples of this kind of society. These people probably had little understanding of their surroundings and the natural events that overtook them.

In the early tribes the leaders no doubt were the individuals best able to cope with the problems of the day. In the primitive tribe this leader would have been the strongest physically even if he had not much intellectual power. We can see this principle in operation today in tribes of lowland gorillas where one powerful male leads the band.

Man's cultural progress is marked by an evolution away from the leadership of the physically strong toward leadership by the intellectually strong. Even today, however, we find nations and states ruled by physical bullies, thus falling into a more or less primitive class. Brute physical strength has now been replaced by military power or by great economic power, but the same principle is involved. In any case, the highest culture of man is to be found, without exception, in those states led by rational intellectuals—men with a knowledge of their cultural traditions and with the ability to think rationally and with discipline.

Probably the beginning of reason in the modern sense came to men about 10,000 years ago. We shall understand by the *dawn of reason* that point in time when men ceased simply to react to their environment and began to use their wits to produce modifications of their environment. This happened not all at once, but gradually, in many isolated places, over a considerable period of time.

1.1
The Beginnings
of Social Man

It is not clear how men came to realize that they could plant crops of food and harvest them. Early tribes probably lived among herds of bovine animals in a symbiotic relationship, protecting the animals from their enemies in exchange for a few of their number for food and hides, for a long time before the animals became truly domesticated. It must have taken countless generations before some primitive hit upon the idea of constraining the animals' movements. Evidence seems to indicate that the goat was the first to be domesticated by man. Dogs must have been used in the hunt and for protection of the group, but they were probably not domesticated in the same sense as goats. The next step in the man-animal relationship was the practice of husbandry, the selective breeding of their domesticated stock.

Tribes of village dwellers lived in the plains regions of Europe after the last Ice Age, 8000 to 7000 B.C. These villagers lived along rivers and lakes and built lodges of heavy timbers. Analysis of the substrate at these sites indicates that hunting and foraging accounted for only about 20 percent of their livelihood. There is considerable evidence of domesticated animals and plants. This remarkable assembly of facts indicates that these first village dwellers had taken the key step toward the development of a tradition and culture.

Sometime between 7000 and 3000 B.C. large sites such as the Hungarian Plain and Mesopotamia became the cradles of the first truly urban-centered societies. The technology of these people was fairly typical Neolithic (*new stone*), with pottery forms and stone tools comprised in the bulk of it.

The planting and harvesting of crops was the single development that led men inevitably to the establishment of semipermanent homes and the beginnings of society. As tribes turned to agriculture, human population began for the first time to increase significantly. At this point in time, the human population probably was not more than a few million individuals. Agriculture brought a need to know when to plant and when to reap—that is, a need for a calendar. With agriculture came a more acute awareness of property rights and the concept of ownership of objects that one could not carry with him and that had to be accounted for. Within each social group there was born, sooner or later, the need to specialize duties within the group. At first the specialties could be accomplished by individuals who excelled in some skill or other. Later there was a need to think abstractly and to record data in some form more efficient than making marks upon the bark of a tree. Archaeological finds have turned up small pieces of flint with tally marks around the edge that were probably used at this time as small computers to keep track of the days of the month. The commerce master, or priest, who could do abstract reasoning must have had the power of a god among his people. He passed his learning on by patient teaching of the select few who were to inherit the priesthood. The term *priest* is used here in its most general sense.

Thus agriculture was the anchor that brought a drifting humanity to permanent rest at various sites on the planet. This coming to rest was at once a spur to civilization and the beginning of serious problems, as we shall see.

1.2
Reckoning
Time
Time is one of those peculiar concepts that is with us from our earliest awareness of things outside ourselves. Time is a primitive concept, and one that is extremely difficult to define. For this reason, it is taken for granted by each of us until we are led by our study to a more critical examination of it.

Temple of Amen-Ra at Karnak, Luxor, Egypt. The picture helps one visualize the enormous massiveness of temples constructed by the ancient Egyptians. The temple was constructed with its long axis pointing to the setting on the summer solstice sun, in about 3000 B.C. St. Peters Church in Rome would fit nicely into one end of the temple. **(Courtesy of the Egyptian State Tourist Administration.)**

A useful base for the ordering of events, and explanations of immediate phenomena around them, had to be found by the earliest men. The most obvious cyclic event was the day, with its sun-up and sun-down routine. Without questioning why it was so, the cavemen must have watched the slow progress of the sun and moon and must have learned to order their routine actions without conscious thought. To be caught too far from the protection of the tribe and shelter with the sun low in the western sky was tantamount to a death warrant. The cyclic functions of their bodies would have also been taken for granted without thought at first. Seasonal changes meant moving the tribe to more hospitable localities. These events may have been simply accepted without thought for untold millennia.

Imagine the triumph of the first human who watched with reason the changing of a stick's shadow upon the ground, to be led in thought to the concept of using such a shadow as a kind of clock by which appointments could be made and kept between members of the tribe. What a magnificent revelation must have been the design of the first standard clock-stick. Can anyone now appreciate the wonder of the first human who discovered and pondered his own pulsing heartbeat?

Cyclic events no doubt occupied the thoughts of many early men. Indeed, some of the objects involved in such events were worshipped universally by men as gods.

In order to establish a unit of time, in short to think of time in a useful way, we quickly realize that all units of time depend upon some cyclic motion of bodies in space. A few examples of motions used as a basis of time are the repeated orbits of the earth about the sun, the spinning of the earth on its axis, the swinging of a pendulum of a certain length, and the vibrations of a tuning fork at a certain precise frequency. No matter how we try to think of time, we always come back to some physical motion that we can observe and make use of as a standard.

Time has been taken as an absolute property of nature by men for so long that it has been only since Newton, and more specifically within the last two centuries, that we have come to regard time as relative to events and motions that occur around us. The relative nature of time can be illustrated by answering the following question: Would time have any meaning at all if there were no motion in the universe? The very idea of motion, or no motion, involves the concept of time.

A child in today's society learns, sometime between the ages of two and five, to count objects by matching each object to be counted with a finger or toe. It is common knowledge that those who are poorly educated can

**1.3
Reckoning
Objects—Numbers**

easily be cheated in any transaction involving more property objects than they have fingers and toes—whether the property objects are coins or pigs. Without some knowledge of numbers and the ability to write them down and manipulate them in abstract fashion, no commerce between men could exist.

For just this reason the ancients must have developed abstract numbers almost concurrently with the development of stable communities. Tally marks on bits of stone from prehistory lend weight to this assumption. With the coming of the concept of personal property, a way of keeping track of it had to come also. Our earliest writings—Indian Sanscrit, Babylonian and Assyrian cuneiform—make repeated reference to laws governing measures of grain and other commercial commodities. It seems quite likely, in view of the nature of the need for numbers, that men had numbers of some sort long before they had a written language. The Incas used knotted strings for recording quantities before they had any written language. There is fairly general agreement today among scholars that this was indeed the case.

In even the smallest communities, there would have been leadership that sooner or later would exact a tribute or tax from the membership. This would have been in the form of a certain portion of the goods or produce of the individual, and hence the need again for abstract numbers. The emergence of money as a substitute for objects in commerce would only have further intensified the study of numbers and abstraction.

The Indians were responsible for what we now call arabic numerals. These numerals have stood the test of need and facility in Western culture better than the many more cumbersome numerals devised along the way. The Roman system of numerals does not, for example, lend itself well to abstract manipulation. (Write your zip code in Roman numerals.) Several schools of Greek philosophers contributed the first important work in the discipline of mathematics. Their geometry dominated human culture even to the days of Galileo.

The period beginning with the Renaissance brought the development of algebra that has been refined to a beautiful abstract discipline by such giants as Newton, Fourier, and Gauss.

**1.4
Ancient
Technology**

Most often technology is regarded strictly as something resulting from the work of scientists. If this were true, there would have been no technology in the world until men like Galileo got around to using the scientific method of investigation. Obviously this was not the case.

Perhaps the first technology came into existence when the first primitive men learned to use clubs and sticks as weapons. In this case, any sort of tool or technique employed consciously by men, and not by animals, to some useful end can be called technology.

Agriculture brought with it a host of technological advancements. These were implements and techniques that were constantly improved in both material and form. The working of hides, and later the weaving of cloth, might be thought of today as insignificant technological advancements, but for the ancients these advances constituted the difference between survival and extinction in hostile climates. One might well imagine that *Homo neandertalensis*, a now extinct subhuman, failed to survive because of failures to develop just such primitive technology. Of course, other factors were probably involved as well.

It is a curiosity of the nature of technology that it must constantly be guarded and nourished by a culture if it is to survive and grow. In this way, technology has had to depend upon traditional education of the young in each culture. The ability to communicate tradition, in whatever form the communication takes place, is one of the unique human properties. Without such education each generation would have had to learn again and invent again the whole of technology. If education were to cease for even a short period, man would be plunged back countless thousands of years, with technology soon crumbling to dust. Thus each new generation of men may be regarded as at one time both the leaders of tomorrow and the howling barbarians who, without education, would tear down the culture.

Metals must have occurred naturally in only very small quantities. Smelting probably got its start from accidental collection of bits of molten metal in fires. Once men began to work metals, the way was open for technological development of coins and jewelry, plows and implements of war. Superior knowledge in metalworking of some tribes and early nations gave them military superiority over their neighbors. Thus did Alexander the Great conquer much of Asia Minor and North Africa—an incredibly huge empire for that stage of human development. Alexander was a fourth century B.C. student of Aristotle. Superior technology, of course, was not the only reason for military supremacy in cases such as this, but technology was certainly an important ingredient in the success formula. In Alexander's case one might well argue that superior military technique and the main force of character of the man himself were the important factors in his victories, and that he might well have succeeded with stone weapons. These facts notwithstanding, it is clear that the side with the technological superiority has a considerable advantage.

An army on the move, even today, is very similar to a primitive tribe of man. The army, like the primitive tribe, moves on, challenging and killing all who stand before it, stripping a living from the lands in its path in the most destructive way. Man's willingness to turn technological advances into military advantage has, unfortunately, persisted to the present day. Modern butchery is less personal than the sword and spear of the ancients, but just as fatal and far more efficient.

1.5
Nature and
Superstition

Another unique property of man is his great and persistent curiosity. From earliest leisure he has observed events and surroundings with keenness and surprising depth of perception. The heavens were a never-ending source of amazement to him. Facing a hierarchy of phenomena upon which he had no direct influence, his reason led him to invent explanations.

Science as we understand it today did not exist in early times except in very rare cases that certainly did not dominate human intellectual activity. Instead, men developed elaborate superstitions to explain that which was beyond their influence. As might be expected, for a variety of reasons many of these superstitions were canonized and elevated to the status of religious dogma. It was inevitable that superstitions, along with rules of moral conduct, would be woven into the fabric of early religions. Temporal leaders of early tribes and states no doubt found it very convenient to be able to appeal to the higher authority of the deities. Many objects and processes qualified as the seat of the deities, e.g., the sun and moon and natural forces such as wind and rain. These objects were all a necessary part of early man's mode of life, and so it was natural to think of them as capricious deities capable of granting favors to their dependents or of making things miserable for them by withholding their favors or stirring up trouble.

The point here is that the scientific method of logical inquiry was not the normal mode of intellectual thought for man. Superstition, as manifested by religion in many varied forms, was the normal mode. Early men no doubt did not make a distinction between their religion and the balance of their relationships with other men. There must have existed a totality of order in which all aspects of life were controlled intimately by religious belief. The religious leader of any group would naturally be a man educated in the traditions and abstractions of the society, call him priest, commerce master, teacher, or whatever. He must have been all these things. Such traditions of leadership still exist today in some of the more ancient religions.

For whatever reasons, however, men did observe and learn eventually to record their observations. Warring states and religious zealots have had, down through the ages, a most distressing habit of destroying one another's written records. Undoubtedly a great deal of what men have recorded of their thoughts, observations, and dreams has been thus lost to us. We have little written record of what might have been highly intellectual cultures before 3000 B.C. The Assyrians in particular we know to have been vicious and unrelenting, having destroyed entire populations to the last individual along with all their cultural works, even to the point of diverting rivers to submerge the ruins of their cities. Other such disasters destroyed cultures in turn down through man's Neolithic and Bronze Ages. Examples from recorded history are the annihilation of the Jewish people in the great uprising against Rome about A.D. 70, the annihilation of many of the Mayas and Aztecs by the Spanish conquistadors in America, and the destruction of the American Indian culture within the United States. Only a few remnants of these peoples can be found today. Several pages could be devoted here to similar atrocities.

Owing to the work of a Christian fanatic in Yucatán, much (in fact, almost all) of the written records of the Mayan culture in Mexico has been lost to us through outright destruction. The Mayas seem to have been good astronomers. They had an accurate calendar, and excellent mathematics, nearly all of which is irretrievably lost to the tradition of man. The Mayas or neighboring people seem to have made and used floating compasses.

1.6 Written Language

The need to carry on commerce no doubt accounts for the evolution of written records and language. Many of the early writings were of picture form with the characters themselves becoming, in time, more and more abstract. We do not really know who first conceived of an alphabet of abstract symbols, but once it was conceived, the custodians of the language achieved a new freedom of thought and expression previously undreamed of. It is a peculiarity of abstract language that in its use, the user refines his mental processes and builds creatively upon the traditional culture. Much of our thinking is done in terms of words that are themselves abstract ideas. This is perhaps a subtle point, but an extremely important one nonetheless.

The man who first recorded an idea in abstract form to have other men read and understand it must have experienced a revelation beyond our powers to appreciate today. Reflect for a moment on the immensity of his realizations that such communication could be generally available and limited only by the effort of those individuals involved in it.

Because of the importance of counting and recording and maintaining the written record of the community, the priest, occupying a prominent building within the community, must have been the living seat of culture for untold generations. Records show that even as late as 500 B.C. much of the tradition of cultures was memorized by members of chosen sects and handed down by education in verbal form.

The Egyptian Book of the Dead is a remarkable example, as is the Hebrew Bible, of a combined recorded teaching of a culture. Both books set down a moral code of conduct couched in religious terms, and both give a great deal of insight into the daily routine and commerce of the people who created them. There are striking similarities between these books and other writings that came out of Mesopotamia. These books all speak of "measures of grain" and standards of both weight and measure indicating an advanced commerce perhaps as early as 3000 B.C. in their respective source regions.

**1.7
Calendars**

Certain numbers, such as 6, 7, and 60 with their multiples, are found throughout antiquity. Some systems using them persist even today. Have you ever wondered why the week has 7 days or why the circle is divided into 360 equal angular parts?

The Babylonian calendar had 360 days in the yearly cycle. It is not possible to date its origin with any accuracy, but the exact date is of little importance, since it no doubt was a continuation of some earlier tradition. The Babylonians were apparently aware that the 360-day calendar did not stretch far enough to cover the yearly cycle, and so Babylonian rulers and religious leaders declared feast days to take up the slack.

Feast days are fairly common in almost all early cultural traditions, depending for their proper celebration upon some sort of calendar. It is not very surprising to note that these feasts were always associated with some seasonal event that could be relied upon to repeat itself year after year. Many cultures celebrated the coming of spring with feasts such as Easter (the goddess of fertility by that name). In like fashion a common feast day was held on the winter solstice when the days cease to shorten and begin again to lengthen. This feast is very close to the Christian feast of Christmas, as well as a number of other religious feasts. It should not be at all surprising that various religions have taken advantage of well-established traditional feasts in order to celebrate some religious observance of special significance.

The earth year, the time for one complete revolution around the sun (sidereal year), takes 365.2563 rotations of the earth upon its own axis. The Julian calendar of Rome, still B.C., included 365 days in the year with every fourth year, or leap year, having 366 days. The $365\frac{1}{4}$-day year of the Julian calendar was slightly more than 11 minutes too long, amounting to the loss of about ¾ day in each century.

The Mayas had a surprisingly good calendar that seems to have been based upon careful astronomical observations. They were an agricultural people with such technological developments as irrigation included in their tradition. Their calendars were so important to them that the object itself was worshipped as a part of a religious hierarchy of objects and symbols. This was, of course, also true in numerous other cultures.

The calendar used in most parts of the world today is the Gregorian calendar, adopted in 1582 A.D. It compensates for the error of the Julian calendar by providing that the last year in each century be a leap year only if that century can be divided by 400. This calendar is still in error, obviously, by that tiny fraction of a day.

In Chap. 2 we shall investigate further the progression of thought concerning time and motions, and the disciplines that grew out of the first questions—those posed by early men—about the nature of things.

We shall examine in the next chapter some engineering feats of the ancients that still puzzle us today. Men of the Neolithic era apparently had a facility with massive stone that we are hard pressed to duplicate today with all our machinery. There are on Easter Island in the Pacific Ocean magnificent monoliths that were possibly brought hundreds of miles across the open sea and somehow set upright on the island. The problem of loading these stones, transporting them, unloading them, taking them through the surf, and then erecting them baffles us today.

1.8
Barbarians or
Craftsmen

In the Andes Mountains there are monoliths of tremendous mass apparently dragged up to the 18,000-ft level and erected there. The source sites of these stones make the engineering feat seem almost incredible. We would have great difficulty reproducing the effort today.

The pyramids of Egypt, Mexico, and South America attest the wonderful skill of their designers. There are measurements involved in the closing mechanisms, and tolerances in the construction, that command our purest admiration for the builders' skill.

We are only now discovering that many of the remaining buildings of this era (massive stone structures for the most part, now in ruin) were apparently used as fixed astronomical observatories. The astrology and numerology that persist today in our society probably had their true origin in the tradition based upon early observations made from these observatories. It is now apparent that these early astronomers had the ability to

Fig. 1.1 Aztec calendar, carved upon a 25-ton monolith, unearthed in Mexico City in 1790. It was curved and dedicated to the sun during the reign of Axayacatl, the sixth Aztec emperor. This is eloquent evidence of the antiquity of calendar development by the many different peoples on earth, sometimes at widely different times and places. **(Courtesy of the Mexican National Tourist Council.)**

predict eclipses of the moon and to fix precisely the rising and setting points of the sun, the equinoxes, and the summer and winter solstices. The equinoxes are those points in the spring and fall when the sun stands exactly over the equator at noon. The summer and winter solstices are those points at which the days begin to get shorter and longer respectively.

Problems 1   What do you think some of the earliest tools might have been? The earliest weapons? Which probably came first?

2   Debate the idea that numbers preceded written language.

3   Contrast the function and scope of early religion with religions existing today.

4   Mesopotamia was once famous as the verdant grainery of the civilized world.   Can you guess why it is so desolate today?

5   What function does written language have in culture?   If we still had no written languages, how would our culture be different from what we know?

6   How would a sightless society keep time?

7   Where do you think the numbers 6, 7, 12, 60, and 360, often used by the ancients, came from?

8   With only the tools of the ancients, how would you go about erecting a 40-ton monolith on an island?

Bresler, Jack B.: "Environments of Man," Addison-Wesley, Reading,   *Bibliography* Mass., 1968.

Butterfield, H.: "The Origins of Modern Science," 2d ed., Macmillan, New York, 1957.

Lockyer, J. Norman: "The Dawn of Astronomy," M.I.T. Paperback Series, M.I.T., Cambridge, Mass., 1964.

Chapter 2
Star Watchers

Warriors' temple and
El Castillo.
(Courtesy of the
Mexican National
Tourist Council.)

2.1
Stonehenge
As we look back through the gray mists of time, back to perhaps 3000 B.C., it is hard to visualize the kind of people who must have lived then. All that we know now we must glean from the few relics they have left. We do know that these people liked to work with large boulders. They apparently were preoccupied with the idea of creating structures that would stand the test of time. The pyramids, for example, are still with us after many thousands of years, and no doubt countless generations in the future will be able to observe these same pyramids.

One of the great relics left behind for us is found in England. Stonehenge was built probably around 2000 B.C. Let us pause for a moment and speculate on the kind of people who must have been involved in the building of Stonehenge.

We know that agriculture must have been of tremendous importance to them. And because of their preoccupation with agriculture, they would have had to devise a system of keeping track of time. From childhood these people learned to tell time, probably to rather good accuracy, by observation of heavenly bodies.

It is true that they left no record in the form of a written language involving abstract characters so that we could understand the intricate details of their daily lives and their motivations, but it is certainly open to question whether these people were the howling barbarians that we often visualize them as being. Probably their lives were well ordered around an agricultural base.

The monument they have left behind at Stonehenge is a denial of the howling-barbarian idea. The planning of Stonehenge and development of its various phases probably required the collective lifetimes of a number of people and relied upon a rational communication among those people with some learning and obviously some engineering skill.

The craggy blue stones forming the outer circle of Stonehenge, each weighing thousands of pounds, had to be brought many hundreds of miles from a mountaintop in an entirely different part of the British Isles. The massive monoliths and lintels that form the inner circle of Stonehenge, stones weighing many, many tons, had to be dragged into position and erected on their sites with marvelous engineering skill. They were aligned with remarkable precision. This fact alone cries out that these people, far from being barbarians, were a highly skilled and technically oriented society, even though the materials with which they worked happened to be stone. There is some small evidence in the stone itself that the people might have been of Mycenaean origin, i.e., coming from a particular region of the Mediterranean.

At the time that Stonehenge was erected, the British Isles might very well have had a balmy climate, with weather approximating that of some of the Mediterranean areas we know today. There have been times when lands lying in the far northern latitudes have been green, free from snow and ice, and fairly balmy in climate.

A young American professor of astronomy, Gerald S. Hawkins, has recently hypothesized that Stonehenge, built about 3000 to 2000 B.C., is a very accurate computer for predicting the position of the sun and the moon and various eclipses. Using a large and accurate diagram (see Fig. 2.1), this young professor laid down a gridwork so that he could record the coordinates of each of the stones on the grid. Putting this coordinate information into his computer, and solving for all possible positions and alignments of stones, he was able to show that Stonehenge is a kind of computer predicting eclipses and correct position of the sun and the moon at midwinter and midsummer. It predicts the solstices and can be used to keep accurate track of the seasons as they progress. Such information on the seasons would have been of vital importance to these people.

The argument has been put forth that the monument Stonehenge was a religious monument and had nothing whatever to do with astronomy, or anything else in a practical sense. It should be pointed out, however, that in dealing with the ancients, religious motivation and economic need cannot be separated. In the early days, the religious needs were synonymous with other needs. Whether or not Stonehenge was a religious

Fig. 2.1
Replica of
Stonehenge showing
major alignments.

monument is really a moot point. Assuming that it was a religious monument, this still would not conflict with the idea of its being used as a very accurate computer, a masterpiece of useful engineering. Perhaps the positions of the sun and the moon were important factors to these people not only for planting their crops, but also as gods in the sky. Indeed, these gods probably were thought to control the seasons, weather, etc.

We shall see that theology and religious activity are very much entwined in the functioning of human intellect, in the development of philosophy, and in the acceptance of certain models as explanations of the physical universe.

**2.2
The Mayas** One of the great tragedies in the known history of the Western world was the deliberate destruction by a bishop of nearly all the written records of the Mayan civilization. These were systematically gathered together over the course of a short span of time and destroyed as works of the devil. Only a few tablets survived this annihilation. A great part of what surely must have been a record of the insights of these very interesting people has been lost to tradition. Only a few of the relics of what we might call the science of this period remain.

From what little we do know of the Mayas, it seems certain that they erected large structures that were used for the purpose of astronomical observation. We might think of these as observatories from which information was gained that was used as a basis for constructing the Mayan calendar.

The Mayan calendar was surprisingly accurate and no doubt was created for agricultural and religious purposes. The Mayas, too, were excellent workers in stone. From the relics of these civilizations, it is obvious to even the casual observer that the sun and the moon were gods to them, subjects of religious worship and reverence. Again we have an example of the duality of religious and practical concern that must have dominated the lives of the ancients.

It has been suggested that civilizations that will exist here on earth thousands of years in the future will dig through the dirt and bring up relics of our civilization that might amount to collections of Coke bottles, aluminum beer cans, and similar "objects of art." Certainly most of our major works will by then have decayed back to the soil. Perhaps these people will conclude that we were howling barbarians on the basis of the same kind of evidence that leads us to judge those who lived around 3000 B.C.

The study of ancient cultures, an enormously important and interesting field of study, must rely on the scientific evidence produced by archaeologists and anthropologists. The tendency has been to accept only what can be objectively demonstrated. We should not lose sight of the fact, however, that much of what occurred during the time of the ancients simply was not recorded or has been lost and remains, therefore, not subject to any attempt on the part of present-day man to reconstruct objectively.

The pyramids of the sun and the moon in Mexico, the great pyramids in Egypt, and all the highly developed works of the Neolithic era are irrefutable evidence that the ancients were highly intelligent, highly articulate, and highly technically developed societies. Agriculture was surely the basis for the existence of all these early societies. As it became possible for the majority of the people to provide for the needs of all, a small minority was able to turn to intellectual activities. Priests, kings, and nobles had leisure to sit down, reflect calmly, and use their intellects for design purposes. This they obviously did. It seems probable that many of these Neolithic intellectuals were of the priest class. These early thinkers contributed to foundations of modern science.

Try to imagine yourself seated at night before the entrance of a hut, thousands of years before Christ (in the age before smog!). The night sky is beautifully lighted by stars that hang there in myriad millions. Watching night after night you have given names to prominent constellations. You also have observed the apparent motion of the entire mass of stars from east to west as the night goes on. You have observed a daily motion of the sun from the eastern horizon to the western horizon.

2.3
Motions in the
Heavens

The ancients were quick to observe that certain bodies in the heavens appeared to move in relation to the star background. They noticed, on a succession of observations night after night, that a few of the bright objects, rather than remaining fixed relative to the other stars in their view, moved through the star background in a general easterly direction.

There is no doubt at all that these "wandering stars" became the subject of mythology. Stories were invented to explain their visits to the various constellations. These wandering stars were, of course, the planets moving in their orbits around the sun.

In making this statement, we have already assumed a particular model; that is, we have assumed that the planets are bodies that move around the sun in some regular fashion. A *model* is a conceptual device that orders events or phenomena. *Facts* are always perceived in a manner that is predetermined by the model. In this case the model calls for planets that orbit the sun. Some of the planets appear to move slowly and others relatively fast. It was observed that even the sun appeared to move eastward against the star background as time passed.

The ancient Greeks observed that the sun moved in a way that always brought it back to the same relative position against the star background in the period of one year. Thus, it was possible for these people to construct a calendar from the observations of the sun's position relative to the star background. Records from this period tell of special events that occurred, such as eclipses and the appearance of strange wandering giants, the comets. These comets must have been dreadful objects. Historians tell us that at the time of these special events in the sky, the people themselves became unsettled. Therefore, such events were inevitably considered signs or predictors of momentous things to come within human society.

It was at such times that great catastrophes befell populations and kings decided to go to war with other nations. The comets and eclipses were often associated with the birth or death of some outstanding individual in the local society. The heavens themselves became the object, and in part, the framework of the religious beliefs.

During this early period, we find the origins of something that was to persist until the time of Copernicus in our own so-called Western civilization. People began the tradition of thinking of those objects and motions that they observed in the heavens as distinct from the events that occurred here on the surface of the earth. The earth appeared to these early people as a tremendously massive body, the extent of which no one had any idea. By comparison, the bodies in the heavens appeared as small points of light. The largest objects were, of course, the sun and the moon, both of which subtend approximately the same angle in the sky, i.e., they appear to be about the same size.

In light of these facts, it is not strange at all that, to the ancients, the objects in the sky seemed to be quite apart and different from objects here on the earth. Certainly it could not have occurred to the earliest men that the earth is related in any way to the heavenly objects. Any irregularity observed in the sky, e.g., comets and eclipses, must have been the cause of great wonder and terror to these people.

2.4
The Greeks Several hundred years before Christ, the Greeks living in Alexandria established an institution that was much like the present institution of technology. It was an institution that involved a kind of museum library, a place where learned men gathered and students came for study at the

feet of these men. At that time, the few men in society who had mastered the art of writing clustered here and forged the first strong links of philosophy. This was the first true university.

If you had been an inquisitive landowner, or a noble, in the early Roman Empire, the ideal place for you would have been the university at Alexandria. A great many early writings were stored there in the historical museum. It is a tragedy that this precious library was repeatedly attacked and destroyed by fanatics. Similar atrocities are familiar to us in more recent history, e.g., indiscriminate destruction of works of art and literature by virtually all participants in World War II.

During the golden age of Greece and Alexandria, many names of philosophers were immortalized. Such names as Socrates, Anaximander, Anaxagoras, Aristotle, and many others come down to us today. Their philosophies, while primitive in form, were in many cases the beginnings of modern concepts and models that we hold to be correct today.

The Greek philosophers were the first to do the sort of thing that is completely obvious to us today; i.e., they were the first to ask *why*. The question why led them to the propounding of various philosophies. In this Greek period the structure of matter was closely examined by intellectual effort. Atomicity of matter was proposed as a model, and persists even today, the only difference being that today we have ways of extending our senses to measure the existence of such things as atoms and molecules. Amazingly, through the sheer force of intellect, the early Greek philosophers were able to develop such models without the aid of acute sensory perception. Sensory perception was not considered to be of fundamental importance.

One of the interesting schools of philosophy during this period was the mathematical society known as Pythagoreans. It was through the work of this society that the world was given all the fundamental principles of that branch of mathematics known as geometry. The philosophical point of view of the Pythagoreans was that all objects and all events in the world can be represented in terms of numbers. This point of view, however, was not shared by many other Greek philosophers. Aristotle, one of the greatest of the Greek philosophers, rejected out of hand the mathematical point of view of the Pythagoreans. He chose to put his faith in non-mathematical forms and in efforts of sheer human intellect.

The Greek philosophers put forth the idea of the perfection of the circle as that curve which has no beginning and no ending, but moves on continually. This assumed perfection of the circle was an idea that was to stay with the philosophy of men through all the Roman period and the Dark Ages in Europe.

It is in this same period that we find the emergence of modern Western monotheistic religions and the demise of the ancient polytheistic religions. We find the roots of the Hebrew and Christian religions and others, such as Zoroastrianism, Buddhism, and Hinduism, in about this same period, some predating others by hundreds of years, of course.

While this text is not a treatise on religions, it is nevertheless important that we realize that the early development of science was unavoidably caught up in the fabric and structure of religious beliefs.

2.5 Early Astronomical Models

The historical development of science can be typified as a succession of rather well-defined events. A number of ideas are put forth, and a few observations are made by a large number of men over a period of time. At various points in the history of science, there comes one man who gathers together all the ideas and all the observations of those who preceded him and synthesizes these into a uniform philosophy that embraces the whole of physical existence. Aristotle, in the fourth century B.C., was one of these great synthesizers. As we have said, Aristotle rejected out of hand the mathematical model of the world—the idea that the world was reducible in terms of mathematics—and chose to believe rather that all true information could be obtained by sheer intellectual effort. Aristotle even mistrusted observation. He thought of human senses as being imperfect and, therefore, subject to all sorts of errors that one really could not know. For this reason, the basis of his synthesis was a kind of commonsense approach to a description of the world. Aristotle believed that all objects have certain natural motion and that this motion proceeds according to a natural course. That is, all objects fall toward the center of the earth. By this time the idea of the earth as an enormous ball had already taken firm root. It was shortly later, in the third century B.C., that Eratosthenes determined the approximate diameter of the earth. All bodies that moved, according to Aristotle, did so because of an applied force. There were natural forces that tended to always attract objects toward the center of the earth, and there were so-called unnatural forces deriving from some other origin that caused bodies to move in directions other than toward the center of the earth.

A central point here is the idea that all bodies in motion move only because there is a continuous force applied on them. Aristotle embraced the idea of the motion of heavenly bodies in perfect circles. He made a clear distinction between the elements that make up the earth and the bodies that exist in space. These were two separate worlds for Aristotle, the world of the celestials and the world of the earth.

Fig. 2.2 The Lyceum of the School of Athens, popularly known as the Lyceum from the habit of conducting classes on the steps, was founded by Aristotle in the fourth century B.C. *after he completed his duties as teacher to Alexander the Great.* (**From a painting by Raphael.**)

We might well pose the following question: If the Greeks already understood that the earth is a huge ball, why did the myth of the earth as a flat, continuous plane persist even to the time of Christopher Columbus? In order to understand this it is necessary also to understand that the philosophy within the body of society was the property of a few individuals. No system of mass education existed here. Even through to the time of the establishment of the University of Paris, in the twelfth century, the general population was not educated. People not of the clergy or lacking sufficient wealth were not educated in the philosophies. Therefore, we should not wonder too greatly that, even though the idea of a spherical earth persisted among the philosophers, a much stronger mythical belief continued to exist within the general population. Education, after all, was a highly proprietary thing. And those who were educated jealously guarded their knowledge and position within society.

We need to keep in mind also that books and written documents of any sort were rare and were kept as the private property of those few individuals who could afford, either by religious association or by sheer wealth, to own such. There were no printing presses, no mass production of anything in written form. Instead, documents to be preserved over a period of time had to be laboriously copied by hand, a page at a time. The total number of documents in existence up to the time of Gutenberg was miniscule.

Aristotle hypothesized that all heavenly bodies are firmly attached to huge crystal spheres, all of which center upon the earth. These concentric spheres were presumed to have different radii and were further assumed to rotate in a way that accounted for the apparent motion of the bodies. The moon and sun each had its own sphere, as did the wandering stars. A single great sphere was supposed to contain all the fixed stars. This model of the universe was to dominate philosophy for 20 centuries.

In the thinking of the philosophers, the heavens and objects therein appeared as something completely different in basic elemental structure from objects observed on the earth. The substance of the earth was divided into the several elements: air, water, fire, and earth. And while this may seem to us to be a primitive breakdown, to the Greeks it nonetheless was an obvious and logical division.

While the whole of Western Europe was plunged into the countless wars, frustrations, and chaos of the Dark Ages, we find the rise of the Islamic science. One man during this period, Alhazen, working at Alexandria around 1000 A.D., succeeded in measuring the depth of the earth's atmosphere by measuring the curvature of the earth from the refraction phenomena of light. He also described the refractive operation of the human eye. It is a pity that more of the writings and teachings of the Islamic philosophers of this period were not preserved and taken to heart by philosophers of the Western world. Many of the things that the Islamic philosophers were able to develop were lost to Western culture. Islamic science did, however, contribute much to Western culture.

In the next chapter we shall begin with Aristotle's ideas concerning astronomy and follow these ideas as they develop through the philosophies of Hipparchus, Ptolemy, and Thomas Aquinas. The embodiment of these ideas became a part of the dogma and structure of the early church. We shall follow this development through to the models of Copernicus and Kepler.

Problems 1   Can you imagine a Neolithic society in which a distinct separation of religion and general practice existed?

2   It is now pretty well established that the same society that built Stonehenge understood the eclipse. How could these people have laid out circles and eclipses on the ground without a written language?

3   Assume you live in the Neolithic Age. If you have a stone with magnetic properties, how would you make a compass out of it?

Clagett, Marshall: "Critical Problems in the History of Science," University of Wisconsin Press, Madison, 1959. *Bibliography*

Cohen, I. Bernard: "The Birth of a New Physics," Anchor Science Study Series, Doubleday, Garden City, N.Y., 1960.

Harvard Project Physics: Text and Reader No. 2, Holt, New York, 1968.

Holton, G. J., and Roller, D. H. D.: "Foundations of Modern Physical Science," Addison-Wesley, Reading, Mass., 1958.

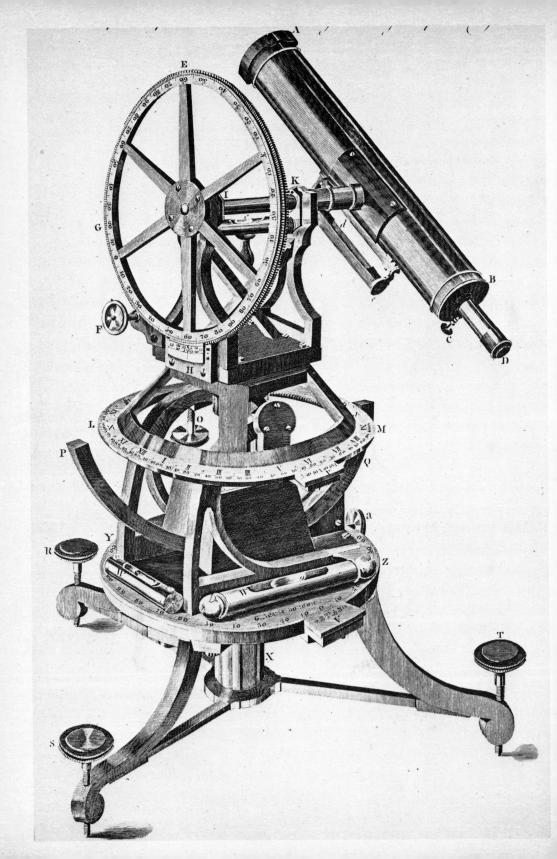

Chapter 3
Music of the Spheres

Astronomical telescope. (The Bettman Archive.)

3.1
Aristotle
In order to understand fully Aristotle's philosophy on the form and structure of the universe and the nature of motion, it is necessary to understand that he made a complete distinction between the elements that are comprised in the earth and those elements that are comprised in the celestial bodies. He visualized these as being two completely different sets of materials and therefore subject to two completely different kinds of laws. We might be tempted at first to ridicule this idea. But before we ridicule Aristotle, we should remember that he had no direct way of knowing what the bodies in space are. So it was quite natural for him to think of heavenly, or celestial, bodies as being composed of something entirely different from earthly materials.

Aristotle, perhaps one of the greatest of the Greek philosophers, was born in Macedonia in 384 B.C. At the age of seventeen he was sent to Athens for his formal study. Subsequent to his studies there, where he was closely associated with Plato, he became the private tutor to Alexander the Great. In 335 B.C., he returned to Athens and founded the Lyceum, a school for advanced study and research.

One of the great tragedies in human history is the fact that the writings of Aristotle—many hundreds of books—were lost to the Western world for a period of almost 15 centuries. Of the hundreds of books, constituting a complete work of philosophy and history, only a small fraction survived the 1,500 years it took to rediscover them. That part that survived, however, became at the hands of Thomas Aquinas a part of the foundation of Christian theological philosophy in the thirteenth century. It persisted for several hundred years, until approximately the time of Copernicus, as a part of church dogma.

Aristotle's books covered all aspects of philosophy, political science, history, natural philosophy, biology, geology, astronomy, and ideas of motion and mechanics. Aristotle was the father of the science of biology, being the first to arrange the animals into various kingdoms and classifications. He recognized the similarity between the different animal types. He also was the first to appreciate geological evolution through the observation of strata.

Considering the tools with which Aristotle and his contemporaries had to work, it is incredible that such an astounding work of human intellect could have been accomplished by one man. Imagine the prodigious effort required in Aristotle's time to write somewhere between three and four hundred complete manuscripts. The lifetimes of many scholars in Western civilization have been spent in the efforts of translating correctly, from the original Greek, the manuscripts of Aristotle.

In considering the translations of these original works, we need to keep in mind that the translation is not merely the substitution of word for word, from Greek into Latin, which was the first translation. The scholar had to be completely familiar with the vernacular of Aristotle and the grammatical form that was current in his day. From this knowledge, he had to be able to interpret what Aristotle was attempting to say.

We have already mentioned that Aristotle was the contemporary of Alexander the Great. He was a contemporary of Zeno of Citium, Epicurus, Diogenes, and Euclid. In literature, he was a contemporary of Demosthenes, Xenophon, and Aristophanes. In fine arts, he was a contemporary of Aristoxenus, Apelles, and Praxiteles.

It is worthy of note that the sculpture of this period of Greek history has never been surpassed. Only a few of the Greek sculptures have survived intact, but those that we do have remind us daily of the magnificence and beauty of these people.

Most of the political philosophies, including democracy and the various other ideologies, are a product of the Greek philosophers.

To the Greek philosophers the questions *what was, what is,* and *what will be* were open questions. It is this fact that sets the Greeks apart from all others in early human history. For others there was always a stock answer to these questions which precluded further inquiry, in many cases religious teaching.

A great many of the Greeks, even those of otherwise opposing schools of philosophy, embraced the idea of a fundamental unifying and ordering principle that operates below the surface chaos of the universe. *What is* was for them the question, "What is the nature of matter?" *What was* and *what will be* were questions of the nature of change of both substance and position.

Aristotle fully realized that for every explanation given there could always be the further question, "Why?" This process might go on without limit. Aristotle, therefore, adopted the concept of *first principle* as the foundation assumption of his model. Observe now the simplicity of and satisfaction to be derived from this model.

"There is a center of the universe toward which all things terrestrial tend in their special order, and around which all things celestial revolve in their spheres."

This first principle was attributed to the prime mover, God. The terrestrial elements were supposed to be four: earth, water, air, and fire, in their decreasing order of tendency toward the center. The fifth element, of which celestial objects were composed, was supposed to be quintessence, unlike the four terrestrial elements.

In the beginning the universe might have been a chaotic distribution of these elements. Applying the first principle to the chaos, the elements sought their "natural place" in concentric spherical shells, each element resting on the one below it. Earth was first, then water, and so forth, with the moon resting in the first celestial sphere. The celestial objects alone rotated in perfect spheres such that their distance from the center of the universe remained unchanging. This model of the universe is finite, reaching from the center outward to the final sphere in which the fixed stars are imbedded and full (a plenum).

Notice how satisfactorily this plenum model "explains" what had by then been observed. If a chunk of earth is lifted upward, it departs from its natural place. When released, it will, naturally, return to its natural place. Notice the use of the word *natural*, which harkens back to the first principle. Bodies, such as those of men, were supposed to be mixtures of the elements. Hence it follows that, in such a body, there will always be at least one element that is not in its natural place. Therefore, the body must ultimately decay with its elements returning to their natural place.

Aristotle was convinced of the "truth" of his model. This is a good place to pause and examine the nature of *truth* as regards science. The *descriptions* resulting from the application of Aristotle's model were all subject to test. The *explanations* of the model are never subject to test. So it is with all science models. Through history, model descriptions have converged while explanations have changed, often drastically, with model revolutions. The sole valid test of any science model is its ability to explain those phenomena that it claims to be able to explain. The explanations always rest upon a collection of basic assumptions that *are* the model. It is for this reason that science never deals with ultimate truth.

We are now ready to define *science* as a rational attempt to develop models and means to test these, without concern for ultimate truth.

The philosophical question *what should be* is clearly beyond the scope of science, though science may help illuminate problems in this area. In addition there are many problem areas, e.g., the determination of art excellence, in which science methods are also not applicable.

Lucretius (Titus Lucretius Carus, first century B.C.) was in nearly all things opposed to the aristotelian model. He proposed a model in which only material things and void exist. It is well worth the effort here to compare and contrast his model with that of Aristotle, since even today many of the dualities in model persist.

In Lucretius' model the universe is infinite in both time and space and has no beginning, nor any end. It is composed, not of the five elements of Aristotle, but of many different kinds of microscopic, and therefore insensible, primordial atoms. These atoms, the final discrete bodies that make up all material things, determine the total characteristic of the various physical objects according to their special properties, their arrangement, their combinations of various types, and the amount of void contained within the body. Thus a lighter body was for Lucretius a body that contained both light atoms and considerable void. He described the way that water seeps through apparently solid rock, and was profoundly influenced by such examples of apparent void spaces in solid bodies. In addition he anticipated Newton by stating the fundamental principle that all matter is characterized by its resistance to any change in its motion. Notice that he did not say any change from rest. Heavy atoms resist change in motion more than lighter atoms. Here we find the first really clear statement of the *principle of inertia*.

Motion for Lucretius had nothing to do with prime movers or a center of the universe. Indeed, for him there was no such center, and motion was due in all cases to the interaction of bodies. He observed dust particles in bright sunlight moving in random patterns, jerking suddenly this way and that. Thus he was the first to describe brownian motion and to ascribe the motion to collisions with microscopic and invisible particles.

Man, second only to God in the hierarchy of Aristotle's model, was for Lucretius just an atomic accident like all other living things. Growth was due to ingestion of food, the atoms of which are like those of the body and, therefore, used to build the body mass. In like manner a tree absorbed its atoms for growth from the soil. There is a very important principle here which we must not pass by. Lucretius stated clearly, and with copious illustrations, that matter can neither be created from nothing nor be annihilated. It was inconceivable for him that atoms could disappear or appear from nothing. All matter had to be accounted for.

Lucretius made no special case for celestial bodies. To him these were just more atoms, and the earth was just one of an enormous number of bodies in infinite space. Needless to say, this model for man and earth has been odious through the centuries to theologians, for whom Aristotle's model was nearly ideal as a religious vehicle.

Decay was for Lucretius a normal process of movement and redistribution of atoms of many different kinds. You should pause here long enough to draw up a balance sheet that compares the basic assumptions and explanations of the plenum model of Aristotle and the atomic model of Lucretius.

Lucretius' model is known by philosophers as *materialism*, first described by Leucippus (fifth century B.C.) and expanded into a full description of the universe by Democritus (460–370 B.C.). We know of their work, however, only through the writings of Epicurus and Lucretius.[1]

Aristotle believed that all motions that occurred in a direction other than toward their natural center (a falling motion) were unnatural or violent

[1] See Lucretius' poem "De Rerum Natura," translated in Beatty and Johnson, "Heritage of Western Civilization," vol. 1, 2d ed., Prentice-Hall, Englewood Cliffs, N.J.

motions caused by violent forces. In this way of thinking, the speed at which a body traveled was supposed to be proportional to the amount of force exerted on the body. That is, the harder you push on a body in violent motion, the faster it will move. The basic idea here is one that might seem very natural to us, if we overlook the influence of friction. Bodies were assumed to remain at rest until a force operated on them. It was further imagined that in order for a body to remain in motion, a continuous force had to be applied to the body.

Today we can observe the motion of a satellite around the earth, circling time after time. We know that it will continue to circle because we have direct evidence that it will. This, in Aristotle's point of view, would require a continuous force acting in the direction of the motion in order to maintain the body at a certain speed, providing that the body is of earthly material. This would be natural motion for a quintessential body. In Aristotle's behalf, we need to keep in mind that bodies moving in space were thought to be subject to an entirely different set of laws. For Aristotle, this kind of reasoning made common sense.

In general, the Greeks mistrusted the senses. That is, they were always skeptical of direct sensory evidence. They maintained that the only true road to truth is the human intellect.

Aristotle's concept of perfect circular motion was a geometric concept that persisted for centuries and became part of other points of philosophy. The perfection of the circle as the prescribed motion of all celestial bodies was embraced by the Catholic Church, when Aristotle's works became available, as a beautiful and satisfying model for the universe. It was not until the time of Johannes Kepler in the early seventeenth century that the idea of the perfect circular movement of all heavenly bodies was finally overthrown by direct evidence.

Through the later work of Hipparchus (second century B.C.) and Ptolemy (second century A.D.), the perfect circular motion of celestial bodies proposed by Aristotle was drawn into a beautiful and surprisingly complete model for prediction of the motion of all bodies in space. In particular, Hipparchus and Ptolemy were concerned with the motion of the so-called wandering stars, which we now know to be the planets of our own solar system.

3.2
Ptolemy's
Epicycles

Ptolemy, in the second century A.D., several hundred years after the death of Aristotle, observed that the motion of the sun around the earth (and notice here that we do not say the earth around the sun) was not perfect and circular. This seemed at first glance to defy the aristotelian model. Hipparchus had observed earlier that during the winter months the sun is physically closer to the earth than in the summer months. After a long and tedious mathematical analysis, Ptolemy introduced a model in which he could account for the apparent change in the sun's path around the earth. He explained this by theorizing that the sun moves in a double circle.

In this theory, the sun was imagined to move in a large circle around the earth, and at the same time to revolve in a much smaller circle with its center on the larger circle. This is illustrated in Fig. 3.1. This earth-centered system of Ptolemy has come to be known as the *geocentric* model.

In Fig. 3.1 we see that by adding the two circular motions of the sun together, the double circular motion produces exactly the desired results. The small circle, or epicycle, of Ptolemy accounted for the nearness of the sun during the winter months, as well as the observed fact that the sun apparently moves faster through the heavens during this period of time and relatively slower in its orbit during the summer months.

If you believe that it was a simple matter for the Greeks to observe the motion of these planets, you need only go out and attempt to duplicate the observations. Remember, they had no telescopes to use in making their observations. The motions they observed were painfully slow, requiring many years for a complete cycle. The motions were projected along a path against a star background. It is no easy task to arrive at either the heliocentric (see below) or the geocentric model for astronomy by such simple observations.

In about the third century B.C., Aristarchus proposed what was, according to him, a much simplified model. This model required all the bodies to move in circular orbits around the sun (*heliocentric*). It seemed quite reasonable to Aristarchus to do this, as it greatly simplified the apparent motion of all the bodies. There was one problem with his heliocentric model, however. If the heliocentric model was true, then the earth, like the other planets, must rotate in a circle with the sun at the center. At the end of a 6-month period, the earth must be on the far side of its orbit about the sun relative to its starting position. Refer to Fig. 3.2.

If the same star is observed from the earth on the first of January and again on the first of July, then relative to a background of stars that are much further distant, the star in the foreground must appear to have shifted slightly. Again refer to Fig. 3.2. Such an apparent shift in the position of the near star would be called a *stellar parallax*. No stellar parallax was, in fact, found by the Greeks. This is not surprising, however, considering that they had no sophisticated method of observing the positions of stars relative to one another. Such a stellar parallax does exist, but the angular dif-

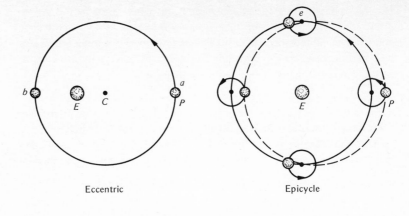

Eccentric   Epicycle

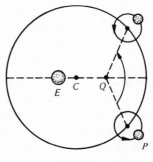

Equant

*Fig. 3.1 Shown here are three devices used by Ptolemy to explain the various motions
of the sun and planets as seen from the earth, assuming that the earth is at or near the
center and all motions are perfect circles or combinations of perfect circles.
Eccentric: The earth is imagined to be off-center (C). The planet, or sun, orbits the
center at uniform angular rate. An observer on the earth then sees the body at b
closer and traveling at a greater angular rate than at a. This explains nicely the
apparent motion of the sun against the star background during the year, but fails to
explain retrograde motion in the orbits of the planets. (Retrograde is a temporary
backward motion at some point in the planetary orbit.) Epicycle: The earth is
imagined to be at the center of the solid circle that is the path of an imaginary center
of a smaller epicycle. The planet is assumed to rotate uniformly around this center (e)
and in so doing follows the dotted path. By varying the size of the epicycle and its
rotational period, one can use this model to explain retrograde motion. You should
experiment with a case that produces retrograde motion. Equant: The earth is
imagined to be off the center of the solid circle that is the path of the epicycle center.
In addition, the epicycle center is imagined to rotate in a perfect circle about the
center C,—at uniform angular rate not around C but as seen by an observer at Q (the
equant). Thus, this model combines the eccentric, the epicycle, and the equant.
Ptolemy achieved considerable success using the observations of Hipparchus and these
models in describing such motions.*

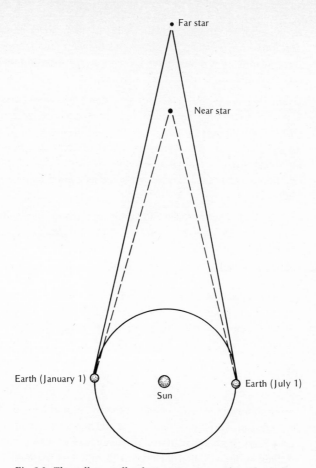

Fig. 3.2 *The stellar parallax for two stars as seen from the earth on opposite sides of its orbit around the sun (heliocentric model). Note that as seen on July 1, the near star is to the left of the far star, whereas on January 1, on the opposite side of the orbit, the near star would be seen to the right of the far star. Prior to use of telescopes, the stellar parallax was not observable.*

ference in the apparent position in the near star is so tiny that it would not have been observable to them.

You can illustrate the phenomenon of parallax by holding one index finger vertically at arm's length from your face. Now hold the other index finger about 2 ft from your face and in line with the first finger. Now close one eye and shift your head first to the left, then to the right. As you do so, observe very carefully the position of the near finger relative to the far one.

As you move your head to the right, the near finger appears to shift its position in the opposite direction or to the left of the far finger. Similarly, if the head is moved to the left, the near finger shifts in the opposite direction, or to the right.

Using the devices illustrated in Fig. 3.1 in the geocentric model, Ptolemy was able at length to generate a remarkably accurate set of circular planetary orbits with superimposed epicycles. These permitted him to predict the positions of all the observable planets for all times of the year. This is the working test of a predictive model. Any model that satisfies the basic function of prediction must be accepted as a good model, regardless of its philosophical basis.

If you are tempted to reject the geocentric model of Ptolemy, reflect for a moment on this question: Do we normally speak of "horizon up" and "horizon down," or do we speak of "sun up" and "sun down"? Don't most people, in their mental patterns and daily speech, even today, operate from the ptolemaic point of view—of the sun circling the earth and not vice versa? You can see from this simple illustration that it was quite reasonable for Ptolemy and his colleagues to think of the earth as being fixed in space and the sun doing the moving around the earth.

**3.3
Aquinas the
Synthesizer** The history of European society in the many hundreds of years following the death of Christ was one of the decline and fall of the Roman Empire—years of savage warfare, of chivalry, of crusades, and in general, of the kind of activity that laid waste to much of the earlier philosophical progress.

In the thirteenth century, Thomas Aquinas succeeded in merging the catechism of the church, i.e., the church's theological teachings, with the Greek works—principally those of Aristotle. It is a curiosity that in writing down the natural philosophy of Aristotle, Aquinas was led to disregard the much more perfect and interesting work of Ptolemy, while embracing the less accurate and less predictive work of Aristotle. With the synthesis by Aquinas of church dogmas and aristotelian philosophy, the church, which was the center of the culture, embraced the philosophical teachings of Aristotle, thus establishing him as an unassailable authority. Having embraced his philosophy, the church instructed all peoples in the Christian world in the philosophical point of view of Aristotle. This fact accounts in large part for the difficulties with the church that were experienced in later times by Copernicus and Galileo.

It seems incredible to us today that all members of a society were required to accept the dogma of the church as the truth of the universe. It is hard for us, in a society where ideas flow as freely as water, to realize that new ideas, even when kept strictly to one's self, were to these people extremely dangerous. Those who held ideas that differed in the simplest way from the accepted dogma of the church were subject to excommunication from the church and suffered economic penalties and in some cases death or imprisonment.

At this time, all facets of life were subject to a very rigorous and constant surveillance by the church. All relationships between men, whether economic, social, or whatever, were subject to strict regulation. The moral code, which included chivalry in Western Europe, was the operational procedure, and no one dared deviate from it. This period in European history is an excellent example of what happens when a particular philosophy becomes the accepted religious dogma of the time. Once philosophy is dominated by rigorous dogma, it literally takes centuries to break away and to gain the kind of freedom that must be present if intellectual progress is to be made.

The period of the decline of the Roman Empire and the ascendancy of the Catholic Church in Western Europe is often called the Dark Ages, and for good reason. The development of the church, however, must be regarded as a result of complex events and ideas, and not necessarily as a cause of them.

As Aquinas embraced the astronomical philosophy of Aristotle, he also perpetuated the idea of the music of the spheres (Pythagoras), the concept of celestial motion in perfect circles. This semimathematical idea of so-called perfect motions persisted to the time of Newton in the seventeenth and eighteenth centuries.

It is a curiosity of human intellect that once an idea, regardless of how ridiculous it might be, is thoroughly ingrained into the population, that idea seems to persist from generation to generation even in light of good evidence to the contrary.

One of the functions of the early Christian church was systematically to drain the best minds out of society. These minds were gathered together into the church clergy. Due to the discipline of the church, monks and priests within the church structure were forbidden to marry and reproduce. This had the unfortunate effect of taking the cream of philosophers and scholars from society by preventing their own regeneration. Europe during this period was literally in the process of genetically selecting against its intelligentsia in favor of the less intelligent segment of society.

3.4
The Breaking
of the
Philosophical
Fetters

Philosophers and scribes were found almost exclusively in the church. However, with the coming of the thirteenth century, and especially in the fourteenth and fifteenth centuries, there emerged in Western society a group of people who were not strictly tied to the church. These were almost invariably from the aristocratic segment of society, people who had both the financial resources and the leisure time to give them the opportunity to carry out detailed investigation. For the most part, the church even in the fifteenth century still could lay proper claim to a large part of the total intelligence in Western Europe. Hence, the philosophy, and particularly the natural philosophy, during this period was heavily dominated by church dogma. With the coming of the Black Plague around 1350, and the great schism in the Catholic Church that followed this by some 30 years, the absolute authoritative rule of the church was at last broken.

Many writers seem to agree that these two events and the Protestant breakaway from the Roman Church helped set the stage for the coming of people like Copernicus and Galileo, Kepler, and later Newton. This was a painful period of European history, again fraught with many wars—the Wars of the Roses, the various religious wars of France and Germany—and a time of indecision within the Roman Church. The period, even though painful, gave rise to a renewal of philosophical thinking and furnished the proper framework in which the birth of modern science was to occur.

3.5
Nicolaus
Copernicus

The following quotations from the preface of the book "De Revolutionibus," written by Nicolaus Copernicus and published in 1543, in the form of a letter to Pope Paul III, will serve to illustrate the kind of restrictions that dominated intellectual existence at that time. In this preface, Copernicus begins as follows:

> I may well presume, Most Holy Father, that certain people, as soon as they hear that in this book on the revolutions of the spheres in the Universe, I ascribe movement to the earthly globe, will cry out that holding such views, I should at once be hissed off the stage. For I am not so pleased with my own work that I should fail duly to weigh the judgment others may pass thereon. And though I know that the speculations of the philosopher are far removed from the judgment of the multitude, for his aim is to seek truth in all things as far as God has permitted human reason to do. Yet I hold that opinions which are quite erroneous should be avoided. . . .

In this paragraph, Copernicus has obviously already apologized in advance for his work to the Pope as the central authority. It has been alleged that the publisher of "De Revolutionibus," and not Copernicus, wrote this preface in the hope of softening the certain critical opposition of the church.

In his work on the heliocentric model for astronomy, Copernicus found it necessary to make a thorough study of the Greek manuscripts beginning with the Pythagoreans on through the works of Hipparchus and Ptolemy.

In the body of his preface, Copernicus continues as follows:

> That I allow the publication of these my studies, may surprise your Holiness, the less in that having been in such travail to attain them, I had already not scrupled to commit to writing my thoughts upon the motion of the earth. How I came to dare to conceive such motion of the earth, contrary to the received opinion of the mathematicians, and indeed contrary to the impressions of the senses, is what your Holiness will rather expect to hear. So I should like your Holiness to know that I was induced to think of a method of computing the motions of the spheres by nothing else than the knowledge that the mathematicians are inconsistent, in these investigations. For first, the mathematicians are so unsure of the movements of the sun and the moon that they cannot even explain or observe the constant length of the seasonal year. Secondly, in determining the motions of these and the other five planets they do not even use the same principles and hypotheses as in their proofs of seeming revolutions in motions. So some use only concentric circles while others eccentrics and epicycles. Yet even by these means they do not completely attain their ends. Those who have relied on concentrics though they have proven that some different motions can be compounded therefrom have not thereby been able to fully establish a system which agrees with the phenomena. Those again who have devised eccentric systems though they appear to have well nigh established the seeming motions by calculations agreeable to their assumptions have yet made many admissions which seem to violate the first principle of uniformity in motion. Nor have they been able thereby to discern or deduce the principal thing, namely the shape of the universe and the unchangeable symmetry of its parts.

In this passage we see that Copernicus was motivated to do his work on the astronomical model by a frustration at the inability of the mathematicians to exactly predict the motions that are observable in the heavens. It seemed perfectly clear to Copernicus that the earth is simply another body like the observed five planets and that it, too, is in motion. It is noteworthy that he still described the motion as *circular motion* around the sun as the center. Copernicus could not bring himself to believe in the physical nature of epicycles. He was disturbed that such a motion should be necessary in order to describe the apparent motion of a body through space. At the same time, however, Copernicus was not successful in his model in accounting for the motions of the planets around the sun. In the end, he was forced to fall back on the epicycle once again as Ptolemy had to describe and accurately predict the position of bodies in space.

The orbit of the planet Mars was particularly troublesome to Copernicus. He was never able to convince most of his readers that the earth, with all its apparent rigidity and immobility, is not at the center of things. He was forced in his arguments constantly to reconcile his new view with the intent and purpose of Deity in creation. He was forced to fall back on a religious justification for his point of view. Even Martin Luther and the followers of Protestantism branded Copernicus as a fool and spoke against his heliocentric theories.

The Bible as interpreted by the church at that time seemed clearly to indicate that the Deity had worked from a blueprint that was geocentric.

H. Butterfield has summed up the position of the militant anti-copernicans of the time in the following way:

> Above all, if you grant Copernicus a certain advantage in respect of geometric simplicity, the sacrifice that had to be made for the sake of this was nothing less than tremendous. You lost the whole cosmology associated with Aristotelianism. The whole intricately dove-tailed system in which the nobility of the various elements and the hierarchical arrangement of these had been so beautifully interlocked. In fact, you had to throw overboard the very framework of existing science, and it was here that Copernicus clearly failed to discover a satisfactory alternative.

> He provided a neater geometry of the heavens but it was one which made nonsense of the reasons and explanations that had previously been given to account for the movements in the sky.

In addition, people at the time simply could not conceive of an infinite universe. They saw rather the finite extent of the universe as being measurable quantities. For them the idea that the universe, containing all its stars and galaxies, extends off to infinity in all directions was completely absurd. Yet the copernican model seemed to demand just exactly that concession. Then, too, there was the problem of parallax, which the heliocentric model clearly demanded. As has been explained, no one at that time was able to physically observe a parallax, and therefore, this was used as patent evidence of the absurdity of the copernican model.

But the proof of the pudding is in the eating. After all, the final test of the goodness of the copernican model, opposed to the ptolemaic model, lay in its ability to predict astronomical positions. It is curious that the copernican model failed to predict as accurately as the ptolemaic model. This seemed to be the final blow. The anti-copernicans pointed to this as the final evidence of falsehood of the model.

In the middle of the sixteenth century Europe was filled with astrologers
and numerologists. It was considered the height of culture to play with numbers, to fit them into all sorts of patterns and then to see what could be made out of the patterns. The astrologers were quite popular in those days and practiced openly. Their services were sought by everyone from kings and queens down to the lowest people in society. One such astrologer, Johannes Kepler, was particularly gifted, and in 1600 he was hired by Tycho Brahe, a Danish astronomer, to analyze the results of his careful observations of the heavens.

Tycho Brahe was a bit of an eccentric. He was the son of a wealthy man, and the King of Denmark granted him an entire island on which to carry on his astronomical observations. His eccentricity and his zeal to demonstrate the truth of the ptolemaic model for the universe led him to design machinery that permitted a kind of astronomical observation that was, prior to this time, completely impossible. The building of this machinery was an enormously expensive project.

Tycho Brahe made astronomical measurements that were one order of magnitude better (only a tenth as much experimental error) than any preceding him. He went to great pains to perfect his machinery and spent long hours making observations, charting positions and times for all the visible wandering stars. He put young Johannes Kepler to work making sense out of his astronomical data. His whole thrust was to demonstrate once and for all that the copernican model was bogus and that the only true one was the ptolemaic model.

He too was carrying on in the tradition of celestial motions occurring only in perfect circles. Kepler worked for a great many years on the data of Tycho Brahe. The more he worked, the more he was confounded by the fact that the data that Brahe's laboratory produced were simply not consistent with either the copernican or the ptolemaic models.

Kepler struggled frantically with this problem and spent many years trying to reconcile the differences. Shortly after the beginning of the seventeenth century he published a book ("Astromia Nova") on the revolutions of Mars, in which we find the first truly great scientific contribution. He had succeeded in interpreting from the data of Tycho Brahe exactly the motions of the planets, and in particular, the planet Mars.

From his careful work, several things of great importance have come. Kepler had read the works of William Gilbert on electrostatic attraction and magnetic effects and was deeply imbued with the idea that, in order for a body to behave as the planets apparently behave in space, there must be some kind of force to hold them in these curved paths. Thus Kepler in

Fig. 3.3
Tycho Brahe in his
observatory.

Tycho Brahe in seiner Sternwarte „Uranienburg" auf der Insel Hven
Nach einem Kupferstich zu Tycho Brahes „Astronomiae instauratae Mechanica" vom Jahre 1602

his paper on Mars referred to the obvious necessity of a force that would keep the planet in orbit. This observation caused Galileo, himself persecuted by the church and the anti-copernicans, to comment that Kepler was obviously a fool. No such force without some mechanical linkage was possible. Nevertheless, Kepler persisted in his point of view, and his

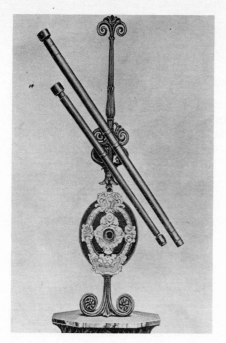 

Fig. 3.4
Two of Galileo's
telescopes.

analyses produced the celebrated three laws of planetary motion. These three laws will be discussed in detail in Chap. 6.

The chief importance of Kepler's work is the fact that he was the first to use very carefully collected empirical data. One of the great curiosities of history is that the errors in Brahe's data were of just the right magnitude to lead Kepler to his laws. If the errors had been smaller, say, only 10 percent as great, Kepler would almost certainly have been misled. His observations and so-called laws were a direct result of the analysis of these data.

At about the same time, a Dutchman invented a device called a *telescope*. The first telescope was an extremely crude device and not really very useful. But Galileo Galilei, an eminent physicist and natural philosopher teaching in an Italian university at the time, was quick to grasp the principle of the telescope. He succeeded in creating a modification of the original design known to this day as the *galilean telescope*. With this relatively low-powered telescope, Galileo took the first great steps in modern science. He solved once and for all the controversy surrounding the copernican versus ptolemaic points of view. Galileo's telescope revealed four satellites clearly revolving around Jupiter, a very embarrassing discovery for the ptolemaics. No less disconcerting were his discoveries that Venus goes through phases in its illumination in much the same manner as the moon, and that the moon itself exhibits a topography not unlike that of the earth in many respects. Now remember that the Aristotle-Ptolemy model demanded perfect spherical objects constituted from the quintessence, all of which revolve around the earth as center. Through the experimental work of Galileo, the ptolemaic model was plunged into a model crisis from which, of course, it could not emerge without drastic changes. We shall have a good deal to say about Galileo in future chapters.

For this achievement, direct measurement by telescope and verification of the point of view of the copernican model, and for his work in the establishment of fundamental mechanics that Newton later developed to a greater extent, Galileo is often referred to as the father of modern science, and justifiably so.

For this work, and for other work involving the motion of bodies at and near the surface of the earth, Galileo was rewarded by the church with trial by inquisition. He was held for many days prior to the actual trial of the inquisitors and was forced to memorize word for word a message of recantation to the grand inquisitor. Having recanted his point of view, he promised the inquisition not to continue his dangerous practice of teaching falsehoods. Galileo was held for many years in later life in general house arrest and was never permitted to teach his ideas again.

Fortunately, Galileo wrote down many of his ideas on mechanics in a book called "Dialogue Concerning the Two New Sciences." This every student should obtain and read thoroughly. This is the first foundation document for modern science.

Bibliography   **Butterfield, H.:** "The Origins of Modern Science," 2d ed., Macmillan, New York, 1957.

Dreyer: "History of Planetary Systems from Thales to Kepler," Cambridge, London, 1906.

Galilei, Galileo: "Dialogue Concerning the Two Chief World Systems: Ptolemaic and Copernican," trans. Stillman Drake, University of California Press, Berkeley, 1953.

Galilei, Galileo: "Dialogue Concerning Two New Sciences," trans. H. Crew and A. De Salvio, Macmillan, New York, 1914.

Harvard Project Physics: Text and Reader No. 2, Holt, New York, 1968.

Heath, Sir Thomas Little: "Aristarchus of Samos, the Ancient Copernicus," Clarendon Press, Oxford, 1913.

Holton, G. J., and Roller, D. H. D.: "Foundations of Modern Physical Science," Addison-Wesley, Reading, Mass., 1958.

Koestler, A.: "The Watershed" (biography of Johannes Kepler), Anchor Science Study Series, Doubleday, Garden City, N.Y., 1960.

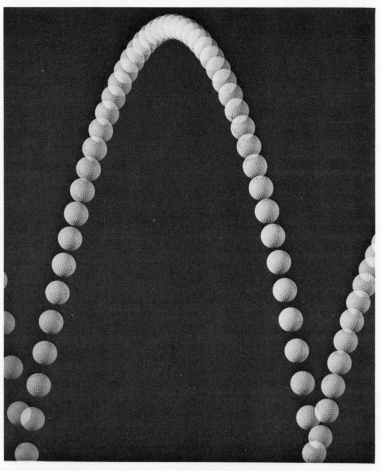

A stroboscopic shot of a golfball bouncing on a hard surface. Can you estimate from the size of the ball how high it has bounced? Can you estimate the length of time in the interval between exposures of the ball? Use your knowledge of motion under constant acceleration to help you. (Courtesy of Dr. H. E. Edgerton, M.I.T., Cambridge, Mass.)

Chapter 4
Motion

Aristotle's model includes a description of motion in terms of natural motion, the tendency of the elements to return to their natural place under the impetus of the prime mover. In this model all other motions are regarded as unnatural or violent motions due to the application of some violent force.

Lucretius, on the other hand, regarded motion as due simply to the interaction of real objects. In this model there is no prime mover or violent force. Similarly, Lucretius did not recognize a center of the universe, nor did he see earth as a body fundamentally unique in the universe.

We come now to a more detailed examination of the *description* of motion, without saying, for the moment, anything about what causes motion. In order to describe motion, we must agree upon some basic ground rules. This chapter uses some simple kinds of motion, along with some graphic techniques, to illustrate these ground rules and to refine some definitions to a point where they have highly specific meaning. This is a bit tedious, but it is quite necessary, since we need to have precise language when we come to examine what causes motions.

The techniques and ideas of this chapter should be studied with considerable care, since they form the basis for a good understanding of what follows. Reinforce the ideas by working as many of the problems at the end of the chapter as possible. Laboratory measurements are encouraged here as a definite aid in further reinforcing the concepts.

All nature is characterized by motion. Bodies whirl and dance in odd patterns. Most motions—the ones that attract our attention—are complicated, e.g., the motion of a rocket blasting off on its way to the moon. If we are to make any real sense out of a description of such motions, we will have to begin very carefully by agreeing on some ideas and definitions. It is not enough to have a passing idea of what *speed* means. One key to understanding all natural processes is a clear understanding of motion.

**4.1
Which Observer
Is Right?**

We have already had a look at the confusing problem of the description of motion in the heavens. The systems of Ptolemy and Copernicus, although they come surprisingly close to describing accurately these motions, are quite different in one important respect: each model tries to describe the motion from a different point of view. How, then, can they both come so close to proper description?

In order to examine this question more closely, let us imagine that we are standing beside a highway. A car goes by at a constant speed of 50 mi/h.

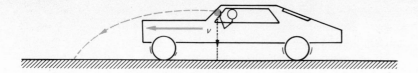

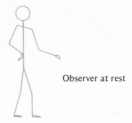

Observer at rest

Fig. 4.1

(See Fig. 4.1.)   Just as the car passes us the driver drops an orange out his window.

Now let us try to describe the motion of this orange. The orange, from our point of view, will follow the dotted path shown in the figure until it strikes the ground, since it has both forward and downward motion. In order to further simplify the description, let us assume that there is no air resistance. This kind of model assumption is common in science. Common sense tells us that the wind would, in reality, have quite an ef-fect, but we can pretend for the moment that it does not. The orange moves forward and downward with increasing speed under the influence of gravity.

But what does the driver see if he watches the orange? From his point of view the orange drops straight down from his hand along the side of the car (remember, no wind). He would not describe the orange as having any forward motion at all relative to himself. He would describe only the falling motion of the orange. Who is right, the driver or us?

The answer to this question must be a relative one. We have seen that the description of the motion of the orange depends entirely upon the point of view, or rather the state of relative motion, of the two observers. Both are correct in their descriptions of the same motion, even though they give different descriptions. Can you predict how a person in a sec-ond car going 50 mi/h in the opposite direction would describe this same motion?

We shall call the point of view of each of these observers by a special name: *frame of reference*. Each of us is born with a built-in frame of reference. We are at the center of it, and we subconsciously measure motions relative to ourselves. Almost as soon as we learn to follow moving objects with our eyes as infants, we begin subconsciously to transfer our frame of reference, while we are in motion, to fixed objects on the ground, such as houses and telephone poles. In such cases, we learn to think of ourselves as doing the moving and of the ground as fixed.

We say that the sun comes up and goes down. This assumes that the earth is fixed in space with the sun moving around it. We do not normally speak of "horizon-up"; rather, we say "sun-down." Hence, in our common speech and standard mental patterns, we are ptolemaic, or more correctly, aristotelian.

We speak of a collision between a car and a wall as "the car ran into the wall," and not as "the wall ran into the car." It is perhaps surprising to learn that both are perfectly good descriptions.

If we accept Copernicus' idea that the motion we assign to the sun is really due to a rotation of the earth upon its axis, then we might better use such phrases as "horizon-up." This is absurd. We just do not talk like that. Yet, we would be perfectly correct in doing so. Try thinking of all the motions you commonly see and describe these from an unusual frame of reference. For example, try describing the motion of a white rag tied on a bicycle tire at the rim, as the bicycle passes by, from the earth frame of reference. You will probably infer a circular motion for the rag. Which frame of reference is implied here?

The problems mentioned thus far seem trivial. Yet equivalent descriptions of motions of various kinds—descriptions that seemed quite different on the surface of things—baffled the best minds of pre-Renaissance Europe. The attitude that "there is only one correct point of view" prevailed in their thinking.

In order to be more precise in our description of motions, we will have to develop a pictorial system of some sort so that we can tell one another exactly where a moving body is at any given time. We have implied here that a proper description of motion requires reporting successive positions of a body in motion at specific times.

It is clear that we must have some mutually agreed-upon unit of length. It does not matter much what this unit is so long as it is the same for all observers. Following the same logic, all observers must have clocks that tick at equal intervals.

The simplest kind of motion we can describe is the motion of a body that moves always either backward or forward along a single line. The body never leaves this line (Fig. 4.1). We can then divide this line into equal parts or segments each of unit length (Fig. 4.2). We can further subdivide each unit length into equal fractions of a unit length to any degree desired within our ability to resolve the tiny distances (Fig. 4.3). But something important is missing. Which of the unit marks do we call *zero* in our numbering scheme? This turns out to be a matter of personal preference, a matter of arbitrary choice (Fig. 4.4). Which sense will be positive and which negative? Again, this is an arbitrary choice. Let us call to the right of a zero *plus* (+) and to the left of a zero *minus* (−). Similarly, motion

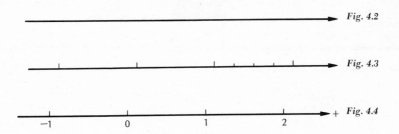

Fig. 4.2

Fig. 4.3

Fig. 4.4

to the right will be called + and motion to the left −. It will be of convenience to place ourselves as observer somewhere along this line. The point that will reduce our reporting work to a minimum is zero, which we shall call by a new name, the *origin* of the frame of reference (Fig. 4.5). Now we can report the position of a body at any time as +4.15 at 10:32 h, and then again as +7.38 at 10:35 h. However the body got from the +4.15 position to the +7.38 position, obviously it did so in 3 min. Do you know whether the body moved smoothly along between the beginning and end points during this period of time?

Fig. 4.5

This one-dimensional frame of reference is not very useful, since we seldom see bodies moving in a single straight line. Things become a good deal more interesting if we add a second line to our frame of reference (Fig. 4.6). This, however, leads to some problems.   What angle should the two lines make at their intersection?   We shall see that a 90° angle is most convenient for description.   Where should the origins of the two lines lie? Since we can choose any point on either line as its origin, it will make good sense, from the point of view of keeping records, to have the two origins lie on top of one another at the point where the two lines intersect.

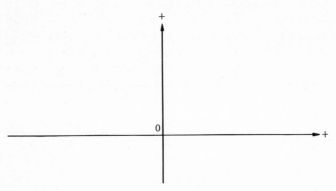

Fig. 4.6

With this frame of reference we can describe more kinds of motion.   We can, for example, describe the motion of an ant on a board by reporting successive positions and times (Fig. 4.7).   We can lay our frame of refer-

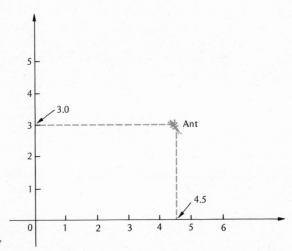

Fig. 4.7

ence right on the board and leave it fixed relative to the board. We can
describe the position of the ant at time t as 4.5 units to the right and 3.0
units up. Instead of saying to the right and up, we can give each line a
short name. Let us call the horizontal line x and the vertical line y.
Numbers to the right of zero on x will be $+$, as will numbers above zero on
y. We shall refer to these lines now as the x and y axes of our two-dimensional frame of reference. The ant's position now would be reported as
$x = 4.5$, $y = 3.0$ at t.

Everything is not flat, though, and we recognize that even our x, y frame
of reference does not describe all kinds of motion. If we add a line called
z through the x, y origin coming straight out of the paper (at right angles
to both x and y), we shall be able to describe any kind of motion whatever
(Fig. 4.8). Now we can pinpoint a fly no matter where he is by giving his
x, y, z coordinates (numbers) and the time.

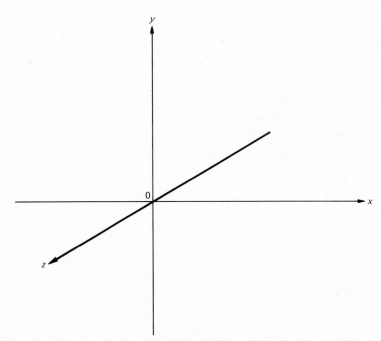

Fig. 4.8

For most of our discussions we shall need to use only the two-dimensional
frame of reference. This will greatly simplify our handling of numbers.

4.2
Some Useful
Ideas

In the following chapters it will be necessary to make use of the formal description of motion. Words such as *acceleration* must have a precise meaning for everyone. We shall begin now to develop these precise meanings. The next sections should be read slowly and carefully, and then reread.

Suppose we wish to calculate the distance in Fig. 4.9 from the ant to the origin. We know the ant's position to be $x = 4.5$, $y = 3.0$ (units). An examination of the triangular figure shows the unknown distance d. The triangle has one $90°$ (right) angle, so we can use a very useful and ancient geometric relationship to solve the problem. The rule states that *the sum of the squares of the two sides of a right triangle is equal to the square of the hypotenuse.* The sides are the lines that make the right angle. The remaining side is the hypotenuse. Thus, the solution to our problem can be found as follows:

$$d^2 = x^2 + y^2 \qquad\qquad [4.1]$$
$$d = \sqrt{x^2 + y^2}$$
$$= \sqrt{(4.5)^2 + (3.0)^2}$$
$$= 5.4 \text{ units} \qquad\qquad [4.2]$$

This formula is an expression of the *theorem of Pythagoras.*

And so the ant is 5.4 units from the origin of the frame of reference. We might also wish to know in what direction the ant may be found relative

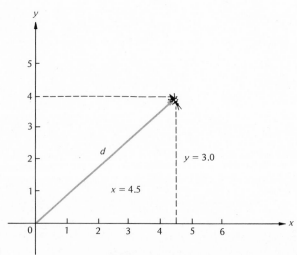

Fig. 4.9

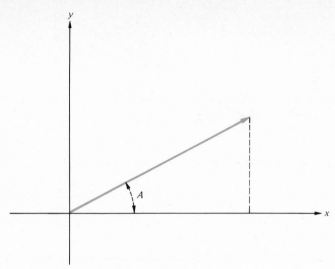

Fig. 4.10

to the origin. The direction is really well established by the x and y coordinates, but there are some useful relationships to be found in asking the question anyway.

The direction to any point in the frame of reference can be established as an angle between one of the axes of the frame, and a line drawn from the origin to the point, e.g., angle A in Fig. 4.10.

Any triangle that contains one 90° angle, no matter how large or small it is or what the other two angles might be, is called a *right triangle*. There is a set of special definitions concerning right triangles; if used properly, these definitions can help us solve the direction problem above.

The right triangle of Fig. 4.11 will be defined as follows:

> sine of angle $A = a/c$ (where c is the hypotenuse)
> cosine of angle $A = b/c$

and similarly,

> sine of angle $B = b/c = $ cosine of angle A
> cosine of angle $B = a/c = $ sine of angle A

and

> tangent of angle $A = a/b = $ cotangent of angle B
> tangent of angle $B = b/a = $ cotangent of angle A

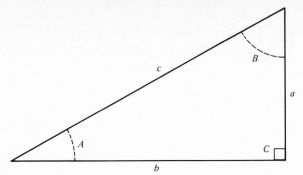

Fig. 4.11

These definitions can be used to solve for an unknown angle or side from a knowledge of other angles or sides of the triangle. Thus, they show a number of useful relationships between angles and sides of any right triangle. We can greatly simplify these by shortening them as follows:

$$\sin A = a/c = \cos B$$
$$\sin B = b/c = \cos A$$
$$\tan A = a/b = \cot B$$
$$\tan B = b/a = \cot A$$

Our first reaction to these definitions might be one of panic. This is not necessary, however, since this is as much of trigonometry as we shall be using in this text. The problems at the end of this chapter are designed to help you get these definitions and their use perfectly clear. Before working through a few of them, look at the following example from our ant problem.

Remembering that our problem was to find the direction of the ant from the origin, let us look again at Fig. 4.11. Side a of the right triangle is the one opposite angle A; it has the value of 3.0 units. The side adjacent to angle A and opposite angle B is b, which has the value of 4.5 units. Notice that, for example, the tangent of angle A would be

$$\tan A = \frac{a}{b} = \frac{3.0}{4.5} = 0.667$$

The nice feature about these trigonometry definitions is that mathematicians have long since calculated all possible values of these ratios for all angles that can occur in a right triangle. In Appendix A of this book you can find the angle whose tangent is 0.667. Look it up at this time. If you find the angle to be about 33.667°, you have used the table correctly. It is important that you now work some of the problems at the end of the chapter so that you will become proficient in the use of the trig table.

The ant is now known to be at a point 5.4 units from the origin on a line that has a direction relative to the x axis of 33.7°.

The line drawn from the origin to the ant we shall call by a special name, *displacement*. The distance between the ant and the origin is just 5.4 units, but this information does not tell us where to look for the ant. When we add the information concerning the angle A, we say the ant lies at 5.4 units at 33.7° relative to the x axis from the origin, and we have completely specified the ant's position, or displacement, relative to the origin. Displacement, then, includes both *distance* and *direction*. If we place an arrowhead on the line at the ant's end, we have a displacement vector $\vec{d}$.

4.3 Motion Defined

A *vector* is a line in a frame of reference whose length signifies a magnitude, such as 5.4 units of length, and whose direction and arrow indicate the direction and sense of the quantity represented. We can now distinguish carefully between *scalar* quantities, which record only magnitude or numbers, and *vectors*, which record magnitude *and* direction (Fig. 4.12).

If we specify that the *speed* of a car is 50 mi/h, we have stated a *scalar* quantity, 50 mi/h. But we have no idea from this information where the

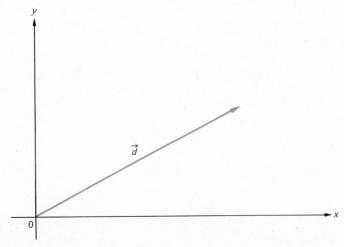

Fig. 4.12

car is going. If we have a report of both the *speed* and *direction* (and sense) of the car, we have all the information needed to specify what the car is really doing, i.e., we know its vector *velocity*.

In the study of motion we are obviously going to find vectors of considerable use. We can do some very interesting things with a knowledge of frames of reference and vectors. Get into the habit of carefully distinguishing between scalar and vector quantities. It will help to write down a list of examples of both scalar and vector quantities in common experience. A partial list is shown below. Add your own list to it.

SCALAR	VECTOR
Distance (d)	Displacement $(\vec{d})$
Speed (v)	Velocity $(\vec{v})$
Time (t)	Force $(\vec{F})$

Up to now the ant has been standing still in our frame of reference. Now we can let him move about freely, and we can begin to describe his motion. Suppose our first sighting of the ant is at $x_1 = 4.5$, $y_1 = 3.0$ at time t_1. At some time later, t_2, we take another sighting on his position and find it to be $x_2 = 6.0$, $y_2 = 3.0$. In the time interval $t_2 - t_1$ the ant moved in some unknown way through a change in displacement, $\vec{d_2} - \vec{d_1}$ (the arrows above the letters indicate vector quantities).

This brings us to a special problem. How do we add and subtract vector quantities? In Fig. 4.13 we can follow the idea of vector addition quite easily. A useful rule for the procedure is as follows: Starting with any one of the vectors to be added, establish its tail as the origin. Now slide one of the other vectors parallel to itself until its tail rests at the head of the first vector. Continue lining vectors in this fashion in any sequence desired until the final vector is in place. The *resultant* vector, the vector that is equivalent to all the vectors added up, is the vector drawn so that its tail lies at the tail of the first vector (origin) and its head lies at the head of the final vector in the addition. Do not worry about moving the vectors around parallel to themselves. This in no way alters their value.

We are now in a position to measure the average velocity of the ant during the time interval $t_2 - t_1$. Since the *velocity* is defined as the *time rate of change of displacement*, in this case the ant's velocity over the interval would be

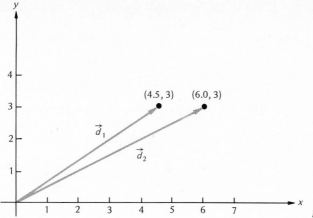

Fig. 4.13

$$\vec{v} = \frac{\vec{d_2} - \vec{d_1}}{t_2 - t_1} = \frac{\Delta \vec{d}}{\Delta t}$$

The Δ's mean *change in* whatever quantity follows. It is pretty clear that the answer is not just scalar. Since velocity is a vector quantity, we must report both a magnitude and a direction for the average velocity. The vector resulting from adding $\vec{d_2}$ and $-\vec{d_1}$ together ($-\vec{d_1}$ is just the vector $\vec{d_1}$ with the arrow on the other end pointing directly opposite) has a magnitude $\Delta \vec{d}$ of 1.5.

The length of $\Delta \vec{d}$ can be found without trigonometry by using a straight-edge and a protractor, drawing the vectors $\vec{d_2}$ and $-\vec{d_1}$ very carefully on graph paper (to scale) and then simply measuring the length and direction of $\Delta \vec{d}$ on the diagram (Fig. 4.14).

If we divide the magnitude of $\Delta \vec{d}$ by the time interval, we have the magnitude of the desired velocity vector. This is, when direction is added, the average velocity over the time interval Δt:

$$\vec{v} = \frac{1.5}{\Delta t}$$

In a similar way, *acceleration* is defined as the *time rate of change of velocity*. The change in velocity is found by subtracting the velocity of the body at the beginning of the time in question, $\vec{v_1}$, from the velocity at the end of the interval, $\vec{v_2}$. This new vector is then divided by the scalar time interval to find the acceleration vector.

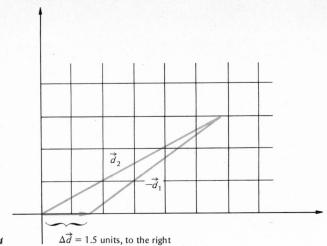

Fig. 4.14 $\overbrace{}$ $\Delta\vec{d} = 1.5$ units, to the right

$$\vec{a} = \frac{\vec{v_2} - \vec{v_1}}{t_2 - t_1} = \frac{\Delta\vec{v}}{\Delta t}$$

These motion definitions will not be difficult once you have practiced using them. Just remember that the velocity is a description of the way the displacement is changing in time, and the acceleration is a description of the way the velocity is changing in time.

A word of caution is in order here. One of the most common mistakes in working with vectors is that of attempting to add vectors that represent different quantities, e.g., displacement and velocity, which results in a nonsense vector. Only vectors that represent the same physical quantity and have the same length scale may be added to achieve a vector that represents the same physical quantity.

Example An airplane travels over the ground from point A to point B, a distance of 200 mi, in $\frac{1}{2}$ h. If the wind travels relative to the ground at 50 mi/h toward the south, at right angles to the direction AB (east), at what heading and speed must the aircraft fly to make good the groundspeed indicated?

In order to travel 200 mi east in just $\frac{1}{2}$ h, the airplane must make good a velocity with respect to the ground of 400 mi/h east. Suppose that we adopt a scale for the 200-mi displacement vector of 1 cm = 100 mi, and for the velocity vector of 1 cm = 50 mi/h. There is nothing at all wrong with this selection of scale or any other convenient scale so long as all displacement vectors have the same scale and all the velocity vectors have the same scale.

The vectors indicated in the problem are

1 Wind velocity relative to the ground of 50 mi/h south

$\downarrow \vec{w}$ (1 cm)

2 Displacement eastward from point A, 200 mi to point B,

$A \qquad \vec{d} \qquad B$
$\xrightarrow{\hspace{2cm}}$
(2 cm)

3 Velocity of the airplane relative to the ground of 400 mi/h eastward

$\xrightarrow[\hspace{3cm}]{\vec{v_g} \text{ (8 cm)}}$

The proper way to state the problem is to ask what velocity vector when added to the wind velocity vector will result in a ground velocity vector of 400 mi/h east? The unknown vector sought here is, of course, the desired velocity of the airplane with respect to the air. This is almost the same problem as the speedboat crossing a river with a swift current, trying to get to a point exactly on the opposite bank. The boat must head up-stream in order to compensate for the current if it is actually to go straight across the river.

The airplane must head north of east if the wind is blowing toward the south in order to travel over the ground straight east. The vector solution is correctly shown here. Note that the air velocity vector lies north of east and has a length of about 8.1 cm. This means that the airplane would actually have to fly on this heading at a speed of 8.1 × 50 = 405 mi/h, relative to the air. This is consistent with common sense.

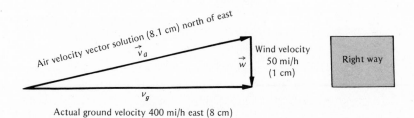

Air velocity vector solution (8.1 cm) north of east
$\vec{v}_a$

Wind velocity
50 mi/h
(1 cm)
$\vec{w}$

Right way

v_g

Actual ground velocity 400 mi/h east (8 cm)

A common error in this type of problem is to try to add displacement and velocity vectors in an attempt to find the vector solution.

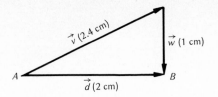

We have added here the two vectors $\vec{d}$ and $\vec{w}$, in such a way that they result in the velocity vector $\vec{v}$. The unknown $\vec{v}$ turns out to be directed too far toward the north and only 2.4 cm long, indicating a desired speed of only $2.4 \times 50 = 120$ mi/h. This is obviously nonsense. We have added apples and oranges to produce a meaningless vector as a solution. Be very careful in your solutions not to repeat this kind of error.

4.4
Motion in a
Straight Line
under Constant
Acceleration

Up to now our units have been arbitrary. We can look now at a series of examples that makes use of the information in the last three sections and also uses the mks (meters, kilograms, seconds) system of units.

Example A car starts from rest and begins to accelerate uniformly toward the east along a straight road. The acceleration is a constant 10 m/s² — an increase of 10 m/s in the velocity each second. How fast will the car be traveling at the end of 10 s? How far will it have gone during this interval?

The best way to work this problem dealing with straight-line motion is to ignore the vector directions, since they all are aligned. A graphic solution will give us the clearest understanding.

First we shall plot the graphs of velocity vs. time and acceleration vs. time for the 10-s period. We must be careful to choose the units along the axes so that suitable distances result. It is conventional to plot the time along the x (horizontal) axis and the scalar values of velocity and acceleration along the y (vertical) axis (Fig. 4.15).

Since the motion of the car starts from zero, the first plot point on the v-vs.-t graph is (0,0). The acceleration is constant, so the velocity will increase by equal amounts in equal times. Hence, the plot of v vs. t is a straight line rising to the right as t increases. If v increases by 10 m/s each second for 10 s, the final speed will be 100 m/s ($t = 10$, $y = 100$ on the graph). The acceleration-vs.-time graph is an easy one since a is constant. It is just a straight horizontal line at $a = 10$ m/s².

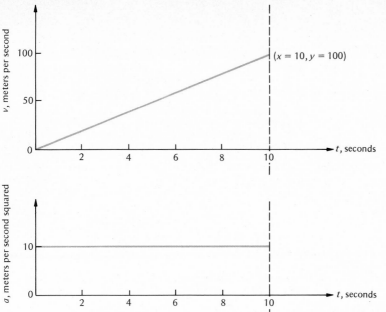

Fig. 4.15

Now think carefully about the next two points. If we calculate the area of the rectangle that is formed by the acceleration line and the t axis out to 10 s, we get an area of 100 units, the units being m/s² × s = m/s. These are the units of velocity, and the 100 m/s is no accident. *The area under the acceleration-vs.-time curve at any time t is just equal to the total change in the velocity up to that time.* Turning our attention to the v-vs.-t graph, let us calculate the area of the triangle formed by the velocity line and the t axis. This area turns out to be 500 units, the units being m/s × s = m. If you have not already guessed it, this represents the distance traveled by the car in the 10 s, 500 m. *The area under the velocity-vs.-time curve at any time t is equal to the total change in the displacement up to that time* (Fig. 4.16).

It is possible to write down some simple equations from these results that will help us find solutions in any case in which the acceleration remains unchanged during the motion. Where t is any time after $t = 0$, the velocity and displacement are

$v = at +$ (any initial velocity at $t = 0$)

  $= at + v_0$

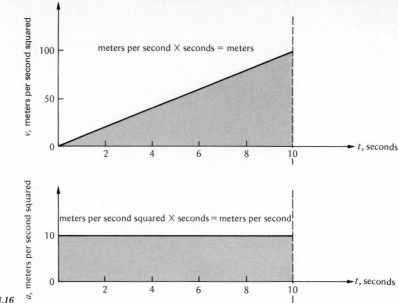

Fig. 4.16

(in our example, $v = 10 \times 10 + 0 = 100$ m/s)

$d = \frac{1}{2}at^2 + v_o t + d_o$

(in our example, $d = \frac{1}{2} \times 10 \times 10^2 + 0 + 0 = 500$ m).

A car traveling 50 m/s begins to brake at a constant negative acceleration of -5 m/s². How fast will the car be going after 7 s of such braking? How far will it have gone in this period?

Now there is no need to graph the motion, since we already know how to solve the problem of constant acceleration. The -5 m/s² acceleration means that the car's velocity is decreasing rather than increasing. Applying the formulas above, we get

$v = at + v_o = (-5 \times 7) + 50 = 15$ m/s
$d = \frac{1}{2}at^2 + v_o t + d_o = \frac{1}{2} \times -5 \times 7^2 + 50 \times 7 + 0 = 227.5$ m

There are similar problems at the end of this chapter. Turn to these now and work as many of them as is necessary to get the idea firmly in hand.

Do not let the superficial grasp you now have fool you into ignoring the problems.

Most motions do not occur in a straight line. Because of the vector na- **4.5** ture of the three motion quantities we have defined thus far, we must be ***Motion in a*** very careful to apply the proper rules of vector addition in order correctly ***Circle*** to find changes in displacement and velocity.

Circular motion is a good example of nonlinear motion and one that we shall encounter frequently in this text (Figs. 4.17 and 4.18). Suppose that a ball whirls around on a string 1 m long at a rate of 10 complete circles per second (angular frequency f). Do you think that there is any acceleration of the ball? Let us analyze this motion. The speed (scalar) is quite easy to find from a simple formula that relates angular frequency f and circular circumference $2\pi \times R$ to the speed:

$$v = 2\pi\, fR$$
$$= 2 \times 3.14159 \times 10 \times 1$$
$$= 62.8 \text{ m/s}$$

The velocity, however, while its magnitude is constant, has a constantly changing direction. Does the changing direction mean that there is an acceleration on the ball? It certainly does.

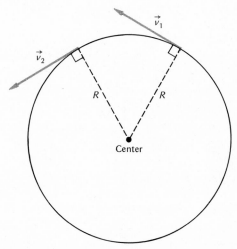

Fig. 4.17

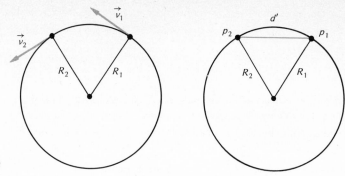

Fig. 4.18

If a heavy ball were rolling along a level table in a particular direction and you wished to change this direction, you would have to push the ball from the side at a desired angle. In doing so you would be accelerating the ball even if its rate of rolling did not change (directional change only). Similarly, a car going around a corner undergoes an acceleration always directed toward the center of the turn.

In just this way the ball on the string must be constantly pushed or pulled sideways if it is to remain in circular motion. This is accomplished by the string. If we calculate the time rate of change of velocity for the ball, this analysis results in a very useful formula. This formula is generally useful for all problems of uniform circular motion, many of which we shall be analyzing presently.

Note that the two radii, R, and the change in displacement, d', form an isosceles triangle [two sides equal in length (Fig. 4.19)]. Note further that the two velocity vectors and the change in velocity vector, $\overrightarrow{\Delta v}$, form a sec-

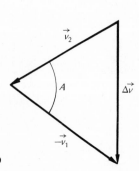
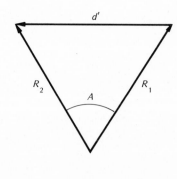

Fig. 4.19

ond isosceles triangle. The two radii are each perpendicular to a velocity vector; hence the angles included between the equal sides of the two triangles are equal to each other. From this knowledge we can proceed to say that the ratio of a side to the base of one triangle is equal to the ratio of a side to the base of the other triangle.

$$\frac{v}{\Delta v} = \frac{R}{d'} \qquad\qquad [4.3]$$

Remember that

$$\frac{\Delta \vec{v}}{t_2 - t_1} = \vec{a} \qquad\qquad [4.4]$$

Since vector direction is accounted for in the geometry, only scalar values need be considered. Thus from Eq. [4.3] above,

$$\Delta v = \frac{vd'}{R} \qquad\qquad [4.5]$$

and dividing both sides of the equation by $\Delta t = t_2 - t_1$,

$$\frac{\Delta v}{\Delta t} = \frac{v \times \dfrac{d'}{\Delta t}}{R} = \text{acceleration} = \frac{v^2}{R} \qquad\qquad [4.6]$$

Thus we see that in uniform circular motion, the body is accelerated by an amount equal to the square of its speed divided by the radius of the circle, and with an accelerated direction pointing always toward the center of the circle (Fig. 4.20). This proof is probably originally the work of Christian Huygens, Newton's contemporary.

4.6 Galileo on Motion

Galileo Galilei was born in Pisa in 1564. This is the same year that Michelangelo died and Shakespeare was born. As a young man his curiosity and genius led him to challenge established ideas. This made him many enemies. Like Plato and Archimedes, Galileo put his faith in his ability to test directly through experimentation any reasonable hypothesis. This was quite a radical position at the time, since it challenged the aristotelian ideas and the authority of the church.

His copernican point of view in astronomy led him to write the book "Dialogue Concerning the Two Great World Systems," which was con-

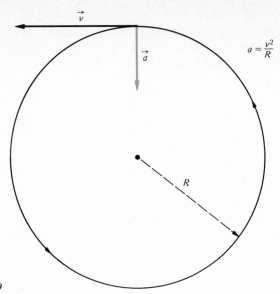

$$a = \frac{v^2}{R}$$

Fig. 4.20

demned by the Catholic Inquisition. In another of his books, "Two New Sciences," written later, we find his treatise on motion. We shall examine this work in some detail.

It had been known since 1330 that bodies of different mass fall at the same rate. It remained for Galileo to redirect attention to this experimental fact in his book. He hypothesized that massive bodies fall with constant acceleration and then proceeded to predict a number of results that could be experimentally checked. In a translation of his own words: "A motion is said to be uniformly accelerated, when starting from rest, if it acquires, during equal time intervals, equal increments of speed."

Having defined uniform acceleration *and* hypothesized that bodies near the earth fall in this manner, Galileo had only to test the hypothesis. He could neither measure terminal velocities of falling bodies directly nor measure with sufficient accuracy the short time intervals of fall involved, so how was he to test his hypothesis? He had to find some quantity that he could measure with sufficient accuracy. He was forced to rely on mathematics to indicate a measurable quantity in the problem.

The velocity at impact of a falling body would be given by

$$v_{\text{final}} = a \, \Delta t \qquad\qquad [4.7]$$

where Δt is the time of flight of the body during which it accelerates, starting from rest.

We have already found that the distance traveled by the body in time Δt would be

$$d = \tfrac{1}{2}a(\Delta t)^2 \qquad\qquad\qquad [4.8]$$

We notice that this can be written as

$$\frac{d}{(\Delta t)^2} = \tfrac{1}{2}a \qquad\qquad\qquad [4.9]$$

Now Galileo's hypothesis can be written as: *Uniformly accelerated bodies move in such a way that the ratio $d/(\Delta t)^2$ remains constant.*

The distance d was for Galileo an easily measurable quantity, but Δt was still unmeasurable with any accuracy. His need to measure finally drove him to invent a water clock capable of measuring very short time intervals (Fig. 4.21). With his water clock he was able to demonstrate the

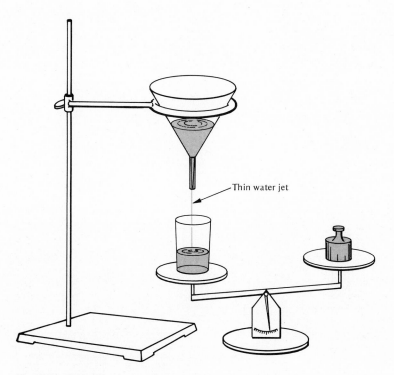

Fig. 4.21. The galilean water clock. A thin jet of water drains from the reservoir above into a collecting cup during the time of the motion to be measured. The water thus collected is carefully weighed and the period of time thereby calculated to good accuracy.

acceptability of the hypothesis as stated above. The galilean water clock is a timing device that allows water to flow out of a container through a small opening at a constant rate. By measuring the amount of water drained during an experimental time interval, Galileo was able to calculate the time interval with good accuracy.

It is this pattern of logic and experimentation that is important here. Galileo's systematic extension of human measuring capability and his formulation and testing of hypotheses were a revolutionary new behavior for man. This insistence on direct observation and persistence in methodology established the foundation of modern science upon which men like Newton were to build.

Problems Problems in science are a key part of your learning process. If you refuse to stop trying until you have worked through all the problems here, you will have gone far toward making these ideas your permanent possessions. If you do not honestly try to work the problems, you will probably not have any permanent understanding. Consider each one carefully. It may help to draw a picture of the physical situation and then to sketch in your frame of reference.

1 Galileo's need to measure short time intervals led him to design a water clock. Describe another clock that Galileo might have con-

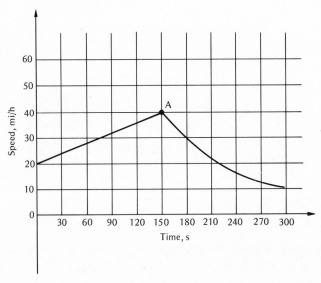

Fig. 4.22

structed at his time that would do equally as well for measuring short time intervals.

2   A certain right triangle has one acute angle equal to 23° and a hypotenuse equal to 15 m. Find the other acute angle of the triangle and the lengths of the two legs.

3   The tangent (tan) of a certain angle in a right triangle is 1.732. One of the legs of the triangle is 0.55 m long. If this is the side opposite the angle above, calculate the length of the hypotenuse. Use the pythagorean theorem to check your answer.

4   Figure 4.22 shows the speed of a car moving along a straight road plotted against time. From this graph plot the acceleration of the car during this same time.

    a   At what time does the car reach maximum speed?

    b   How far has the car gone during the positive-acceleration portion of the trip?

    c   Is it possible for the velocity of a car to abruptly begin decreasing as at point A on the graph?

5   Two cars are initially at rest facing one another but 2 km apart on a straight road. They begin to accelerate uniformly, one with acceleration $a_1 = 2$ m/s, and the other with acceleration $a_2 = 3$ m/s. At some time later they will meet along the road.

    a   At what time will they meet? (*Hint:* Solve this algebraically.)

    b   At what distance along the road will they meet?

    c   What will be the speed of each at their meeting? (Be very careful to keep the signs of the motion quantities in mind.)

6   Sketch the graphs of distance, velocity, and acceleration vs. time for the motions of Prob. 5, remembering to take into consideration the sign convention you have chosen. Analyze these graphs for areas under curves and slopes of curves.

7   A cannon ball is fired vertically upward at an initial speed of 50 m/s. Assuming the acceleration of gravity to be 10 m/s², plot the graphs of distance, speed, and acceleration vs. time for this motion.

    a   What is the maximum height reached by the ball?

    b   Calculate the final displacement of the ball after it has returned to earth from the speed-vs.-time graph.

8   The cannon ball in Prob. 7 is again fired with initial speed of 50 m/s, but this time it is fired at an angle of 70° above horizontal. Use component vectors to solve the following:

    a   What is the maximum height reached by the ball?

    b   What is the horizontal range of the ball?

c Show by a graph how the angle above horizontal at which the ball is fired is related to the horizontal range of the ball.

9 A certain river is W meters wide and flows at a rate of R meters per second. A man has a speedboat capable of going V meters per second through the water. If this man wishes to make a trip across the river to a point directly opposite his starting point, what direction must he head relative to the line of sight to his objective?

10 A jet fighter is flown through a vertical loop 1 km in diameter. When exactly on top of the loop, the pilot experiences weightlessness.

a At this point what force is causing him to move in a circle?

b What force causes him to move in a vertical circle at the bottom of the loop?

c What is his velocity at the top of the loop?

Bibliography **Cohen, I. Bernard:** "The Birth of a New Physics," Anchor Science Study Series, Doubleday, Garden City, N.Y., 1960.

Physical Science Study Committee: "Physics," Heath, Boston, 1965.

Project Physics: Text, Unit 1, Holt, New York, 1970; "Project Physics," Reader, Unit 1, Holt, New York, 1970.

Chapter 5
Newton

Astronaut Shepard
in weightless
condition during
simulated
weightlessness on a
KC-135 aircraft.
The KC-135 Air
Force plane, flying a
parabolic curve,
creates a weightless
environment as a
training exercise in
preparation for the
astronauts'
extravehicular
activities on the
lunar surface.
(Courtesy National
Aeronautics and
Space
Administration.)

From Chap. 4 we have an idea of frames of reference and how to describe motions of simple kinds. As it happens, this is really all we need to know in order to begin the study of the heart of the problem, i.e., what causes motion to change.

This is precisely the question posed by Galileo in 1632, in "Dialogue Concerning the Two Chief World Systems." In this dialogue, the motion of a perfectly round, bronze marble upon a polished steel plane is examined. If the marble is placed at rest upon the plane and the plane is tilted from horizontal, the marble will accelerate toward the downward edge of the plane. This is common experience. If the marble is thrown up the slope initially, it will slow down, stop for an instant, and then move downward as before.

If the marble is set at rest upon the horizontal plane, it will remain at rest. But if it is given a certain initial velocity, it will continue to move with this velocity unchanged, provided that friction is assumed to be zero (remember that velocity has direction as well as magnitude). In this self-evident proof from general experience, we have the statement of a law of motion later formalized by Newton.

Remember that an acceleration is said to occur when either the direction or the magnitude of a velocity is changed or when both are changed. The purpose of this chapter is to examine this problem in detail and to discover ideas that will permit us to predict motion changes in a body in a useful way.

5.1
Mass vs. Force

Most people have a very good intuitive feeling for mass without having a formal definition. Force, too, is generally appreciated as a thrust or a shove on a body. Suppose we examine the question of what mass really is.

Many descriptive definitions are typical responses to this question, e.g., "mass is that which occupies space," or "mass is that which has weight," etc. We can best attack the question with an illustrative problem. Suppose we have two irregularly shaped solid bodies, plus a bit of string, a meter stick, and nothing else with us in deep space enormously distant from any celestial object. The problem is to find the mass of the two solid bodies. All the objects are essentially weightless.

We normally establish the mass of a body on earth by weighing it on some device that compares its weight with a standard weight. The kilogram (kg) is such a standard and has a weight of 9.8 N (newtons) at sea level on earth. But our irregular masses in space have no apparent weight and neither of them is a 1-kg mass.

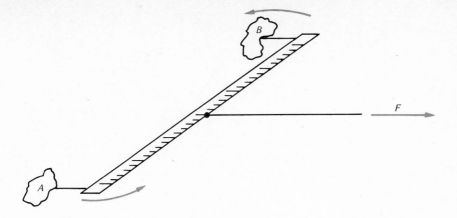

It is clear, then, that we shall be able to express the mass of one only in terms of the mass of the other. We cannot specify their mass in terms of a standard. One possible solution exists. There is no weight, so we cannot weigh B against A on a beam balance (Fig. 5.1). By attaching A and B to opposite ends of the meter stick with bits of string, and fixing a third string intermediate between them, we can accelerate both A and B by pulling on the intermediate string. If this string does not pass through a certain point on the meter stick, a rotation of the stick relative to the string will occur. The intermediate string attachment can now be slid along the meter stick until a pull on the string produces no rotation of the meter stick, i.e., both A and B are accelerated equally by the pull.

Without proving it for the moment, we can argue that the resistance of A to acceleration is proportional to the resistance of B to acceleration in exactly the same ratio as the ratio between L_B and L_A, when no rotation exists and A and B are accelerated equally (Fig. 5.2). We can call these resistances to acceleration *inertial mass*. Hence,

$$\frac{m_A}{m_B} = \frac{L_B}{L_A}$$

If we arbitrarily accept m_A as our standard inertial mass, the mass of any other object, e.g., m_B, can be found by a similar experiment in terms of m_A.

$$m_B = \frac{L_A}{L_B} m_A$$

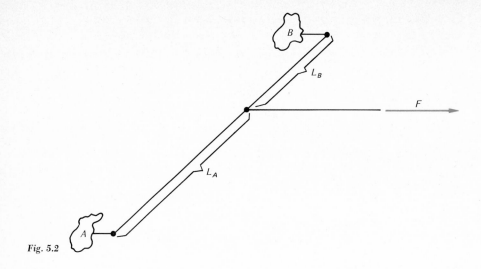

Fig. 5.2

In our tiny laboratory in space, we can now find the mass of anything, without the presence of a measurable gravitational force, in relation to our standard mass, m_A.

We can define *force* simply as that which produces a measured acceleration of a mass. Since acceleration is a vector quantity, force must also be a vector. The ratio of force to measured acceleration we shall simply call *mass*.

$$\frac{\text{Force}}{\text{Acceleration}} = \text{mass}$$

Note particularly that it is not possible to define mass without reference to force, and similarly we must include the idea of mass if we are to understand what we mean by force. This mutual dependence between mass and force shows that neither is an independent quantity. The dependency is usually written as

$$\vec{F} = m\vec{a} \qquad\qquad [5.1]$$

which should be interpreted as follows: The acceleration of a body of mass m is in the same direction as the applied force and has a magnitude equal to the applied force divided by the inertial mass.

This implies that if no force is applied to a mass, it will have zero acceleration. This, of course, is exactly the point developed by Galileo; it is often called the *principle of inertia*. Objects (masses) free from forces will continue with unchanged velocities. When a body slides over a tabletop, it comes to rest in short order, but it is not free. It is, instead, subject to gravitational force, which sets up a retarding force of friction between the body and the tabletop. If we were to slide a flat puck over a very smooth ice surface dusted with a fine snow, we would come close to a good demonstration of this principle, since the retarding force due to friction is, in this case, greatly minimized.

Another situation will serve to further illuminate the idea of mass apart from gravitational force. Suppose you are in a spaceship drifting along in remote space with motors shut off. Inside with you there is an office safe which weighs several hundred pounds back on earth but which drifts freely inside the spaceship. You also have a common marble of very small weight when on earth. If you push on the marble, it will reach a very high velocity away from you in a short time. However, if you push with the same force on the safe, its velocity will change very slowly as it moves away from you. Now suppose you move to the opposite side of the ship into the path of the two bodies; which do you think will be easier to stop, the slow-moving safe or the fast marble?

The marble, of course, can be caught with ease. The safe, however, can be stopped only by exerting a force over a much greater period of time. In fact, if you wait too long to begin slowing the safe, you had better get out of the way to avoid being crushed between the safe and the wall of the ship.

There is a seed of a new idea here, i.e., the final speed of the safe and the marble depend not only on the force but also on the time during which it is applied.

There is no need here to make a great issue of the exact nature of time, since our intuitive idea of time intervals is all that is required for our present study of mechanics. Newton conceived of time as being absolute and quite independent of the presence or motion of bodies in space. When you think about it for a moment, however, it becomes pretty obvious that without bodies in motion, or more generally, without measurable changes of some kind, time has no meaning.

**5.2
*Newton's Idea
of Time***

Objects that move in a reliably cyclic way, always repeating the cycle exactly, are usually the basis for counting time. To the extent that the cycles are regular, the motion is a good basis for counting time. We do not use human pulse rate as a basis for counting time because, although the normal period for heartbeats is about 1 s, the rate varies for different individuals and even within the same individual.

We can use a small fraction of the annual period of the earth's rotation around the sun as a basis, since it is a reliable period based on the simple regular motion of the earth. Is this unit the same as what we call a second? From what is our basic unit of time derived?

The establishment of a standard unit of time depends upon very careful observation of a periodic motion. Mechanical systems that produce this kind of motion are called *clocks*. There are many clocks in nature not designed by men. How many of these are you aware of?

Newton spoke of an inner sense of "before" and "after" in events, and so it seemed to him that the essence of time does not depend upon any clock. Newton had no direct information on the motion of microscopic particles moving at very high velocities. His idea of time as an absolute one-directional quantity was valid for all macroscopic physics.

Try to imagine a society of men in which sight simply never existed as a physical sense. Given all the other normal human senses, how would sightless men keep track of time? How might two observers from this blind society describe the falling of a tree with reference to time?

5.3 Aristotle's Physics

For some 2,000 years the philosophical point of view of Aristotle dominated the thinking of scholars, although as we have already seen, not all Greek philosophers were in agreement with Aristotle. The known works of Aristotle, some 50 volumes of which have survived, out of several hundred, are an encyclopedic record of Greek philosophy, much of which was Aristotle's own creation. The works of Aristotle date from before 322 B.C. and deal with all phases of human intellectual interest.

Few ideas of today are really new ideas. Most ideas of physics were developed, at least in part, by the Greeks, e.g., atomicity and the heliocentric solar system. Aristotle held that natural motion of all earthly bodies is to fall toward the center of the earth. He supposed that the rate of fall is directly proportional to the object's weight. He also appreciated the retarding influence of a viscous medium like water upon the natural falling motion. Motions that do not involve natural falling were termed *violent* motions. Violent motions always required the application of a force as a motive agent. Remove the force and the body must come to rest. It was quite in keeping with common experience to see motion in this way, since nothing was known of friction at this time.

One might ask why Aristotle did not check his hypotheses experimentally. At this time algebra was unknown; you will recall that this was the age of geometry. Geometry is far less applicable to quantitative problems and was held somewhat in contempt by Aristotle. His physics seemed to him

perfectly evident. So evident and logical did it seem, in fact, that it was
embraced by scholars in general until the seventeenth century. It is important to realize here that quantitative mathematical procedures were
quite cumbersome about the time of Galileo.

Galileo Galilei, who spanned a long period during the sixteenth and seventeenth centuries, was an extremely abrasive personality. He was aggres-
sive and often tactless in his questioning of established philosophy. A
number of scholars had questioned in private, but it required the wit and
persistent drive of this man to establish once and for all the quantitative
inquiry technique of science. For this reason, he is credited with origi-
nating modern science.

It remained, however, for Isaac Newton to synthesize the ideas and observations of Galileo and others into a uniform mechanics. The heart of this
synthesis is that it demands that celestial objects be subject to the same set
of laws as earthly objects. We recognize in this model the materialist
philosophy of Lucretius (55 B.C.), who had been regarded for centuries by
the church as an antichrist and whose philosophy was repugnant to aris-
totelians. We shall begin now to study in some depth the laws of newtonian mechanics, which have permitted us to put men on the moon.

**5.4
Newtonian
Mechanics**

The assumption of Galileo that any change in the measured velocity of a
body must be brought about by a net force is the foundation of this
mechanics. This concept of natural motion as unaccelerated motion
departs radically from Aristotle. Galileo's search for a quantity that
increases by equal amounts in equal distances led to the conclusion that it
is the square of velocity, not the velocity itself, which increases linearly
with increasing distance under constant force.

$$v^2 = cd$$

where c is some constant. You might wish to check this result by rolling
a marble down an incline at various angles to horizontal. Remember that
a change in either direction or magnitude of the vector velocity, or a
change in both, constitutes an acceleration (Fig. 5.3).

From the aristotelian point of view, a constant force is required to maintain the constant velocity of a body. From the newtonian point of view,
objects that are either at rest or in uniform motion (constant velocity) will
continue unchanged so long as no force is exerted. This poses the immediate problem of finding some force responsible for the accelerated motion of celestial bodies. This principle is often called *Newton's first law
of motion*, or the *law of inertia*.

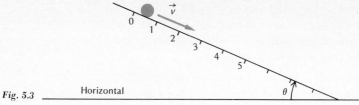

Fig. 5.3

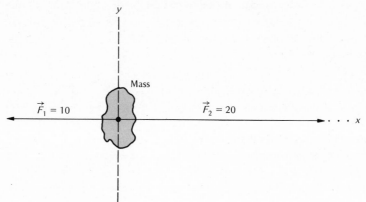

Fig. 5.4

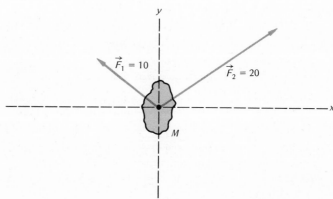

Fig. 5.5 $\vec{F}_2 + \vec{F}_1 = \vec{F}$ or $\vec{F}_1 + \vec{F}_2 = \vec{F}$

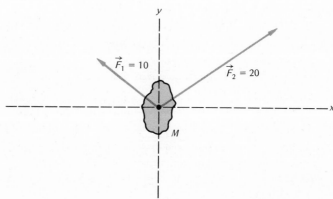

Fig. 5.6

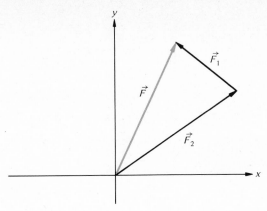

Fig. 5.7

If more than one vector force acts upon a body, the motion of the body will change according to the resultant force (Fig. 5.4).

If a force $\vec{F_1}$ acts to the left along x on the mass m, and force $\vec{F_2}$ acts simultaneously to the right along x, the resultant force $\vec{F}$ is found by adding the force vectors diagrammatically as shown in Fig. 5.5. $\vec{F}$ is found to be to the right along x and of magnitude 10.

If $\vec{F_1}$ and $\vec{F_2}$ in Fig. 5.6 act simultaneously on m, the resultant $\vec{F}$ will be found in the same way according to vector addition. The easiest way to get a useful solution to this resolution problem is to construct this vector addition on graph paper, taking care to preserve the magnitude and directions of the vectors. The magnitude and direction of $\vec{F}$ can then be read directly from the diagram (Fig. 5.7).

In Fig. 5.8 we find a boy pulling along the wagon handle with force $\vec{F_1}$. The weight of the wagon, $\vec{F_2}$, pulls the wagon down against the earth,

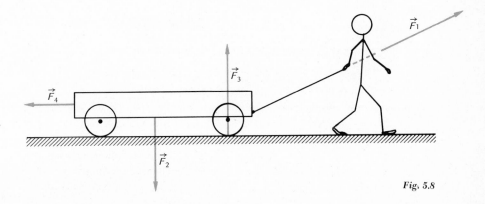

Fig. 5.8

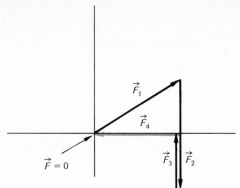

Fig. 5.9

while the earth pushes upward on the wagon, $\vec{F}_3$. $\vec{F}_4$ is a retarding force of friction. If the wagon moves along horizontally with constant velocity, Newton's first law says that no net force exists. Hence, $\vec{F} = \vec{F}_1 + \vec{F}_2 + \vec{F}_3 + \vec{F}_4 = 0$. Figure 5.9 shows how this happens. If the boy were to stop pulling, $\vec{F}_1$ would go to zero and $\vec{F}_4$ would slow the wagon until its velocity reached zero, at which point the force of moving friction, $\vec{F}_4$, would also go to zero.

This first law of Newton is really just the formalization of the principle of inertia developed by Galileo.

The most important contribution of Newton was his insistence upon a detailed analysis of the forces that cause changes in motion of bodies. We have already seen a definition that relates force and mass:

$$\vec{F} = m\vec{a}$$

This definition is often quoted as a complete statement of Newton's second law of motion. This definition, however, states only a special case of the far more general second law, i.e., the case in which mass remains constant.

Newton focused his attention on a quantity that is far more fundamental in nature, *the product of mass and velocity, $m\vec{v}$.* Since velocity is a vector quantity, it follows that the product mv is also a vector quantity. But why should we consider $m\vec{v}$ and not $m^2\vec{v}$ or mv^2 or $m^3\vec{v}$ or any of a host of other possible products? The answer is that there is something that is experimentally very exciting and fundamental about $m\vec{v}$. We shall now give this quantity its usual name and proceed to examine it carefully.

Momentum $= m\vec{v}$
$\qquad = \vec{p}$
$\qquad \equiv$ kg $\cdot$ m/s $\qquad$ [mks] $\qquad\qquad\qquad\qquad$ [5.2]

The symbol $\vec{p}$ will henceforth be used to represent the momentum of a body or of a collection of bodies in a system with definite boundaries in space.

Newton's second law, stated in approximate form, is given by

$$\vec{F} = \frac{\Delta \vec{p}}{\Delta t}$$

$$\quad = \frac{\Delta \overrightarrow{mv}}{\Delta t} \qquad\qquad\qquad\qquad [5.3]$$

This reads as follows: *The force on a body is equal to the time rate of change of the body's momentum.* To illustrate this we can look at a ball that bounces off a rigid wall (Fig. 5.10). The ball has an initial momentum of $\overrightarrow{mv} = \vec{p}$ and a final momentum of $\overrightarrow{m'v'} = \vec{p}'$ after collision. Obviously, there has been a change in its momentum during the collision with the wall. In fact, whatever force is exerted upon the ball is acting during the time that the ball is physically in contact with the wall. The second law states that

$$\vec{F} = \frac{\Delta \vec{p}}{\Delta t} \qquad\qquad\qquad\qquad [5.4]$$

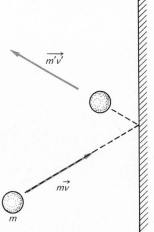

$\overrightarrow{m'v'}$

$\overrightarrow{mv}$

m

Fig. 5.10

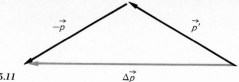

Fig. 5.11

Suppose that $\Delta t = t_{final} - t_{initial} = 1$ s. The force, then, is

$$\vec{F} = \frac{\vec{p}' - \vec{p}}{1}$$

which may be found diagrammatically (Fig. 5.11) by performing the vector sum indicated.

Since $\Delta\vec{p}$ has the same direction as the force on the ball, we note that the force in this case is perpendicular to the wall, not in the direction of either $\vec{p}$ or $\vec{p}'$. If the magnitude of $\Delta\vec{p}$ happens to be, for example, 100 kg·m/s, the force on the ball is

$$\vec{F} = \frac{\Delta\vec{p}}{\Delta t}$$

$$= \frac{100}{1} \text{ kg} \cdot \text{m/s}^2 \qquad \text{or N} \qquad \text{perpendicular to the wall and outward}$$

But what about the wall? Does the ball exert any force upon the wall? Experience tells us that it does. The wall recoils from the blow of the ball. If the wall is rigidly tied to the earth, there will be no noticeable motion of the wall.

Suppose now that the wall is not fixed; instead, it is mounted on a frictionless surface. If the wall is initially at rest in our frame of reference, common experience predicts that it will recoil from the blow of the ball (Fig. 5.12). It will perhaps be easier to visualize what happens if the ball is thrown perpendicularly at the wall. While the ball and wall are in contact, each exerts a force upon the other. From Newton's second law it is possible to state what will happen in each case. The force upon the ball is

$$\vec{F}_b = \frac{\Delta\vec{p}}{\Delta t}$$

$$= \frac{\vec{p}' - \vec{p}}{\Delta t} \qquad\qquad [5.5]$$

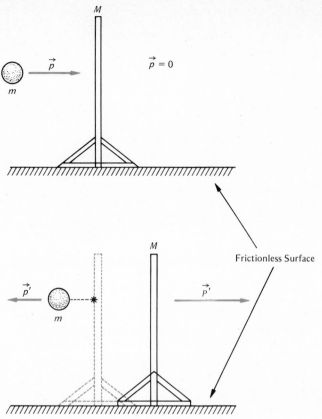

Fig. 5.12

and sketching the solution for $\Delta\vec{p}$ here (Fig. 5.13), we see that a fairly large force has been exerted upon the ball to change its momentum. But it is the wall that has exerted exactly this force upon the ball.

So, also, we can find the force upon the wall as follows:

$$\vec{F}_w = \frac{\overrightarrow{\Delta P}}{\Delta t}$$
$$= \frac{\overrightarrow{M'V'} - 0}{\Delta t} \qquad\qquad [5.6]$$

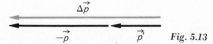

Fig. 5.13

and diagrammatically the solution for $\Delta\vec{p}$ is

$$\vec{P'}$$

simply the wall's momentum after collision. It is the ball that is responsible for this force. Indeed, the forces upon the wall and upon the ball are identical in magnitude and oppositely directed. This is often referred to as the *action-reaction principle*. It was one of Newton's fundamental mechanics postulates. Often it is stated more formally in the following form: *For every action there is an equal and opposite reaction.* The wall increases in momentum toward the right (direction of the force due to the ball), and the ball increases in momentum in the opposite direction. We can now set $F_B = F_W$, being careful to equate only the magnitudes of the two vectors. From Eqs. [5.5] and [5.6] we can write

$$\frac{\vec{p'} - \vec{p}}{\Delta t} = \frac{\vec{P'}}{\Delta t} \tag{5.7}$$

Now Δt is the same time period for both, the time of physical contact. Equation [5.7] says that the two force vectors have the same magnitude. In the algebra, however, it is very important to note the fact that $\vec{F}_B$ is directed toward the left and $\vec{F}_W$ toward the right. It is possible to take this into account by using a sign convention that says that all vectors toward the right will be positive $(+)$ and all toward the left negative $(-)$. Now we can modify Eq. [5.7] in vector form:

$$-\frac{\vec{p'} - \vec{p}}{\Delta t} = \frac{\vec{P'}}{\Delta t} \tag{5.8}$$

Simplifying and multiplying both sides by Δt, which is the same time interval for both,

$$\vec{p} - \vec{p'} = \vec{P'} \tag{5.9}$$

The vector diagram (Fig. 5.14) illustrates the equality. Typically $m \ll M$; hence, even though $\vec{P'}$ is quite a large momentum, $\vec{V'}$ is quite small and consistent with good sense.

There is a result here of enormous significance. A careful review of the whole procedure will make this apparent.

1   Our system contained only two bodies—the ball and the wall. No external force was permitted to act on either body, i.e., the wall rested upon a frictionless surface (an isolated system).

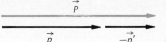

Fig. 5.14

2   Initially, only the ball was in motion in the frame of reference with momentum $\vec{p}$.

3   We assumed that both bodies exerted equal but opposite forces upon one another during the collision period Δt.

4   We concluded that the momentum of both the wall and the ball changed in such a way that the total momentum of the isolated system remained constant.

$$\vec{p} = \vec{p}' + \vec{P}'$$

or, writing it in terms of masses, $\vec{mv} = \vec{m'v'} + \vec{M'V'}$ where we have understood the primes to signify post-collision quantities.

It is tempting to generalize even further and to say that, in an isolated system as we have defined it, the sum of the vector momenta at any time is constant. We can state this symbolically as

$$\sum_{i=1}^{N} \vec{P_i} = \text{constant} \qquad [5.10]$$

where $\sum_{i=1}^{N}$ means the sum of all momenta for a total of N bodies, for an isolated system containing N masses. This is an immensely powerful principle if it turns out to be true. For example, it predicts that nothing that happens inside the system can possibly alter the sum of the momenta of its bodies.

Suppose that a system contains only one body—a bomb. If the bomb explodes into five fragments, will the sum of the momenta of the fragments equal the initial momentum of the bomb? All experimental evidence gathered to date on experiments of this kind indicates that the momentum of the system is precisely conserved no matter what happens. The power of this experimentally demonstrated principle will become increasingly apparent as you read further. At this point it is suggested that you go into the laboratory and try to demonstrate that the principal hypothesis is false.

Example A ball of putty of mass $m_2 = 4$ kg is lying motionless on a frictionless surface (Fig. 5.15). A marble of mass $m_1 = 0.2$ kg is fired into the center of the putty ball with initial velocity $v_1 = 15$ m/s. The marble imbeds itself in the putty in an "inelastic" collision, and the combined mass moves to the right with speed $\vec{V}'$. We shall now attempt to solve for $\vec{V}'$ using the principle of *conservation of momentum*.

When you approach any problem in physics, there are key questions that you should answer before you make any attempt to find an algebraic solution. Get into the habit of asking them.

1 Is this an isolated system or are there significant external forces with which one must deal?

2 Are the observed motions and changes in motion described from an *inertial frame of reference*? An inertial frame of reference is one that is unaccelerated. Always make sure that the frame of reference is *not* itself subject to change in velocity. (This point will be further illustrated in connection with circular motion.)

3 What is the physics of the situation, i.e., which natural laws apply to the observed phenomena?

In this case we are dealing with an isolated system, since no external forces are allowed to act on either body. The frame of reference is arbitrarily taken as that frame in which the putty ball is initially at rest. The frame is *inertial*, since the observer is not subject to any accelerating force. The physics applying to the case is the principle of conservation of momentum, which is generally stated as

$$\sum \vec{P} = \text{constant}$$

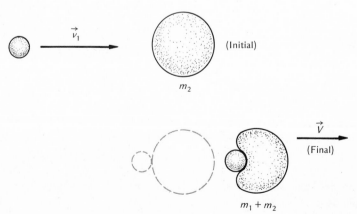

Fig. 5.15

in an isolated system such as this. It can be stated for this problem as

$$\overrightarrow{m_1 v_1} + \overrightarrow{m_2 v_2} = (m_1 + m_2)\, \vec{V'}$$

However, since $\vec{v_2} = 0$, this can be simplified to

$$m_1 \vec{v_1} = (m_1 + m_2)\, \vec{V'} \qquad\qquad [5.11]$$

Since m_1, m_2, and $\vec{v_1}$ are all known, the solution for $\vec{V'}$ is simple. Dividing both sides of the equation by $m_1 + m_2$ and reversing sides in the equation,

$$\vec{V'} = \frac{m_1}{m_1 + m_2}\, \vec{v_1} \qquad\qquad [5.12]$$

$$\vec{V'} = \left(\frac{0.2}{4 + 0.2}\right) \times 15 \quad\text{to the right}$$

$$\vec{V'} = 0.7 \text{ m/s} \quad\text{to the right}$$

At this point one further question should always be asked, and while it may seem trivial, it is extremely important even for experienced scientists.

4   Is the solution reasonable in magnitude and dimension, and is it consistent with what was intuitively expected?

In this case, a small mass with relatively high velocity collided with, and stuck to, a much larger mass. The resulting velocity of the combined mass was much smaller, and this is just as expected. Equation [5.12] sets one velocity equal to another velocity multiplied by a ratio of masses, so that the result is dimensionally correct as well as reasonable. Until you have the hang of asking all four of these questions automatically, make yourself a checklist and use it on every problem. Unless you do this, you will waste valuable time and develop thought patterns that will be hard to overcome later. Above all, do not attempt blindly to "plug" numbers into equations you find throughout the chapter.

In following the mechanics of Newton through the centuries from the **5.5** publication of "Principia," dozens of brilliant men expanded the work of *Energy* Newton to a highly refined materialistic model of the universe, a model which, incidentally, still holds today for macroscopic (large) bodies moving at speeds much less than the speed of light. The newtonian idea of momentum still applies even for microscopic bodies, though some of the basic definitions have changed somewhat. We shall illuminate these points further in later chapters.

The world is made up of bodies that get moved around or have their states of motion changed by forces. A fundamental question arises at this point. When a force acts on a body through some distance and for a finite time, is there something fundamental, other than altered momentum, transferred to the body by the motive agent? It is possible to apply a force to a body without changing its momentum ultimately. Such a force will simply produce a change in position of the body; for example, we might apply a force of 10 N to stretch a spring by 1 m. Is anything transferred to the spring in the process? Or we might lift a heavy rock from the ground up to chest height. Again, is anything transferred to the rock by virtue of this change in position, and does it *cost* the motive agent anything to do this?

Men struggled with these questions for some time. The result was that the newtonian model was enlarged to include the concept of work and energy. The model simply says that it is energy that is transferred from the motive agent to the body in any case where a net force acts through some distance to produce either a change in momentum of the body or a change in its position *or* both of these changes together. This idea has turned out to be extremely useful, as we shall see shortly. Let us now turn to a detailed consideration of work and energy.

Recall that it was Galileo who discovered a fundamental relationship in the experiment in which a ball is rolled down a very hard surface. He found that

$$v^2 = cd$$

where $v =$ ball's speed
               $d =$ distance down the plane
               $c =$ some constant

The thing that is particularly interesting here is that it is the square of v that increases with the distance d in linear fashion. This is the key to a very fundamental relationship, as we shall soon see.

In ordinary usage the word *work* has almost limitless meanings. You *work* hard trying to understand this chapter. An accountant *works* very hard at his calculations. A piece of machinery does not *work* properly, etc.

The scientist has a very precise quantitative definition for *work*. In a way it is consistent with popular definitions. Work means the product of a force and a distance through which a body is moved by the force.

$$W = Fd \qquad\qquad [5.13]$$

However, the force F is only that portion of the force lying in the direction of the distance d. For example, in the problem of the boy pulling the wagon, the pull on the tongue of the wagon is not aligned with the distance through which the wagon actually moves (Fig. 5.16).

In order to find the work done on the wagon, the distance d is multiplied by the component of F lying in the direction of d,

$$F_d = F \cos 0 \qquad\qquad [5.14]$$

Now the work done on the wagon is given by

$$W = (F \cos 0)(d) \qquad\qquad [5.15]$$

This is reasonable, since it is only the force component F_d that has been useful in moving the wagon through distance d. The wagon has not moved upward at all. In practice the component F_d can be found by carefully constructing the force vector diagram and measuring directly.

The units of work in the mks system are a composite of those of force and distance.

$$W = \text{newtons} \times \text{meters}$$
$$\equiv \text{joules}$$

The *joule* is the mks unit of work. If it is known how many joules of work have been expended in moving a body from one point to another, the total energy expended is also known in the same units.

But there are really two ways in which we can change the external energy of a body. We can change the speed of the body by applying a net force, and this changes the *kinetic energy* of the body. Or we can change the

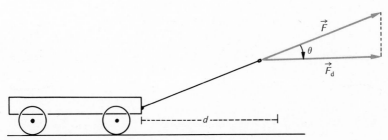

Fig. 5.16

position of the body relative to some variable force, i.e., its *potential energy*.

The kinetic energy is rather easy to visualize. For example, in a gravitational system such as that at the earth's surface, a bowling ball of mass m dropped from a height of 10 m will accelerate downward at the rate of 9.8 m/s². The kinetic energy, or energy of motion, of the ball increases linearly with the distance through which it falls.

Now recall that Galileo found that this distance is proportional to the square of the velocity of the ball. Since the gravitational acceleration close to the earth is nearly constant, we can check this result using our constant-acceleration equations from Chap. 4.

$$y = \tfrac{1}{2}at^2 + v_o t + y_o$$

The initial speed, v_o, is zero in this case, and $y_o = 10$ m above the ground or zero plane. So, as we see in Fig. 5.17,

$$y = \tfrac{1}{2}at^2 + y_o$$

can now be set equal to zero at the time t when the ball strikes the ground.

$$\tfrac{1}{2}at^2 + y_o = 0$$

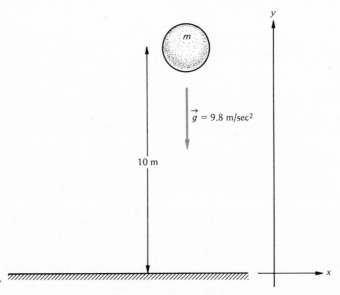

Fig. 5.17

or rearranging ($g =$ acceleration of gravity),

$$-gt^2 = -2y_o \qquad\qquad [5.16]$$

The time t can be found in terms of the velocity from

$$v = at + v_o$$
$$v = -gt$$

and solving for t,

$$t = -\frac{v}{g}$$

Substituting this value in Eq. [5.16],

$$-g\left(-\frac{v}{g}\right)^2 = -2y_o$$

and

$$v^2 = 2y_o g$$

y_o is the distance traveled by the bowling ball when it strikes the ground. We can, therefore, recognize in this result the same result found experimentally by Galileo,

$$v^2 = (2g)(y_o) \qquad\qquad [5.17]$$

since $2g$ is a constant.

The bowling ball will have reached a final velocity the instant before striking the ground of

$$v_{final} = -gt_{final}$$

t_{final} can be found from Eq. [5.16] as

$$t_{final} = \sqrt{\frac{2y_o}{g}}$$

Substituting this value into Eq. [5.17], we find that

$$v_{final} = -g\sqrt{\frac{2y_o}{g}}$$

or squaring both sides,

$$v_{\text{final}}^2 = g^2 \, \frac{2y_o}{g} = (2g)(y_o) \tag{5.18}$$

and again we have Galileo's result.

The momentum of the ball at this point is $mv_{\text{final}} = m\sqrt{2gy_o}$. If the soft ground stops the ball in a distance of 3 cm in a time of 0.2 s, what work did the ball do upon the ground? It is quite reasonable that the ball will be able to do an amount of work on the soft ground equal to that amount of work done on the ball by gravity as it falls from y_o. Since the gravitational force is constant, this work is calculated as

$$W = Fd$$
$$= mg \times y_o$$

that is, the force of gravity times the distance through which the ball drops. Now notice that by multiplying the right side by $\frac{2}{2}$, we get

$$\tfrac{1}{2}m \times 2gy_o$$

From Eq. [5.17] we know that

$$2gy_o = v_{\text{final}}^2$$

and so we can now rewrite the work expression as

$$\text{Work} = mgy_o$$
$$= \tfrac{1}{2}mv_{\text{final}}^2 \tag{5.19}$$

Pay close attention to the fact that the first of the solutions reports the work done as a function of *original position*, y_o, and the final solution reports the work done as a function of *final velocity*. This last solution is called the *kinetic energy*:

$$\boxed{KE = \tfrac{1}{2}mv^2} \tag{5.20}$$

The first solution is called the *gravitational potential energy*:

$$\boxed{PE = mgy_o} \tag{5.21}$$

It is not a coincidence that these two values are equal.

We can interpret the bowling ball problem in this way: At a height of y_o above the ground, the ball will have potential energy mgy_o; i.e., if it is dropped to the ground, it will be capable of doing work mgy_o on the ground or any object placed upon the ground, such as an aluminum plate. As it falls to ground level, its potential energy mgy_o goes to zero, and its energy is now expressed as kinetic energy, $\frac{1}{2}mv_{final}^2$.

There is an enormously important principle involved here. At the top (y_o) the kinetic energy is zero and the potential energy is maximum, mgy_o. At the bottom, where $y = 0$, the potential energy is zero and the kinetic energy is a maximum, $\frac{1}{2}mv_{final}^2$, and

$$mgy_o = \frac{1}{2}mv_{final}^2 \qquad\qquad\qquad [5.22]$$

In fact, at any point in the path of the ball the sum of its instantaneous potential and kinetic energies will always be the same. To illustrate the power of this concept, suppose we ask this question: What is the velocity of the ball at a point 1 m above the ground? Now, if

Total energy = KE + PE = constant

then we can write

$$\frac{1}{2}mv_o{}^2 + mgy_o = \frac{1}{2}mv_1{}^2 + mg \times 1$$

and since $v_o = 0$, this simplifies to

$$mgy_o = \frac{1}{2}mv_1{}^2 + mg$$

Collecting terms in preparation for finding v_1,

$$\frac{1}{2}mv_1{}^2 = mgy_o - mg$$
$$= mg(y_o - 1)$$
$$v_1{}^2 = 2g(y_o - 1)$$

and so

$$v_1 = \sqrt{2g(y_o - 1)}$$

Finding the numerical solution,

$$v_1 = \sqrt{176.4}$$
$$= 13.3 \text{ m/s}$$

The final velocity may be calculated now from

$$\tfrac{1}{2}mv_{\text{final}}^2 = mgy_o$$

$$v_{\text{final}}^2 = 2gy_o \tag{5.23}$$

as we have already seen in Eq. [5.17].

Plotting a graph of the two energies vs. y, we see that the kinetic and potential energies at any y always sum to $\mathscr{E}_{\text{total}}$ (Fig. 5.18). This is known as the *conservation of energy* principle.

Answer these questions before going on.

1 How much work was done in raising the bowling ball from the ground to y_o in the first place?

2 When the ball finally comes to rest on the ground, its potential energy relative to the ground is zero and it has lost its kinetic energy. What happened to this energy?

Nothing has so far been said concerning internal energy such as thermal energy. In summary, we have defined only two kinds of energy: (1) stored or potential energy due to a force that can act to do work—potential energy such as that due to gravitation or such as that stored in a com-

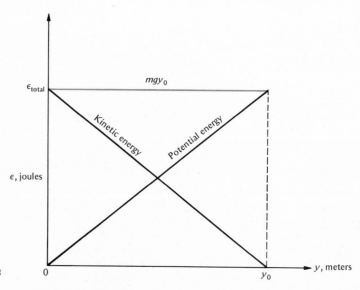

Fig. 5.18

pressed spring; and (2) energy that derives from the relative motion of a body—kinetic energy. A change in either of these energies constitutes work.

$$W = \Delta KE = \Delta PE$$

There is a class of dynamics problems which represent common phenomena and yet which cannot be solved employing solely the principle of conservation of momentum. For example, in the case of a collision of two bodies, we wish to calculate the momentum of either body after the collision. We do not, however, have any information on what occurs physically during the collision. Will one or both bodies be permanently distorted? Will they stick together, or will they rebound? And, if they rebound, how?

5.6 Conservation

Two hard steel spheres of equal size and equal mass undergo a collision as follows: the first mass moves initially toward the center of the second mass at velocity $\vec{v_1} = 20$ m/s, while the second mass is initially at rest in this frame, $m_1 = m_2 = 5$ kg (Fig. 5.19). We are to find the velocity of the first mass after the collision. Again, we shall use primes upon the variables to indicate post-collision values. The frame of reference is inertial, the system being isolated from external forces, and the physics involved seems to be the principle of conservation of momentum.

$$\sum \vec{P_i} = \text{constant}$$

We know that the initial momentum in the system is the momentum of m_1.

$$\vec{p_1} = \vec{m_1 v_1}$$

Hence, whatever the post-collision momentum vectors are, they must sum to $\vec{p_1}$.

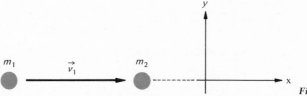

Fig. 5.19

$$\vec{p}_1 = \vec{p}_1' + \vec{p}_2'$$

Since the collision is known to be on-center, no component of motion in any direction other than x will exist. Both will travel in either a $+x$ or $-x$ direction. This simplifies the problem somewhat. Let us now consider the possible reasonable alternatives.

1   m_1 will rebound with a negative momentum, in which case m_2 will go forward with $\vec{p}_2' > \vec{p}_1$.

2   m_1 and m_2 will both move forward with different momenta, the sum of which is $\vec{p}_1$.

3   m_1 will stop, and m_2 will carry forward with momentum $\vec{p}_2' = \vec{p}_1$.

Which do you think will happen? The point is that conservation of momentum alone does not supply the answer. There are unlimited combinations of $\vec{p}_1'$ and $\vec{p}_2'$ that all sum to $\vec{p}_1$. From this point of view any one of the three possibilities might happen.

Recall from the example of the ball striking the wall that during the collision both were subject to equal but opposite forces for the same duration of time, Δt, during which they were physically in contact. Our two hard steel balls are not going to become permanently distorted by the collision. They will each be momentarily compressed, but they will instantly spring back to their original shapes. If we assume that no energy is lost in this process, we have the solution to the problem at hand. If no energy is lost, kinetic energy must be conserved, since no net work was done on the balls.

$$\sum KE = \text{constant}$$

Now we can write this down for the problem:

$$\tfrac{1}{2}m_1v_1{}^2 = \tfrac{1}{2}m_1v_1'^2 + \tfrac{1}{2}m_2v_2'^2 \qquad [5.24]$$

Note that the kinetic energy may be written in terms of the scalar value of momentum as

$$\tfrac{1}{2}mv^2 = \frac{p^2}{2m}$$

$$= \frac{m^2v^2}{2m}$$

$$= \frac{mv^2}{2}$$

So Eq. [5.24] may be rewritten as

$$\frac{p_1{}^2}{2m_1} = \frac{p_1'^2}{2m_1} + \frac{p_2'^2}{2m_2} \qquad [5.25]$$

Multiplying both sides by 2, and realizing that $m_1 = m_2 = m$, so that we can also multiply both sides by m,

$$p_1{}^2 = p_1'^2 + p_2'^2 \qquad \text{conservation of KE} \qquad [5.26]$$

and from conservation of momentum we have

$$\vec{p}_1 = \vec{p}_1' + \vec{p}_2' \qquad \text{conservation of } p \qquad [5.27]$$

The only way that Eqs. [5.26] and [5.27] can be simultaneously true is if either p_1' or p_2' is zero. Therefore, one of the masses must carry off all the original momentum. m_2 is the only one in position to do this. Possibility 3 is the correct state of affairs.

From Eqs. [5.26] and [5.27] it is also readily seen that, in the event of an off-center collision with resulting y-component motions, the two momentum vectors $\vec{p}_1'$ and $\vec{p}_2'$ must lay at right angles to one another. Equation [5.27] may be diagrammed as a triangle such that the square of one side is equal to the sum of squares of the other two sides. This is, of course, the pythagorean theorem for a right triangle.

This is one example of the power of these two conservation principles considered simultaneously. The physics of the situation is not fully delineated by stating the conservation of momentum. A full delineation comes only from simultaneously applying the principles of conservation of momentum and energy.

5.7 Summary

These threads of newtonian mechanics need to be drawn together in a coherent tapestry. At this point you may be somewhat confused by symbolism and what seems to be a large grouping of somewhat unrelated ideas.

The essence of Newton's contribution was to draw together a set of unifying principles—call them *laws* if you wish—that apply universally to all observable physical objects, including those in space. As we have already pointed out, this was a radically new approach in his day and was highly unpopular in some quarters.

Assuming that one can describe motion from any inertial frame of reference, the ideas of Newton provide a completely satisfying explanation for the behavior of all macroscopic objects. If we can describe the way in which the momentum of a body changes with time, we know the force acting upon it.

$$1 \qquad \vec{F} = \frac{\Delta \vec{p}}{\Delta t}$$

If, on the other hand, we know the net force acting upon a body, we can state the rate of change of its momentum, remembering that both $\vec{F}$ and $\Delta \vec{p}$ are vector quantities.

Given an isolated inertial system, we know that the total momentum of the system is at all times constant regardless of interactions within the system. It has been suggested that the total energy of an isolated system — a scalar quantity — is a constant as well.

$$2 \qquad \sum_{i=1}^{n} \vec{p}_i = \text{constant}$$

$$3 \qquad \sum_{i=1}^{n} E_i = \text{constant}$$

In any case, neglecting internal energies such as heat, the sum of the potential and kinetic energies has been shown to be a constant in at least some systems.

This material can be properly assimilated only if the problems and investigations are satisfactorily pursued to completion.

**5.8
A Noninertial
Frame of
Reference**

Up to now, all examples have been highly idealized in order to be consistent with "isolated" systems and "inertial" (unaccelerated) frames of reference. We shall show now that none of these beautifully constructed principles hold in an accelerated frame of reference.

We live, in fact, in an accelerated frame of reference. At the surface of this planet we have a uniform circular motion of speed dependent upon our latitude. From the discussion of uniform circular motion in Chap. 4, it will be recalled that such motions are always accelerated with the acceleration vector pointing always toward the center of rotation. If an observer stands at the equator, his rotational radius is about 6×10^6 m and his period of rotation is one day (Fig. 5.20). His centripetal acceleration is, therefore,

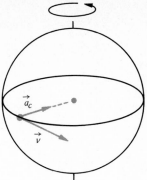

Fig. 5.20

$$a = \frac{v^2}{R} = \omega^2 R = \frac{4\pi^2 R}{T^2}$$

$$\approx \frac{10^1 \times 10^7}{(10^5)^2} = 10^{-2} = .01 \ \text{m/s}^2$$

where the symbol $\approx$ means that this is only a rough order-of-magnitude calculation. If we are then in an accelerated frame of reference, why is it possible to demonstrate the correctness of the newtonian principles in the laboratory?

Imagine a large record turntable, large enough for an observer to climb up and stand on as it rotates in uniform circular motion around its hub, about 50 m in diameter (Fig. 5.21). In this frame of reference, it is easy to demonstrate that the observer's description of the motion of a bowling ball will not agree with that of a second observer standing on the floor near the turntable. If O_1 sets the ball down at his feet and releases it, he will see the ball accelerate directly away from the hub toward the edge of the turntable along one radius. He will therefore conclude that a force is acting on the ball along the radius outward. As he repeats this experiment, he finds again and again a force always directed away from the center hub. He concludes that there is, in fact, a force on the ball, and further

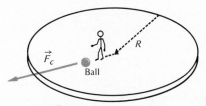

Fig. 5.21

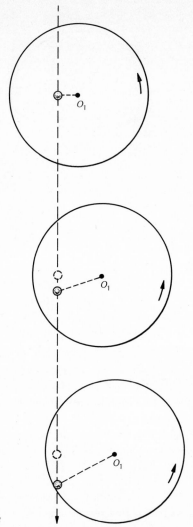

Fig. 5.22

notices that it is greater the further out along the radius the ball is placed, i.e., very small near the hub and maximum near the rim.

Observer O_2, however, describes the same experiments in quite a different way. At the instant before the ball is released, he sees it traveling in a circle with a velocity that changes direction constantly and whose magnitude varies with the radius of the circle.

$$v = \omega R$$

When the ball is released, O_2 sees it move along a straight line with a constant velocity, whatever its tangent velocity happened to be at the instant of release, and concludes that no force is acting after release. Which observer is correct?

The observer seated on the turntable is, of course, accelerated himself, as would be clear if the turntable were very slick, since he would have difficulty staying on it (Fig. 5.22). Hence, O_1 is led to describe apparent forces that do not exist. He is maintained in circular motion at some radius R by a frictional force of the form

$$F = ma = \frac{mv^2}{R} = m\omega^2 R$$

in which the centripetal acceleration v^2/R is the same as that described in Chap. 4.

1   You find yourself lying in the middle of a perfectly smooth, frozen **Problems** pond. The ice is lightly dusted with powder snow and so slick that you cannot even stand up on it. You have no sharp instruments with which to get a grip on the ice. How will you get to the edge of the pond? Explain your method in terms of Newton's laws of motion.

2   You are a 100-kg astronaut in deep space with a massive set of oxygen tanks strapped to your harness. The tanks have a mass of 30 kg. You have become separated from your ship by a distance of 150 m and are drifting steadily away from it at 2 m/s speed. You must act quickly to get back to the ship. You have a small emergency oxygen bottle that will let you breathe for 2 min after disconnecting your back tanks. What velocity must you give the 30-kg tanks in order to return to the ship in time?

3   A high-speed 1,000-kg rocket sled traveling at a speed of 100 m/s is stopped within 300 m by lowering two scoops into a water bath. The scoops are designed to project streams of water at right angles to the sled plate on either side.

   a   What average force must the water exert on the sled to stop it in 300 m?

   b   How long does it take to stop the sled?

   c   What is the average rate of change of sled momentum during this stopping?

   d   If momentum is conserved, where does the sled's momentum go? (*Hint:* Assume constant acceleration to solve for average values. Use the kinematic equations of Chap. 4.)

4   A man leans against the side of a building and pushes as hard as he can, but the wall does not move. Does the man do any work? Is any energy expended? How do you reconcile your answers to the preceding two problems?

5   A 500-kg mass is raised by a crane to a height of 10 m above a piling head and then dropped on the piling. As a result the piling is driven 5 cm into the ground.
  a What is the speed of the mass as it strikes the piling?
  b If the driving mass comes to rest in 5 cm, what is its change in momentum?
  c What total work is done by the driving mass when it is dropped?
  d If the piling moves into the ground for 0.15 s, what work is done on the piling alone? Where does the balance of the energy go?

6   On a straight stretch of highway a Volkswagen of mass 1,000 kg is traveling north at 30 m/s. A Cadillac sedan of mass 2,100 kg is traveling south at 35 m/s, and the two run head on into one another. During the collision both cars are welded into a solid mass.
  a What is the change in momentum for a 100-kg driver of the Cadillac during the collision?
  b What is the change in momentum for a 100-kg driver of the Volkswagen during the collision?
  c How much kinetic energy is lost in the collision? Where does it go?
  d If the impact upon either driver is given by $\vec{F}\Delta t = \Delta \vec{p}$, which driver will suffer most in the collision? Why?

7   Assuming that the moon circles the earth once every 28 d at a distance of some 3.8×10^8 m, what is its acceleration in this motion? What produces such an acceleration?

Bibliography   **Andrade, Edward N.:** "Sir Isaac Newton," Anchor Science Study Series, Doubleday, Garden City, N.Y., 1958.

Cohen, I. Bernard: "Birth of a New Physics," Anchor Science Study Series, Doubleday, Garden City, N.Y., 1960.

Feynman, et al.: "The Feynman Lectures on Physics," vol. 1, Addison-Wesley, Reading, Mass., 1963.

Harvard Project Physics: Text and Reader Nos. 1 and 3, Holt, New York, 1968.

Hoyle, Fred: "The Black Cloud," Harper & Row, New York, 1957.

Newton, Isaac: "Mathematical Principles of Natural Philosophy," transl. Motte-Cajori, University of California Press, Berkeley, 1962.

Physical Science Study Committee: "Physics," Heath, Boston, 1960.

Chapter 6
The Field Idea

Galileo making his
experiments on the
velocity of falling
bodies from the
Leaning Tower of
Pisa. (Courtesy of the
Bettmann Archive,
Inc.)

We have at this point gone well into the mechanics of Newton. Perhaps you have found this tedious, while at the same time somehow exciting.

Newton was a peculiar individual. He was at once brilliant beyond other men of his time and yet deathly afraid of the criticisms of these men. Without the urging of men like the astronomer Halley, he would certainly never have published his momentous book called the "Principia." In the third volume, he set down the mechanics of the world system as a logical extension of his basic mechanics — the mechanics of bodies in isolated systems that we have just examined.

But we are already ahead of our story.

**6.1
Demon Force**
You will recall that Kepler set about to prove the correctness of the ptolemaic model for the universe. He spent years looking for supporting evidence in the mountain of astronomical data that came from Brahe's observatory in Denmark. His principal job with Brahe was to attempt to explain the worrisome orbit of the planet Mars, an orbit that was observed to be rather complicated. Even though Kepler vigorously sought to justify the ptolemaic model with its epicycles and equants, he was torn by a fundamental belief that bodies move in observed ways because of motive forces. He rejected, therefore, the notion of small epicycles, since there was nothing at the center of these small loops that could possibly motivate the planet to move in the supposed circle.

Early in the seventeenth century, Kepler published his book entitled "Astronomia Nova" ("New Astronomy"). His efforts to fit the observations of Brahe on the Mars orbit to the geocentric-equant model had failed. But in this failure lay the beginnings of our understanding of the mechanics of celestial bodies.

So it was Kepler, and not Newton, who first made reference to the necessity of a motive force to explain the motions of celestial bodies. It is a curious twist of human personality that his contemporary, Galileo, himself persecuted by the church for his views, was nettled by Kepler's reference to this motive force. Apparently, Galileo considered the idea of a demon force, which could act upon bodies at great distance from one another, to be preposterous.

We shall be concerned here with the details of Kepler's findings. Keep in mind the fact that Kepler made an enormous contribution to human thought in his refusal to accept the mysticism of celestial numerology and in his demand that some force acting over great distances — a force somehow related to or dependent upon the bodies themselves — was necessary to the observed motions. Thus, while Galileo was busy describing the dynamics of bodies falling at the earth's surface, Kepler was busy with the first description of celestial dynamics.

Accepting Brahe's observations as true representations of the planetary orbits, Kepler set himself to work upon the enormous task of analyzing these data. This analysis is in itself an interesting story, but space restricts our present discussion to the results of his labors.

It matters very little whether you remember which law is number one and so forth, but for the sake of convenience, they are listed here in the traditional sequence.

1   The orbits of the planets establish a series of planes, all of which planes include the sun. These orbits are elliptical, not circular, and have the sun fixed at one focus of the ellipse.

This remarkable observation places all planets in a group with something in common, i.e., their relationship to the sun. The ellipse is not a complicated closed curve. You can generate one by drawing at random two points on a paper (see Fig. 6.1). Now place pins on the points and tie a very loose string to both pins. With a pencil stretch the string tight, and being careful to keep the string tight, draw the curve. The pins represent the foci. The ellipse is the curve of all points for which $R_1 + R_2$ is constant. In Kepler's first law, we have this same situation.

2   An imaginary line drawn from the sun to a planet sweeps out equal areas within the elliptical plane in equal times; e.g., if 30 d are required for the planet in Fig. 6.2 to go from point q_1 to q_2, and if the same 30 d are required for it to go from q_3 to q_4, swept area A_1 equals swept area A_2.

From this it is clear that the planet travels relatively fast near the sun and relatively slow far from the sun in its orbit. This is, qualitatively at least,

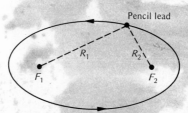

Pencil lead

R_1 R_2

F_1 F_2

Fig. 6.1

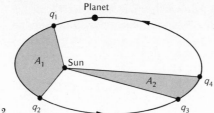

Fig. 6.2

consistent with experience where a force of attraction is assumed between the sun and the planet. If you whirl a ball on a string in a circle and shorten the string as the ball whirls, the angular speed of the ball increases with decreasing circular radius.

3   The ratio of the cube of the mean radius to the square of the orbital period for all planets in orbit about the sun is a constant.

$$\frac{R^3}{T^2} = K \qquad\qquad [6.1]$$

where K is a constant with dimensions m^3/s^2.

This is the experimentally determined relationship that led ultimately to the development of the universal law of gravitation. Note that these three laws of Kepler were derived from empirical evidence and not based upon any theoretical assumption.

Kepler struggled for years with Brahe's data, trying to make the numbers fit first one model and then another, but never getting satisfactory agreement with any model. He made a number of errors of analysis, but these, fortunately, converged in time. Curiously, Kepler was led again and again to elliptical orbits but each time rejected the ellipse as a nonsense solution. As was stated earlier, if Brahe's data had been better (more accurate) by one order of magnitude, Kepler would almost certainly have rejected the elliptical solution. Data gathered by today's instruments do not fit the elliptical orbit. Mercury, for example, has an orbit that wanders rather markedly from elliptical. This development, coming when it did in Europe, represented a marked departure from the more usual nonempirical method of investigation. The empirical method of science began with such men as Kepler and Galileo at a time when Europe was torn by religious and political struggles and North America was not yet settled.

Before the musical genius Bach wrote his first note, Newton had given the world what must be counted as one of the most brilliant works of human intellect, the "Principia." In the third volume of "Principia," Newton used those principles of earthly mechanics developed in the first two books to analyze completely the world system. In this prodigious work, he analyzed the motions of the satellites of Jupiter and Saturn and of the planets orbiting the sun. He calculated the masses of the sun and planets and came very near to describing accurately the earth's mass, density, and shape. He analyzed the tides and deduced that the lopsided earth ought to wobble very slowly upon its polar axis; it does, in fact, wobble with a period of about 15,000 years.

6.3
Universal
Gravitation

Yet in all this Newton avoided the question of what gravity really is, being content to describe only what it does in a manner so complete that today spaceships are navigated to the moon and the planets using very little more than newtonian gravitational mechanics.

In "Principia" Newton synthesized the work of Kepler and Galileo and his own experimental work to produce a mechanical model that all bodies must follow.

We know that the orbit of the earth around the sun is very nearly a circle. Newton reasoned that any body in uniform circular motion about a center of rotation must be subject to a force of the form

$$F_c = \frac{mv^2}{R}$$ [6.2]

where m = the mass of the orbiting body
v = its tangent speed
R = its orbital radius

If you whirl a ball on a string around in a circle, you have already experienced this force. You know that to increase the ball's speed requires increasingly greater effort as v increases. You will also note that the larger the radius R, the smaller the effort you use to restrain the ball. Specifically, the centripetal force is the force directed toward the center or rotation and acting upon the ball. Do not confuse this with the outward pull of the ball upon the string. Added to this was the empirical evidence that Kepler had found, i.e.,

$$\frac{R^3}{T^2} = K$$

We have here two apparently unrelated results. The first, mv^2/R, is a purely analytical statement based on logic. It holds for any and all bodies that are constrained to move in a circle. The second, $R^3/T^2 = K$, is a purely empirical result coming from experimental data. We shall now consider both results together to show that both are keys to a result that has far-reaching impact on our world view. Keep in mind that wherever Kepler's result enters into the argument, this represents real measurements made in Brahe's experiment. Rewriting this expression, we see that

$$\frac{1}{T^2} = \frac{K}{R^3}$$

A body in circular motion has a period of rotation T of the form

$$T = \frac{1}{\text{frequency}}$$

$$= \frac{1}{2\pi\omega}$$

Hence,

$$\omega = \frac{1}{2\pi T} \qquad \text{rad/s}$$

Now the tangent speed of such a body is

$$v = \omega R \qquad \text{(rad/s)(m/rad)}$$

so that the *centripetal force* may be written

$$F_c = \frac{mv^2}{R}$$

$$= m\omega^2 R \qquad\qquad\qquad [6.3]$$

And further, substituting for ω the value in T,

$$F_c = mR \left(\frac{1}{2\pi T}\right)^2$$

$$= \frac{mR}{4\pi^2 T^2} \qquad\qquad\qquad [6.4]$$

which for convenience we can rewrite in the form

$$F_c = \frac{mR}{4\pi^2} \frac{1}{T^2} \qquad\qquad [6.5]$$

At this point, we may substitute Kepler's expression for $1/T^2$ taken from observations as reported in Eq. [6.1].

$$F_c = \frac{mR}{4\pi^2} \frac{K}{R^3}$$

$$= \frac{K}{4\pi^2} \frac{m}{R^2} \qquad\qquad [6.6]$$

Note that this form of the centripetal force includes the observations of Kepler of planets in orbit about the sun. The constant K is truly a constant only so long as the sun is the body at the center or focus. Equation [6.6] establishes the inverse-square relationship between the force and the distance R.

$$F \propto \frac{1}{R^2}$$

The realization of this relationship was of immense importance, as we shall see.

Newton was assisted in his work on centripetal force and circular oscillatory motion by the previous work of his contemporary, Christian Huygens, an eminent Dutch scientist about whom we shall have more to say later.

We can now combine the constant portion of Eq. [6.6] into a single constant K_s:

$$F_s = \frac{K_s m}{R^2} \qquad\qquad [6.7]$$

where the subscript s refers to the fact that it is the sun that lies at one focus of all these ellipses. In another system, such as that of Jupiter with its moons, a new constant is required, K_J, for the centripetal force

$$F_J = \frac{K_J m}{R^2}$$

And for the earth with its moon, still another constant, K_e, is required.

In the case of each new system, the constant K found from experimental observations seemed to be somewhat proportional to the physical size of the central body in the system. Newton hypothesized from this that when the mass of the central body is extracted from the constant, the remaining constant, G, is indeed unchanging regardless of the gravitational system involved.

$$F = \frac{GMm}{R^2} \qquad [6.8]$$

This equation, in which M is the mass of the central body and G is the universal gravitational constant,

$$G = 6.67 \times 10^{-11} \text{ m}^3/(\text{kg})(\text{s}^2)$$

is still merely the expression for centripetal force on a body of mass m providing that $M \gg m$.

$$\boxed{\frac{mv^2}{R} = \frac{GMm}{R^2}} \qquad [6.9]$$

Equation [6.9] is very powerful in that it opened the way for Newton to calculate the relative masses of the planets and to make definite statements concerning the energies of bodies in a gravitational-force field.

The problem of determining a good value for G was complicated by the fact that bodies that can be manipulated in a laboratory attract one another with such a tiny force as to be unmeasurable except by extremely sophisticated techniques. These techniques were not available to Newton. It is possible to gain an accurate value of G by observing large bodies in space *only* if the observer already knows the mass of at least one of those bodies. Nobody has ever been able to devise a scale for weighing a planet, so G had to be measured using small masses for which the mass is precisely known.

We can illustrate the difficulty by taking the example of two identical bags of sand of measured mass $m = 2 \times 10^2$ kg. If we place these such that their mass centers are 1 m apart, the gravitational force of attraction would be approximately

$$F_g = \frac{Gmm}{R^2}$$

$$\approx \frac{10^{-10} \times 10^2 \times 10^2}{10^0}$$

$$\approx 10^{-6} \text{ N}$$

or about the weight of a mosquito. It is very hard to measure experimentally a force of a millionth of a newton with sufficient accuracy to get a good value for G when the mass to be accelerated is so large.

It was not necessary for Newton to have a precise value for G in order to calculate the *relative* masses of planets. We can illustrate this fact by considering the attraction of three bodies. If we select one of the planets that has an observable satellite, e.g., the earth, since it is at hand, we know that

$$F_{em} = \frac{GM_eM_m}{R_{em}^2} = \frac{M_m v_m^2}{R_{em}}$$

where e and m refer to earth and moon, and em refers to the earth-moon system. Similarly, we know that for the sun and earth we have

$$F_{se} = \frac{GM_sM_e}{R_{se}^2}$$

$$= \frac{M_e v_e^2}{R_{se}}$$

Now, considering Eq. [6.9], we can see that

$$M_e = \frac{v_m^2 R_{em}}{G} \qquad\qquad [6.10]$$

and similarly,

$$M_s = \frac{v_e^2 R_{se}}{G} \qquad\qquad [6.11]$$

The ratio of the mass of the earth, m_e, to that of the sun, m_s, is given by dividing Eq. [6.10] by Eq. [6.11]:

$$\frac{M_e}{M_s} = \frac{\dfrac{v_m^2 R_{em}}{G}}{\dfrac{v_e^2 R_{se}}{G}}$$

$$= \frac{v_m^2 R_{em}}{v_e^2 R_{se}} \qquad\qquad [6.12]$$

Notice that the constant G appears in both denominator and numerator in this ratio and therefore disappears. Note too that the relative mass of earth and sun can be found directly from the observation of distances and speeds for moon and sun and earth. It is very cumbersome to deal with the orbital velocities of the moon and earth, but their orbital periods are well known. Equation [6.12] may be rewritten replacing v by its equivalent in terms of the orbital period

$$v = \frac{2\pi R}{T}$$

$$\frac{M_e}{M_s} = \frac{R_{em}{}^3 T_e{}^2}{R_{se}{}^3 T_m{}^2}$$

$$\approx \frac{1}{3 \times 10^5}$$

i.e., the sun's mass is about 300,000 times that of earth.

A similar calculation for Jupiter would be

$$\frac{m_J}{m_s} \approx \frac{1}{1 \times 10^3}$$

i.e., the sun's mass is about 1,000 times that of Jupiter.

From this we can see that the earth is only about one-thousandth the mass of Jupiter and that all the planets together, Jupiter being the most massive, account for only about one-thousandth the mass of the sun. The sun is clearly the gravitational master of the solar system, the center of mass for the whole system being within the sun itself.

Henry Cavendish, born shortly after Newton's death, was responsible for finding a reasonably good value of G from laboratory experiments. This work took place at about the time of the American Declaration of Independence from English rule. At this time, men could finally begin to get good values for the masses of bodies in space by applying Newton's laws directly.

Newton's mechanics made possible the quantitative study of the solar system and the universe beyond the solar system. It might be argued that the science of astronomy had its real beginning with Newton. An exhaustive elaboration and refinement of newtonian mechanics was to occupy the life energies of brilliant men for more than two centuries after his death.

We have been setting down the formal theory of gravitation, but let us pause now to reflect on the theory a bit and to consider some interesting results. At no time did Newton attempt an explanation of "what gravity really is." He was content to develop a quantitative model from which predictions could be made and then checked by observation.

For example, there are several small planets in the solar system that have no satellites. Yet it has been possible to get good values for their masses by calculating the complex orbital changes due to the presence of other planets quite distant from the planets in question. The most striking case of this kind of calculation was the case in which the existence of the planet Pluto was established from calculations based upon the subtle deviation of other planets from a simple orbit. Men "knew" that Pluto existed and where to look for it *before* it was actually seen with a telescope.

No theory is perfect or final. In fact, the word *perfect* is unacceptable as a description of a physical model or theory. Models and theories are useful only to varying degrees. They may be remolded and refined toward the goal of making them embrace a wider range of physical evidence. Models and theories never survive intact and never fully explain all observational evidence. We shall return to this subject again.

With the newtonian mechanics at hand we are prepared to make some interesting observations. Suppose, for example, we wished to know at what altitude and speed a satellite of mass m would hang fixed above a point on the earth in its orbit (see Fig. 6.3). Such a satellite would have its orbital plane coincident with the earth's equatorial plane; that is, it would have to "hang" above a point on the equator. The satellite would

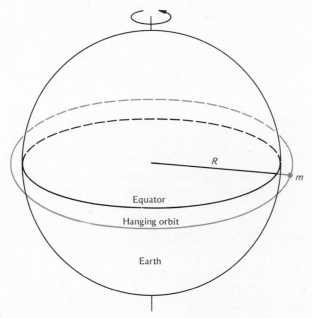

Fig. 6.3

also have to have exactly the same rotational period as that of the earth on its axis. The satellite would make one complete revolution in the same time that its fixed subpoint on the equator rotates once. But where do we begin to solve this problem?

This is clearly a gravitational problem of the kind Newton described. There are no external forces interfering so long as the satellite is substantially above the earth's atmosphere and not close enough to the moon to experience a significant gravitational force due to that body.

Assuming that only the earth need be considered, and considering only a circular orbit for simplicity,

$$\frac{m_s v_s^2}{R} = \frac{GM_e m_s}{R^2} \tag{6.13}$$

Note that R is the distance separating the mass centers of the earth and the satellite. Assume also that $m_s \ll M_e$. It is extremely fortunate that the mass of the satellite can be eliminated from Eq. [6.13] by dividing both sides by m_s:

$$\frac{v_s^2}{R} = \frac{GM_e}{R^2}$$

which simplifies further to

$$v_s^2 = \frac{GM_e}{R}$$

This equation can be solved for R:

$$R = \frac{GM_e}{v_s^2} \tag{6.14}$$

This is a single equation with two unknowns, R and v_s. We do know, however, that the satellite period is $T = 24$ h. Recall now that $v_s = 2\pi R/T_s$. Substituting this value in Eq. [6.14],

$$R = GM_e \frac{T_s^2}{4\pi^2 R^2}$$

$$R^3 = \frac{GM_e T_s^2}{4\pi^2}$$

and solving for R,

$$R = \sqrt[3]{\frac{GM_eT_s^2}{4\pi^2}}$$ [6.15]

Solving for the numerical value of R gives us that separation for which the period T_s will be exactly that of the earth's rotational period.

$$R = \sqrt[3]{\frac{6.7 \times 10^{-11} \times 6 \times 10^{24} \times (8.64 \times 10^4)^2}{4\pi^2}}$$

$$= 4.24 \times 10^7 \text{ m}$$

$$= 6.6 \text{ earth radii}$$

since $G = 6.7 \times 10^{-11}$
$\quad M_e = 6 \times 10^{24}$ kg
$\quad T_s = T_e$
$\qquad = 8.64 \times 10^4$ s

One of the striking features here is that satellites of any mass, so long as that mass is much smaller than the mass of earth, will follow the same orbit with the same period. This result is of considerable importance to an astronaut who becomes separated from an orbiting ship.

Another interesting problem is the one in which the velocity of a satellite is calculated when its orbit is just grazing the planet surface. There is a good reason for doing this, which will later be apparent.

The equation is the same as Eq. [6.14], which now needs to be solved for v_s,

$$v_s = \sqrt{\frac{GM_e}{R_p}}$$ [6.16]

where R_p is the planet's radius if its mass center is near its geometric center. This particular solution is for a satellite grazing the earth where atmospheric friction is neglected. The same expression is, however, just as valid for any similar planetary problem.

Suppose that a hypothetical planet has buried within it a huge deposit of some very dense material, such as gold. Suppose the gold is located near the surface so that the center of mass of the planet is displaced a considerable distance away from its geometric center (Fig. 6.4). Such a planet might or might not be rotating on some internal axis. If it did rotate, it would clearly appear to wobble. This is due to the fact that it would rotate about its center of mass rather than the geometric center.

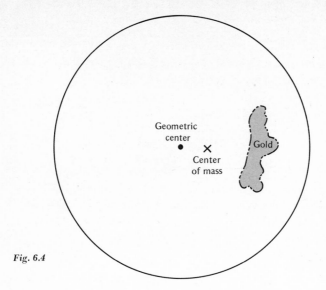

Fig. 6.4

Suppose, further, that it has very slow rotation or none at all. We could observe the motion of a man-made research satellite as it orbits about such a planet. The satellite will, of course, orbit the planet in a close-in orbit with the planetary center of mass as the orbital focus. A careful observation of this orbit will locate the center of mass for us. It may be that Venus is a planet of this type. Intensive research into the Venus problem is now under way.

There are a number of good reasons for placing artificial satellites in orbits of varying heights and speeds. Location of the planet's center of mass is only one. Scientists might wish to make measurements of surface features from varying altitudes. The science of geodesy deals with this problem for the earth.

Scientists might also wish to measure quantitatively the density and chemical composition of, say, a rarefied atmosphere. Other measurable variables would be temperature structure as a function of altitude and the amount and types of radiation present at each level. This list is by no means exhaustive.

To gain facility with this type of problem, work through the problems at the end of this chapter with some care. The calculations you will do have, generally, a very real and present application.

Given a planet in deep space, we could test its gravitational pull by placing a body of known mass at a number of different points in the space around it. At each point we could then measure the force of attraction on the mass. This is exactly what is done when a satellite is placed in orbit about the planet. By recording the magnitude and direction of the force on the satellite for each point in space, we can build up a map of the gravitational *field* of the planet. The field idea is just that—an idea or model that we use to help us think about a problem.

Those who have played miniature golf have probably been frustrated by a "hole" in which the cup sits in the center of a cone-shaped depression (see Fig. 6.5). If the ball is struck too hard, it will roll into the depression, curve toward the cup, and then climb out of the depression again to travel away in some new direction. If, however, the player is lucky, he will hit the ball gently enough so that it will roll slowly into the depression and not climb out again.

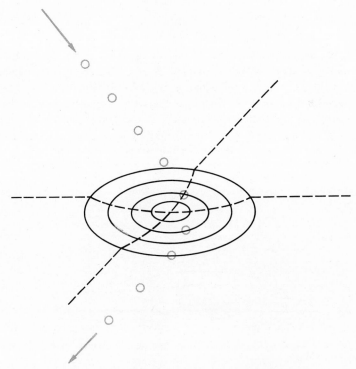

Fig. 6.5

In this latter case, the ball becomes trapped in the depression, eventually losing energy as it orbits about the cup, and finally falling into the cup. This system is quite like the gravitational field surrounding a planet in space. A ball of mass m, traveling through space with less than a certain critical velocity, may pass close enough to the gravitational depression to become permanently entrapped. The loss of energy through friction in the case of the golf ball might correspond to the case of a satellite losing energy through atmospheric friction in the region outside the planet's solid surface. In general, however, unless an atmospheric drag is encountered by the satellite, it will continue in a stationary orbit that will depend only upon its velocity of approach when it was far from the depression.

There is a convention used when talking about the energy of a body within a gravitational field that is potentially troublesome for students. It need not be so. We say that the ball that becomes trapped in the depression has a total energy that is negative. This simply means that it lacks sufficient energy to free itself from the gravitational attraction of the planet. Carrying this idea further, it would be said that the ball with sufficient energy to climb out of the depression and travel away would have a total energy that is positive relative to the gravitational field of the planet (Fig. 6.6).

Of course, the gravitational depression around a planet has no distance limit, but rather extends to infinity. Even though the earth is millions of miles from the sun, it still is bound by gravity to orbit the sun as a permanent satellite. By convention, if the earth were somehow given just enough energy to travel out from the sun so that its relative velocity just dropped to zero as it reached infinity, it would be said to have zero energy relative to the sun's gravitational field. Remember now,

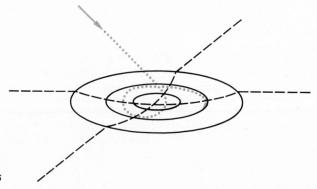

Fig. 6.6

Negative total energy $\longrightarrow$ trapped or "bound"

Zero total energy $\longrightarrow$ just escapes to infinity

Positive total energy $\longrightarrow$ escapes with energy to spare

For mathematics buffs, it should be noted that all negative-energy or "bound" bodies travel in *elliptical paths* of which the circle is just one possibility. Those with positive energy fly through the gravitational field in *hyperbolic paths*, and zero-energy bodies fly through in a *parabolic path*. It is not important for our present purposes to remember this.

Kinetic energy cannot be negative, so how is it that a body that is moving can have a total energy of less than zero? You will recall the principal equation of Newton's theory:

$$\frac{mv^2}{R} = \frac{GMm}{R^2} \qquad\qquad [6.9]$$

Now, in general, kinetic energy is always positive and of the form $\frac{1}{2} mv^2$. Notice that the left side of Eq. [6.9] is quite similar to KE. Multiplying both sides by R and then by $\frac{1}{2}$ will put it in proper form.

$$\frac{mv^2}{2} = \frac{GMm}{2R}$$

$$= \text{KE} \qquad\qquad [6.17]$$

This equation says that the kinetic energy of a satellite in orbit at distance R and with speed v is $GMm/2R$,

$$\text{KE} \propto \frac{1}{R}$$

A plot of this energy vs. the center-of-mass separation distance R would look like Fig. 6.7.

It is something of a curiosity to see from Eq. [6.16] that as the orbital radius becomes larger and larger, the velocity in orbit grows smaller. From Eq. [6.17] we can solve for orbital speed,

$$v = \sqrt{\frac{GM}{R}}$$

which is the same as Eq. [6.16], as it should be. At this point, you should plot the velocity vs. R for a satellite of the earth.

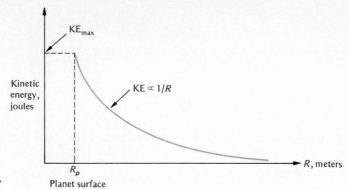

Fig. 6.7

The question of the potential energy is a bit more troublesome. Imagine a satellite at rest rather than in orbit, at a fixed distance R_1 from the earth's center (see Fig. 6.8). We shall hold the satellite at this point against the force of gravitational field to pull the satellite into a new separation, R_2.

The work done by the gravitational field is the product of the force in the direction of motion and the distance moved, ΔR.

$$W = F \, \Delta R = \Delta PE \qquad\qquad [6.18]$$

The difficulty in making the calculation comes from the fact that F changes with R rather than remaining constant over ΔR.

$$F_1 = \frac{GMm}{R_1{}^2}$$

$$F_2 = \frac{GMm}{R_2{}^2}$$

where $F_2 > F_1$. So the simple product $F \, \Delta R$ in Eq. [6.18] is not so simple after all.

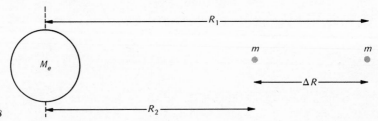

Fig. 6.8

We know, however, that the change in potential energy due to movement from R_1 to R_2 will be one that will result in a tighter binding of the satellite, i.e., it will take more work to pull the satellite away from the earth at R_2 than at R_1. So we know that potential energy must increase in magnitude as the satellite gets closer to the earth. This would indicate some sort of inverse relationship between PE and R. What the exact form of this is we do not yet know.

If the gravitational force were constant over the interval ΔR, we could easily find the work done and hence the change in potential energy by multiplying the force by the distance ΔR. Because the force does change continuously over ΔR, we need some kind of force-averaging technique to find the work done. This is done by summing the product $F \times R$ over many small increments of R, dR. dR is the tiny change in distance under consideration.

It is possible to see how this will work by looking carefully at the graph of F vs. R for our gravitational problem (see Fig. 6.9). In this case the constant of proportionality between F and $1/R^2$ is assumed to be 1, and all units are arbitrary.

$$F_{\text{grav}} = \frac{1}{R^2}$$

As R becomes small, the force of gravitational attraction rises sharply. The problem is to calculate the area under the curve between $R = 1$ and $R = 4$. This area is equivalent to either the work done by the field force in moving the body from $R = 4$ to $R = 1$, or the work done against the field in moving the body from $R = 1$ to $R = 4$.

It is, however, not a simple matter to calculate this area. We might approximate it by subdividing the area into triangles and rectangles until we have nearly the total area accounted for, as in Fig. 6.10.

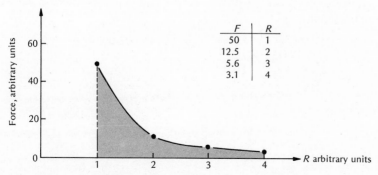

F	R
50	1
12.5	2
5.6	3
3.1	4

Fig. 6.9

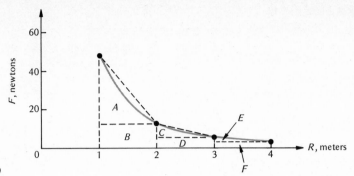

Fig. 6.10

Now an approximation of this area and therefore of the work done can also be found by an elegant technique invented by Newton for just such problems. It is beyond the scope of this text, so only the results of the technique are presented here.

$$W = \Delta U$$
$$= \frac{GMm}{R_1} - \frac{GMm}{R_4} \qquad [6.19]$$

In our problem graphed in Fig. 6.10, the product GMm was taken arbitrarily to have the value of 50. The change in potential energy is then

$$W = \Delta U$$
$$= 50 \left(\frac{1}{1} - \frac{1}{4} \right)$$
$$= 37.5 \text{ units}$$

As you can see, our geometrical approximation method gave an answer that is a little high.

The general form of the gravitational potential energy is

$$U = -\frac{GMm}{R} \qquad [6.20]$$

Recall now that the kinetic energy of a body in stable orbit is

$$KE = +\frac{GMm}{2R}$$

or half as great in magnitude as its potential energy in the orbit.

We can now find the total energy of the body in its orbit (satellite) as the sum of its potential energy (U) and kinetic energy (KE).

$$E_{\text{total}} = \frac{GMm}{2R} - \frac{GMm}{R}$$
$$= -\frac{GMm}{2R}$$

[6.21]

Remember that this energy is negative, indicating a bound body that cannot escape, and is good only for a satellite in stable orbit.

We can have fun now in working interesting satellite problems like the following.

An earth satellite of mass $m = 10^3$ kg is in orbit at a distance $R_1 = 10^7$ m *Example* from the earth's center.

1   How much energy binds the satellite to the earth?

$$M_{\text{earth}} \approx 6 \times 10^{24} \text{ kg}$$
$$G = 6.67 \times 10^{-11} \text{ m}^3/(\text{kg})(\text{s}^2)$$

$$\therefore E_1 = \frac{-GMm}{2R}$$
$$\approx -\frac{6.67 \times 10^{-11} \times 6 \times 10^{24} \times 10^3}{2 \times 10^7}$$
$$\approx -20 \times 10^9 \text{ J}$$

2   How much energy must we expend in order to raise the satellite to a new stable orbit of $R_2 = 10^8$ m?

$$\text{Work} = \Delta E = E_2 - E_1$$
$$= -\frac{GMm}{2R_2} + \frac{GMm}{2R_1}$$
$$= \frac{GMm}{2}\left(\frac{1}{R_1} - \frac{1}{R_2}\right)$$
$$= \left(\frac{6.67 \times 10^{-11} \times 6 \times 10^{24} \times 10^3}{2}\right)\left(\frac{1}{10^7} - \frac{1}{10^8}\right)$$
$$= 18 \times 10^9 \text{ J}$$

About 18 billion joules of energy are required to do this job. This is approximately the energy required to raise a 600,000-lb jetliner from the ground to about 7 km above the ground.

From this problem it is increasingly clear that energy is a prime consideration in space flight. If a certain type of propulsion fuel yields W joules of usable energy per kilogram of fuel mass, and if we wish to make a space journey that calls for a total energy expenditure of E_T, we must carry along a total of N kilograms of fuel, where

$$NW = E_T$$

The problem here is that the fuel itself often constitutes a major part of the takeoff mass of the spaceship and is expended as the ship uses the required energy.

6.5
Summary of
Gravitation

It is difficult to overemphasize the impact that Newton's "Principia" made upon the whole of human society. The effect was not immediate, since only a few scholars at the time were able to read the "Principia" with any real understanding. However, as the full import of the work was made available to the whole of society, the result was predictably dramatic. The geocentric model was once and for all crushed.

Man, at this point in time, found himself suddenly removed from the center of the world. Celestial objects were now to be regarded as nothing very special and, in any case, as subject to the same set of rules as earthly objects and the earth itself. For the first time men had a real glimpse at earth as a relatively tiny planet among a number of sister planets, many of which are more grand and spectacular than earth.

At the same time Newton's preoccupation with detailed mechanical analyses of systems of bodies set the pattern of scientific models and research for hundreds of years to come.

We have seen how Newton expanded the observations of Kepler on planetary orbits into the law of universal gravitation.

$$F_g = \frac{GMm}{R^2}$$

If a smaller body orbits a much larger one under the influence of this force, the gravitational attraction just supplies the centripetal force required to maintain the orbit (Fig. 6.11).

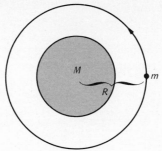

Fig. 6.11

$$\frac{GMm}{R^2} = \frac{mv^2}{R}$$

The orbital speed v is given from this by

$$v = \sqrt{\frac{GM}{R}}$$

and is independent of the satellite mass.

The work done on a body in a gravitational-force field is the difference in either the potential energy U or the kinetic energy KE. The potential energy U in the field is

$$U = -\frac{GMm}{R}$$

If the body is a satellite in stable orbit around a much larger body, the kinetic energy in the orbit is

$$KE = \frac{GMm}{2R}$$

or half the magnitude of its potential energy U. We take U to be negative, since the force is attractive between masses, and therefore, "binds" bodies together.

In the asteroid problem (Appendix D) we note that the minimum energy required to escape from the surface of a body to infinite distance is just the gravitational potential U at the surface. If a body is in orbit around another much larger body, it can just escape to infinity by expending energy equal to its orbital kinetic energy KE.

The mass of the asteroid can be determined experimentally by observing its mean radius and the period of an orbiting satellite at known separation as

$$M = \frac{4\pi^2 R^3}{GT^2}$$

The total energy required for the trip from the earth to another body must include an analysis not only of the earth's gravitational field but also of that of the sun and the body at destination.

Problems 1   If a high jumper can clear a 7-ft bar on the earth, how high could he clear a bar on Mars? (Mars mass $= 6.4 \times 10^{23}$ kg, Mars radius $= 3.4 \times 10^6$ m.)

2   Would you expect the variation in g with altitude above sea level to affect the outcome of the Olympic Games? Compare the broad jump, high jump, and shot-put events in games held in both London and Denver (elevation $\sim$ 5,000 ft above sea level).

3   How much energy must a 10^6-kg spaceship expend to just escape from Mercury to outer space beyond the solar system?

4   The sun and solar system are in orbit about the gravitational center of our galaxy. The solar system orbits under the influence of the gravitational attraction of all masses of bodies within its orbit. If the orbital radius is 3×10^{20} m, and the period is about 2×10^8 years, how much mass is included within its orbit?

5   Uranus has a mean orbital radius of about 3×10^{12} m. What is its orbital period about the sun?

6   Jupiter and Saturn contain most of the planetary mass of the solar system, about one-thousandth the mass of the sun. If they were combined in a single mass and orbited the sun with a period of 4×10^3 s, what would be their mean orbital radius?

7   If we travel from the earth's surface to the moon's surface, a distance of some 3.8×10^8 m, what total minimum energy would we have to expend for a 10^4-kg ship?

8   Assuming that we could inhabit Mars just by transporting people there, and assuming further that energy costs 0.01 cents per joule and that a 10^6-kg ship is required for 100 people,

a What is the total minimum cost per person for the one-way trip to Mars?

b If our present 3.2 billion population is doubling every 35 years, what would be the cost to maintain constant earth population by shipping people to Mars?

9 Asteroid 164 A has a mass of 7×10^{19} kg and a mean radius of 1.6×10^4 m. In our spaceship, we have only 6.3×10^8 J of energy to spend in approaching 164 A. The asteroid spins on its axis once in 6 h. Can we put our ship into a hanging orbit and escape again with energy available?

Andrade, Edward N.: "Sir Isaac Newton," Anchor Science Study Series, *Bibliography* Doubleday, Garden City, N.Y., 1960.

Cohen, I. Bernard: "Birth of a New Physics," Anchor Science Study Series, Doubleday, Garden City, N. Y., 1960.

Feynman, et al.: "The Feynman Lectures on Physics," vol. 1, Addison-Wesley, Reading, Mass., 1963.

Harvard Project Physics: Text and Reader No. 2, Holt, New York, 1968.

Holton, G. J., and Roller, D. H.: "Foundations of Modern Physical Science," Addison-Wesley, Reading, Mass., 1958.

Kilston, Stephen D., et al.: A Search for Life on Earth at Kilometer Resolution, "Icarus: International Journal of the Solar System," Academic, New York, 1966.

Sagan, Carl, and Shlovsky, I.S.: "Intelligent Life in the Universe," 1966.

Chapter 7
Another Kind of Field

Field ion micrograph of a hemispherical tungsten top showing its individual atoms as small white dots.

The idea of a force acting over a distance with no visible connection between bodies has been hard for men to grasp. We have gone a long way with this kind of model in the discussion of gravitation. The evidence for the gravitational force is pretty convincing. Our astronauts have staked their lives on our model of the nature of gravitation, and they have found it a good model. Now we shall turn to the investigation of another force that is of the same general form as gravity but many times stronger.

**7.1
In the
Beginning**

Lightning must have frightened men for countless generations before they learned the art of agriculture. The great forests of those days, stretching for hundreds and thousands of miles over the continents, must have been burned over repeatedly due to lightning. Some species of trees today will not reseed themselves until the severe heat of fire causes the seeds to germinate.

Lightning has been the source of many legendary tales and has entered the literature of every major religion. Yet it has been explained only in very recent times. Nobody guessed that lightning had anything to do with the curious attraction of bits of paper and thread to certain objects such as amber. Even more remote was any idea that lightning could be in any way connected with the magical lodestones that permitted the Eastern hordes to travel over great distances and find their way back. As late as the beginning of the nineteenth century, scientists were still seeking to demonstrate the connection between electricity and magnetism.

The theories that attempted to describe the effects that we know as due to electricity and magnetism were many and very limited in scope, dating from the Greeks of the pre-Christian era. The word *elektron* is the Greek word for *amber*. The attractive force between certain substances had long been noted, but the force that, in some cases, repelled bodies was first observed by Nicolo Cabeo, an Italian Jesuit and a militant anti-copernican. At this same time, Galileo and Kepler were using some of the ideas of "De Magnete," a paper published by William Gilbert in 1600 on magnetism, to support the copernican astronomical model. Cabeo probably sought to point out the error of the Gilbert paper when he discovered that some objects, after attracting one another and coming into contact, violently repel each other.

Gilbert was the first to visualize the earth as a huge magnet. After his momentous paper of 1600, others were quick to experiment with the wide range of materials found by him to exhibit electrical properties.

By the eighteenth century the word *electricity* was in common use. By 1731 it was discovered that the "electric virtue" could be passed from one body to another, and the first serious work was done in classifying bodies as electrical conductors or electrical insulators according to their ability to conduct the electric virtue.

Men then imagined electricity to be a kind of fluid that could flow from one conductor to another—a most reasonable assumption even though they could not see this special fluid. It was Benjamin Franklin who first appreciated that this electrical fluid can neither be destroyed nor created, being rather transported from one body to another.

Joseph Priestley found that a pith ball, attracted to the outside of a conducting vessel in the usual fashion, could be suspended within the vessel with no force upon it whatever. Newton's "Principia" dealt with such a case as this, deriving the result that a small mass within a shell of mass of uniform shell thickness would not be subject to any gravitational force. Priestley was moved by this to postulate that the same kind of inverse-square-law force must be involved in the case of his pith ball. This provides us with yet another excellent example of how one scientist builds upon the ideas of others. This story is repeated throughout the history of science.

**7.2
The Electric
Field**

Charles Augustin de Coulomb (1736–1806) built a highly precise torsion balance that served very well to test the nature of the force at varying distances between charged balls. Such a device had already been built to test the gravitational law of force between masses and to determine the value of Newton's universal gravitational constant G. Coulomb's experiment, begun in 1785, only 9 years after the American Declaration of Independence, led to the first quantitative law for electric charges. The electric force was found to vary as the inverse square of the separation distance between charge centers, and as the product of the quantity of charge on the two balls.

$$F = \frac{kq_1q_2}{R^2}$$

[7.1]

where q_1 and q_2 = the two charges upon the balls

R = the distance between their centers

K is a constant analogous to G in the gravitational law

$$F = G\,\frac{m_1m_2}{R^2}$$

[7.2]

and has become known as the *coulomb constant*. The mks unit of charge has been given the name of the experimenter, as is so often the case. The unit of electrical charge is the *coulomb*,

$$F = \frac{kq_1q_2}{R^2}$$

$$= 9.0 \times 10^9 \text{ N} \cdot \text{m}^2/\text{C}^2 \frac{q_1q_2}{R^2} \quad \text{[mks]}$$

We can now compare the magnitude of these two forces for the same bodies. Suppose that two balls of equal mass, $m = 10$ kg, both having equal charges, $q = 1$ C, are placed 1 m apart. We shall assume that charge is of two different kinds, $+$ and $-$, and that like charges repel one another, whereas unlike charges attract one another. If our two balls are alike in sign of charge, i.e., either both $+$ or both $-$, there will be a mutual force of electrical repulsion acting on them.

$$F_e = \frac{kq_1q_2}{R^2}$$

$$= \frac{9 \times 10^9 \times 10^0 \times 10^0}{10^0}$$

$$= 9 \times 10^9 \text{ N}$$

At the same time, there is a mutual gravitational attraction acting on them of

$$F_g = \frac{Gm_1m_2}{R^2}$$

$$= \frac{6.67 \times 10^{-11} \times 10^1 \times 10^1}{10^0}$$

$$= 6.67 \times 10^{-9} \text{ N}$$

Comparing these two forces,

$$\frac{F_e}{F_g} \approx \frac{10^{10}}{10^{-8}}$$

$$\approx 10^{18}$$

we see that the electrical force is a billion billion times greater than the gravitational force. A more easily achievable charge in a demonstration might be smaller than a coulomb by perhaps a factor of 10^{-3}, but even at one-millionth of the charge the E force is enormous by comparison to gravitation. The similarity between the two force expressions has led to speculation that gravitational force is somehow related to electric charge contained within the masses.

The coulomb experiment, since the forces are so large, can be approximated very simply in your laboratory. It is well worth while to attempt to verify Coulomb's results. Take care to perform your experiment on a low-humidity day, since high humidity will cause excessive leakage of charge from your pith balls through the air.

A microscopic ball of mass 10^{-30} kg carries a charge of -1.6×10^{-19} C *Example* and orbits like a tiny satellite around a ball of mass 10^{-26} kg carrying a similar + charge.

1   If it orbits at a radius of 10^{-10} m, what will its speed be?

This is our old gravitational problem with new variables. Remember that the centripetal force required is provided by the electrical force between charges.

$$F_c = F_e$$

$$\frac{mv^2}{R} = \frac{kq_1q_2}{R^2} \qquad\qquad [7.3]$$

Hence, the orbital speed v is analogous to the speed of a satellite in gravitational orbit,

$$v = \sqrt{\frac{kq_1q_2}{mR}} \qquad\qquad [7.4]$$

except that the mass m of the orbiting satellite does not disappear as before. Since $q_1 = q_2 = q$,

$$v = q\sqrt{\frac{k}{mR}}$$

$$= 1.6 \times 10^{-19} \sqrt{\frac{9 \times 10^9}{10^{-30} \times 10^{-10}}}$$

$$= 1.6 \times 10^{-19} \sqrt{9 \times 10^{49}}$$

$$= 1.6 \times 10^{-19} \sqrt{90 \times 10^{48}}$$

$$\approx 1.5 \times 10^6 \text{ m/s}$$

At $1\frac{1}{2}$ million meters per second, our tiny ball is something of a blur.   This means that each second it will make f complete trips, where

$$f = \frac{v}{2\pi R}$$

$$\approx \frac{1.5 \times 10^6}{2\pi \times 10^{-10}}$$

$$\approx 2.4 \times 10^{15} \text{ trips per second}$$

A million billion trips every second seems an incredible number, yet this is nearly the case for an electron orbiting the nucleus of a hydrogen atom.

2   What is its total energy in this orbit?

Like the gravitational case, the same expressions hold here for the charged balls except that the variables have new meanings.

$$U_g = -\frac{GM_1 m_2}{R} \qquad U_e = -\frac{kq_1 q_2}{R} \qquad\qquad [7.5]$$

$$KE_g = +\frac{Gm_1 m_2}{2R} \qquad KE_e = +\frac{kq_1 q_2}{2R} \qquad\qquad [7.6]$$

Hence, the total energy is

$$E = U_e + KE_e$$

$$= -\frac{kq_1 q_2}{2R} \qquad\qquad [7.7]$$

$$= -\frac{9 \times 10^9 \times (1.6 \times 10^{-19})^2}{2 \times 10^{-10}}$$

$$\approx -11.5 \times 10^{-19} \text{ J}$$

This seems like a very tiny energy.   Let us look at the centripetal acceleration required to hold this orbit.

$$\frac{mv^2}{R} = \frac{kq_1 q_2}{R^2}$$

$$a_c = \frac{v^2}{R}$$

$$\frac{v^2}{R} = \frac{kq_1 q_2}{mR^2}$$

$$= \frac{9 \times 10^9 \times (1.6 \times 10^{-19})^2}{10^{-30} \times (10^{-10})^2}$$

$$\approx 2.3 \times 10^{22} \text{ m/s}^2$$

This is an enormous acceleration. How does it compare with the centripetal acceleration of the earth in its orbit around the sun?

Pause here for just a moment to reflect that we have been able to handle two vastly different problems, at least in scale of distances and sizes of mass, by essentially the same model. Both gravitational- and electrical-force problems obey the same fundamental mechanics. The problems typical of electricity only seem to be different from those concerning gravitation because a number of electrical phenomena involve rather complicated spatial collections of charged particles that either do or do not move about, relative to one another, in time.

Perhaps the best way to unscramble this last statement is to look at one or two simple examples.

**7.3
The
Parallel-plate
Problem**

Robert Millikan's oil-drop experiment, in 1909, demonstrated a remarkable fact about electrical charge. This experiment led Millikan to the observation that all measured charges are composed of a finite number of whole *unit* or *elementary* charges. Recall that Lucretius insisted upon just such a discreteness in nature. Experiments with electricity and those in chemistry contributed over a considerable period to the idea of a "graininess" in electricity. The unit charge was found to be the charge residing on the electrons, $e = 1.6 \times 10^{-19}$ C. This fact was deduced by accelerating tiny charged drops of oil with a known electrical force between two conducting parallel plates.

Before we can fully understand the experimental procedures followed in the modern version of the Millikan experiment, it will be necessary to examine the problem of these conducting plates.

We shall assume a conducting plate, on which electric charges can move about more or less freely, of very large dimensions (see Fig. 7.1). Giving this plate a net charge Q distributed evenly over the plate, we shall next examine the nature of the force on a test charge q^+ placed above the plate. A *test charge* is the tiniest whole charge observed, i.e., the charge on an electron or proton.

The force on q^+ due to charge Q on the plate is directly upward away from the plate if Q is positive, and directly downward toward the plate if Q is negative. We shall assume the former case to be true. If R is the

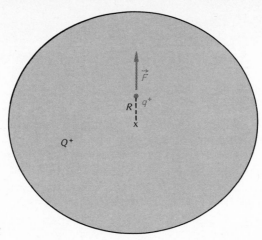

Fig. 7.1

distance between the plate and q^+, we find experimentally that $\vec{F}$ is independent of R so long as R is reasonably small compared to plate dimensions. This experimental result is mathematically verifiable, and perhaps you will want to demonstrate this. Why is the force $\vec{F}$ always perpendicular to the plate?

Now consider two such charged plates parallel to one another with an air gap between them. The plates separated by a distance d have charges of different signs, as shown in Fig. 7.2. Notice that both forces, F^+ and F^-, are directed upward. The total force F is

$$\vec{F} = \vec{F^+} + \vec{F^-}$$

Since F^+ and F^- are independent of where the charge is between the plates, we have a constant force upon q^+, $\vec{F}$, no matter where it is. If the constant force $\vec{F}$ works on the charge q^+ as it moves from the + plate to the − plate, a distance d, we know that the total work done on q^+ by $\vec{F}$ is

Work $= Fd$

F remains constant so long as the charges, Q^+ and Q^-, on the plates remain constant. Let us examine this fact and its implications. Suppose the plates are moved apart to a new separation, d'. The above statement says that the product of F' and d' must be greater than the product of F and d. If d' is $2d$, then $F'd' = 2\ Fd$. Twice the work is done on the charge q^+ in the d' case, provided charges Q^+ and Q^- do not change.

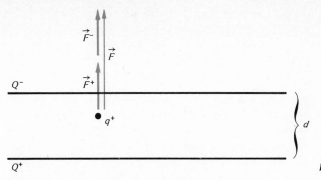

Fig. 7.2

We can use a device known as a battery to place net charges of opposite
sign upon two such plates (Fig. 7.3). You may want to think of a battery
simply as a device that can separate charges of opposite signs. Now let
us connect a battery to the two plates and see what happens. The battery separates charges and puts Q^+ on the bottom plate and Q^- on the
top plate. q^+ accelerates from the bottom plate toward the top plate
under force F such that the work done on it is

$$W = Fd = \Delta KE \qquad\qquad [7.8]$$

provided we pump all the air out of the space between the plates. If q^+
starts from P_1 at rest, it will smash into P_2 with a kinetic energy $\frac{1}{2}mv_{max}^2 =
F \times d$. If we do not pump out the air, air molecules will get in the way
of q^+ and impede its progress. As q^+ strikes P_2, it stops, doing work

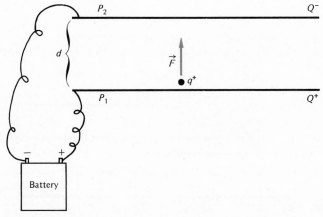

Fig. 7.3

$\frac{1}{2}mv_{max}^2$ upon the plate. This energy appears as heat and is measurable. You are encouraged to try to measure the heat when a steady stream of charged particles strikes P_2. We call a steady stream of charges an *electric current*, and we have meters to measure the rate of transfer of charge.

Now what happens if we leave the battery as is and separate the plates to a new spacing, $d' = 2d$? We find experimentally that the force F on q^+ decreases at the same rate as d increases. That is, the product $F \times d$ remains constant no matter what d is, so long as we use the same battery. We say, then, that this battery is capable of doing only a certain set amount of work on a charge, q^+. If the product $F \times d$ remains constant, then, at the new spacing,

$$F' \times d' = F \times d \qquad \text{and } F' = \frac{F}{2}$$

The new force on q^+, F', is half the original force F (Fig. 7.4).

Some definitions will help clarify these ideas—which are fundamental to an understanding of electricity.

Electric force per unit of charge:

$E \equiv$ electric field intensity

$$= \frac{\overrightarrow{F}}{e} \qquad \text{N/C}$$

Electric potential energy per unit of charge

$$V \equiv \text{electric potential difference} = \frac{U}{e} \qquad \text{J/C}$$

We say that $\overrightarrow{E}$ is the force on a 1-C charge at some point in space. Note that E is a vector quantity with the same direction as the electric force and

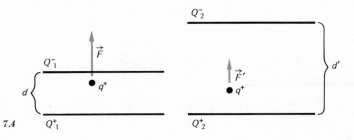

Fig. 7.4

that it is associated always with some point in space. In our two-plate problems, $\vec{E}$ is constant everywhere between the plates so long as nothing changes.

V is the energy available per unit of charge, from some source such as a battery, to do work on the charge. It has its own special unit, the *volt*. Now suppose we have a 12-V battery hooked up to our plates. How much work will this do on a single electron with a charge of 1.6×10^{-19} C?

Electric force: $\qquad \vec{F} = \dfrac{KQq}{R^2} \qquad$ N

Electric field intensity: $\quad \vec{E} = \dfrac{KQ}{R^2} \qquad$ N/C

Electric potential energy: $U = \dfrac{KQq}{R} \qquad$ J

Potential difference: $\qquad V = \dfrac{KQ}{R} \qquad$ J/C

Identities: $\qquad\qquad\quad \vec{F} = q\vec{E} \qquad U = qV$

Notice now the similarities and differences in the electrical definitions shown above. $\vec{E}$ and V are quantities indicating the amount of force or of energy available *per unit of charge*. In the example we wish to know how much work is done on the electron by the 12-V battery. This we find by multiplying the potential difference V (work available per coulomb of charge) by the actual charge to experience the work, $q = 1.6 \times 10^{-19}$ C.

$\Delta U = q^- V$
$\qquad = 1.6 \times 10^{-19} \times 12$
$\qquad = 19.2 \times 10^{-19}$ J

This seems a tiny amount of energy; however, from the following example we can see that it is not trivial.

Two parallel conducting plates are spaced a distance of 2 cm apart and *Example* charged by a 12-V car battery (see Fig. 7.5). A hot filament serving as a source of electrons is placed very near the negative conducting plate, and a steady current of 1 A is measured in the circuit. With what speed do electrons collide with the positive plate? What total work is done by the battery per second? Consider the region of the plates to be evacuated.

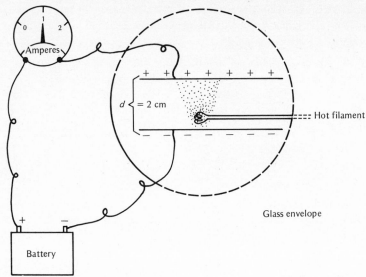

Fig. 7.5

1   The total work done per electron by the battery is, as before,

Work $= q^- V$
$= 19.2 \times 10^{-19}$ J

This is also the change in kinetic energy of the electrons that make the trip.

$q^- V = \frac{1}{2} m v_{max}^2$

From this we can solve for v_{max} as the electron strikes the + plate.

$$v_{max} = \sqrt{\frac{2q^- V}{m}}$$

where $m =$ the mass of the electron
$\qquad q^- =$ its charge

$$v_{max} = \left[\frac{2 \times (19.2 \times 10^{-19})}{9 \times 10^{-31}} \right]^{1/2}$$

$\approx 2 \times 10^6$ m/s

2,000,000 m/s is not a small speed. It results, of course, from the fact that the electron mass is so tiny.

2   If a 1-A current exists in the circuit, this means that 1 C of charge
     (6×10^{18} electrons) is moving through the space between the plates
     each second.   If 1 C of electron charge makes the trip between the
     plates each second, this means that the battery does ($19.2 \times
     10^{-19})/(1.6 \times 10^{-19}) = 12$ J of work each second.   We call the work-
     over-time ratio the *power*, i.e., the rate at which work is done, and
     give it the special unit *watts* where one watt equals one joule per
     second.   Can you explain now why the inside of your television cabi-
     net gets so warm when you have the set on?   Where does this heat
     come from?

The system of plates that has been described thus far is the basis of vacuum tubes in electronics.   Many vacuum tubes have been replaced by
other devices that do not become so hot during operation.   These lower-
heat devices go by a variety of names, such as *transistors* and *FETS*.
They will be mentioned again in a later chapter.

All during the parallel-plate discussion the gravitational field was neglected.   We know, however, that there is no switch that will let us turn off
gravity.   Another look at the parallel-plate problem will yield a very
surprising result.

Suppose a particle of mass m and charge q (either $+$ or $-$) is placed in the
electric field between two charged plates (Fig. 7.6).   For argument, we can
assume a negative charge q^-.   Now the mass m is subject to a gravitational
force downward, mg in magnitude.   If an electric field intensity $\vec{E}$ is placed
across the plates so as to drive q^- upward with a force q^-E that is just equal
in magnitude to mg downward, the particle experiences a zero total force
and goes nowhere.   We can make q^-E the right size by adjusting E's mag-

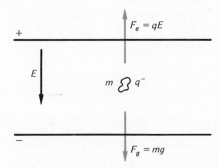

Fig. 7.6

nitude with some sort of black box. We can say for this case that the electric and gravitational forces are just balanced for this particle.

Suppose now that we have a number of particles like this one, all of mass m. Suppose further that we have some way of changing the charge q, both in sign and in magnitude, at will. It is clear that the electric force on the particles depends upon both sign of charge (+ charges will travel downward quickly) and magnitude of charge q. Only a few of many will stand still for a given field intensity E. Remember that all particles have the same mass, and hence, have the same gravitational force upon them. There is no way to change that.

By observing the smallest field $\vec{E}$ that will just bring a few particles to balance, Millikan made an exciting discovery. He found that there is indeed a smallest charge e and that no smaller charges can be found. He also observed that all larger charges are integral (whole-number) multiples of this charge e. This discovery has enormous significance in science models. The charge e found by Millikan is the charge on the electron, e^-, and on the proton, e^+. This means that charge is *discrete* (not infinitely divisible), a fact that gives us the key to atomic models and atomic and nuclear interaction problems.

Although the idea of discrete charge predates Millikan, he demonstrated this fact experimentally beyond doubt. This recent story began with men like Nikola Tesla and J. J. Thomson, who discovered the electron, and continues through the present. It makes fascinating reading and is highly recommended.

Theoreticians have now proposed the existence of special subnuclear blocks called *quarks*. These quarks are assigned certain very special properties and are subject to a set of highly specific limitations on the ways that they can combine to form the observable nuclear particles and photons. From this set of rules one can play the game and account for the existence or absence of all those particles or photons that have been observed or that have never been found even though people thought they might exist. All this is an elaborate model that carries forth the lucretian concept of fundamental building blocks.

**7.5
Magnetism** Probably no area of study has been more obscured for students with complicated models and rules than magnetism. It will not be possible here to give an exhaustive treatment of magnetism, but a few central ideas will suffice to develop the concept of a magnetic field and its implications.

OPTICAL SPECTRA

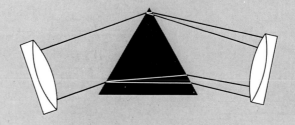

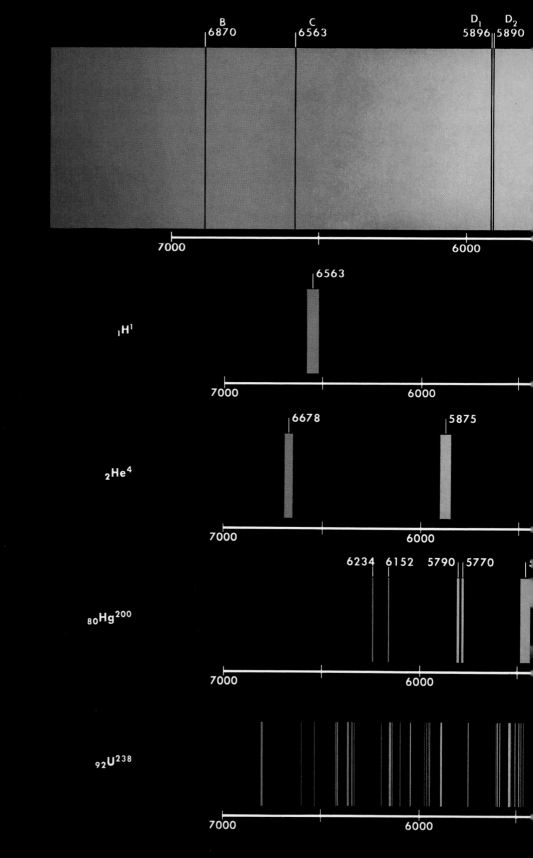

5000   4000

|4861 |4340 |4101

00   4000

|4921 |4713 |4471 |4026

00   4000

4358| 4078||4047

00   4000

Such diverse and fundamental informa
tion on the nature of matter as the compo
sition of distant stars and the structure
of atoms and molecules has been ob
tained by analysis of the light emitted
from any incandescent substance.

In the SPECTROSCOPE, such light, passed
through a slit and a prism, is broken up
into its component wavelengths, which
are observed as colored lines, or light of
different energies, characteristic of the
differences between the various electron
energy levels of the atoms. This EMIS
SION SPECTRUM is CONTINUOUS when the
images of the wavelengths are uninter
ruptedly overlapping; it is a LINE spec
trum when only certain specific wave
lengths are emitted, as shown here for
the elements hydrogen, helium, mer
cury, and uranium.

On the solar spectrum across the top of
this plate appears a series of dark lines
— FRAUNHOFER LINES — forming an AB
SORPTION SPECTRUM: Some of the light
from the intensely hot interior of the
sun is absorbed by the cooler gases of
its outer layers as the light energies
raise the atoms in these layers to higher
energy states; bright lines are not, there
fore, seen for these changes.

The spectra are calibrated in angstroms
(1 A = 10⁻¹⁰ m); the letters are arbitrary
designations introduced by Fraunhofer
for lines important in spectroscopy.

A magnetic field is always the result of a charge or charges in motion relative to a detection charge. No relative motion between charges—no magnetic effects. There is something fundamentally important in the relative motion as it applies to what we have historically described as magnetism.

Suppose we have a long, straight copper wire carrying a current I always in one direction. We say that such a current (charges in motion) creates, or gives rise to, a magnetic field that is cylindrical around the wire, as in Fig. 7.7. Note that I^- is taken to be in the direction of motion of negative charges. If we look along the wire in the direction that the electrons are moving, the field direction is counterclockwise and circular around the wire. Its magnitude depends upon I and upon the distance from the wire at which it is measured.

This much is pure memorization. Without more work in relativity you must, at this point, accept this rule as experimental fact.

How do we know there is such a thing as a magnetic field around this wire? How is it sensed and measured? If a test charge q^+ is placed at point p and held there, it will experience only a force of electric attraction for the electrons in the wire if the wire is charged to a net negative value. The charge q^+ experiences no effect due to magnetism.

If, however, we grasp q^+ and begin to move it in a straight line parallel with the wire and in the direction of I^-, a peculiar force becomes appar-

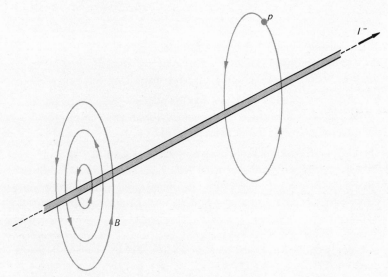

Fig. 7.7

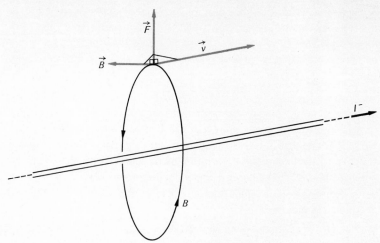

Fig. 7.8

ent on q^+ (Fig. 7.8). As q^+ cuts through the magnetic field B, perpendicular to its field direction, it is accelerated upward away from the copper wire. If we reverse direction with q^+ so that it goes opposite to the electron-flow direction (in the direction of positive current I^+), the magnetic force on q^+ is reversed and is now toward the wire.

Two experimental facts stand out here. First, the magnetic force on q^+ is at right angles to its velocity $\vec{v}$. Second, the magnitude of the force depends directly on the magnitude of $\vec{v}$.

$$F_B = qvB$$

This is indeed strange. The value of v depends upon the frame of reference of the observer, as does I. If we move q^+ directly along with $\vec{B}$ so that the angle between $\vec{v}$ and $\vec{B}$ is zero, there is no force at all on q^+.

If a uniform magnetic field exists into the plane of the page (indicated by crosses, x), we can show both the velocity of an electron or proton and the force on both due to the magnetic field.

The force on the proton as it enters the field is upward, $F_B{}^+ = q^+v_pB$, and follows, always perpendicular to the velocity, as the proton flies through a circular arc of radius R_p (Fig. 7.9). In a similar fashion, the electron curves downward, according to $F_B{}^- = q^-v_eB$, in a circular arc of radius R_e. Although these particles may have the same speed, they have very different masses. If they move in circles at constant speed v, the magnetic force is just supplying the necessary centripetal force, like the satellite in gravitational orbit.

$$F_B = qvB$$
$$= \frac{mv^2}{R} \tag{7.9}$$

If v is known and the radius R also is known for a particle, it is possible to solve experimentally for the ratio of the particle charge to mass, q/m. From Eq. [7.9],

$$\frac{q}{m} = \frac{v}{BR}$$

This ratio tells us immediately what particle we are dealing with, since the ratios q/m of a large number of particles are well known.

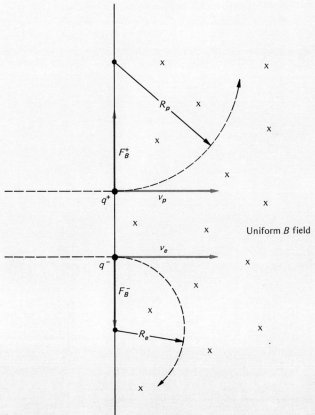

Fig. 7.9

Example   We have a source of many kinds of unknown charged particles.   How can we build an electromagnetic device that will let us identify each type of particle present?

The device shown in Fig. 7.10 is quite simple in concept.   Let us look at it a piece at a time.   The source of unknown charged particles is placed next to one plate of a two-plate system across which any V can be placed, and with either plate P_1 or P_2 positive.   Particles are thus accelerated by V and reach P_2 with speeds of

$$qV = \tfrac{1}{2}mv_{max}^2$$

$$v_{max} = \sqrt{\frac{2qV}{m}}$$

Some of them pass through the hole in P_2 and beyond P_2 into the region between parallel plates P_3 and P_4.   The desired electric and magnetic fields, E and B_1, are maintained between P_3 and P_4, each at right angles to the other, so that charged particles will all experience both a uniform E and B field simultaneously.   These two produce forces on the particles of

$$F_E = qE$$
$$F_B = qvB_1$$
$$\quad = qB_1\sqrt{\frac{2qV}{m}}$$

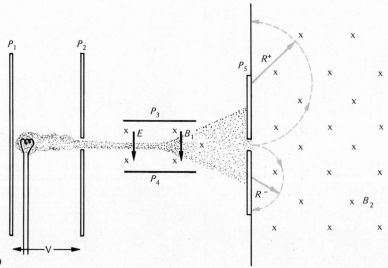

Fig. 7.10

If, and only if, $F_B = F_E$, the particle will have no net force upon it and will pass undeflected through the hole in P_5 and into a second uniform magnetic field B_2. We can solve now for the velocity of particles that pass, undeflected, through the hole in P_5. For these particles

$$F_{B_1} = F_E$$
$$qvB_1 = qE$$
$$v = \frac{E}{B_1}$$

Both these quantities are well known, and so we have a very effective velocity selector that depends only on E and B_1 and does not depend on the mass of the particle.

Now in the new field B_2, the particles will bend either upward (+) or downward (−) through a circular arc of radius R. Since v is known, the ratio q/m can be easily computed from a knowledge of E, B_1, and B_2.

$$qvB_2 = \frac{mv^2}{R}$$
$$\frac{q}{m} = \frac{v}{B_2 R}$$

and substituting E/B_1 for v,

$$\frac{q}{m} = \frac{E}{B_1 B_2 R}$$

This is the principle of the mass spectrograph, with which we have been able to identify a great many atomic particles that nobody has ever seen. The mass spectrograph indirectly measures particle masses by subjecting them to accelerating E and B fields. The reverse side of the plate, P_5, may be coated with a phosphor that gives off a flash of light as particles strike it, just as your television screen does. Can you guess now how your television set might work? See Fig. 7.11.

As discussed earlier, Sir Isaac Newton was one of those rare synthesizers of the work of those preceding him. Newton synthesized the work of Kepler, Galileo, and others into a unified mechanics that for the first time made bodies of earth and the heavens behave according to the same laws.

**7.6
Maxwell and
Lorentz**

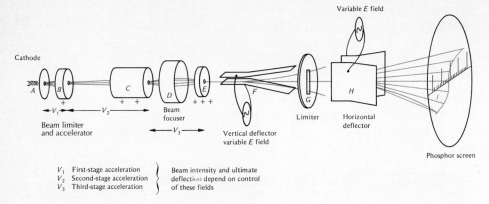

Fig. 7.11 The heart of a working cathode-ray tube. *The drawing shows the essential elements that create the mass of electrons (cathode), accelerate them in a beam (A through E), focus the electron beam and physically limit it prior to entry into the deflector region (D and E), and deflect the beam vertically (F) and horizontally (H) according to two variable signals. The result is a well-focussed beam that traces lines or curves very fast on the phosphor screen.*

Newton's model of the world was enormously important in shaping the thinking of all men in the centuries that followed. What was mysterious and unknowable was reduced in the developing world view to the predictable and knowable. The newtonian world became a giant machine that danced to the tune of precisely known laws of mechanics. The implication was that man, too, rather than being the capricious and unfathomable creation of a god, behaves in patterns that are subject to analysis and according to basic truths. Thus, Freud was led to his model of the human mind. Indeed, pieces of the biological puzzle have fallen into place to the extent that the nature of life as a chemical phenomenon has been advanced to relegate even humanity to the same "giant machine" world view.

James Clerk Maxwell, a Scottish physicist of the nineteenth century, was another synthesizer of the work of those preceding him. Ampère, Coulomb, Franklin, and Faraday were a few of the important links in the model chain that was to be forged by Maxwell. With the insight of genius, Maxwell succeeded in demonstrating, in a paper published in the 1860s, that changing electric fields produce magnetic fields according to a precise relationship. Furthermore, changing electric and associated magnetic fields, created by charges undergoing acceleration, propagate through space and through material objects at a speed that is very close to the measured speed of light. Hence, Maxwell reasoned that light itself is but a propagating electromagnetic wave.

Thus, Maxwell gave body and substance to the mathematical theories of Fresnel and Kirchhoff, theories that had prior to this time been simply mathematic models for the propagation of light waves. Maxwell's work showed that light is indeed a wave phenomenon with measurable electric and magnetic fields that behave according to his wave equation. All rigorous mathematic treatments of light and other electromagnetic phenomena begin with Maxwell's formal model.

Very near the close of the nineteenth century two men made an astonishing discovery. The telegraph had long been in use, and the telephone and phonograph were already invented. Observing cathode rays in a specially designed tube, Nikola Tesla in the United States and J. J. Thomson in England first speculated that the "rays" were actually streams of very tiny charged particles. A series of experiments, perhaps suggested by Tesla, led Thomson to the discovery of the electron.

A few years later another group of scientists, working under Ernest Rutherford, fired a stream of helium nuclei, now called *alpha particles*, into a very thin gold foil. Observing the pattern of particles scattered from the foil, they verified what chemists had roughly guessed for more than a century. Matter is indeed made up of atoms, mostly consisting of empty space. Almost the entire mass of Rutherford's atom, differing from the chemists' model, is concentrated in a very dense and tiny nucleus that also carries the positive charge of the atom.

There followed an amazing burst of scientific experimentation, in which the atoms of the full range of elements were investigated. A marvelous piece of chemistry early in our century placed the atoms of elements in a periodic table according to the number of unit positive charges residing on the atomic nucleus, taking into account as well the manner in which atoms behave toward one another in combining to form molecules.

During the same brief period of history at the threshold of our century, radioactivity of nuclei and x-rays were discovered. The attempt to explain all these things under the newtonian world view failed. There were things here in these tiny atomic particles and in the waves of Maxwell that defied the newtonian world view. The quantum-mechanical model, evolved during the past half-century, is the model that extends the world view to these perplexing particles and waves.

With the coming of quantum mechanics a certain mystery was injected once again into the world view. The mathematical formalism of quantum mechanics, along with the lack of a simple mechanical model, has removed this world view from the grasp of all but a few initiates in society. Its various facets are beyond the grasp, let alone the speculation, of even many scientists. This has created a sort of elite minority in society with a partial return of the balance of society to a pre-newtonian uncertainty. We are no longer so certain about the mechanisms of the "giant machine" point of view.

It is quite useful to think of the whole universe as being populated with particles that are electrically charged. Any one of these charged particles that is accelerated by a force becomes the source of electromagnetic waves. These waves transmit energy through space. We can demonstrate this fact by watching a distant, previously undisturbed, charge dance to the tune of this new wave. This model, the Lorentz model, becomes a little complicated by the fact that charged particles of atomic and subatomic size rarely go about the universe dissociated from other similar particles (Fig. 7.12).

The whole elemental structure of the material universe is determined by the way in which these small bits and pieces come together in an almost infinite variety of patterns. Nuclear particles associate under very mysterious and powerful forces to form incredible tiny atomic nuclei. The positive charge of the nucleus of an atom is normally balanced by an array of negative electrons zipping around outside the nucleus, with the number of positive protons in the nucleus determining what we call an *element*. A large number of atoms, all of one element, brought together will form a viewable sample of the element. This sample has certain definite characteristics that determine how it will react chemically with other elements.

Atoms associate with other kinds of atoms to form molecules that are more or less stable depending upon the electrical forces that bind them together. It is important to see here that all material objects of whatever appearance are composed of molecules and atoms that are themselves formed of tiny particles, many of which are electrically charged. To break molecules down to individual atoms or to strip electrons from atoms requires energy to overcome the electric bonding of these particles and atoms, just as energy is required to take away gravitational satellites of a planet.

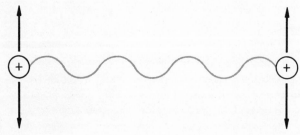

Fig. 7.12

Have you ever asked yourself why you can see through some things and not others? The "seeing" depends upon electromagnetic waves passing through a substance such as glass. Not seeing through implies that somehow these waves are blocked. If a plate of some material such as wood is opaque, our common sense tells us that the plate either absorbs incident waves or reflects them, or possibly does both.

But now let us try to construct a simple model that might explain this phenomenon. We do not insist that the model be a comprehensive representation; we require only that it be useful in our thinking and in predicting results. Suppose that the unknown plate is just a collection of billions of tiny particles, most of which are charged. These particles are bound together in atoms, and if the plate is a pure single element such as lead, the lead atoms are distributed spatially in some more or less regular geometry. The electrons that are the lightest of the particles are somewhat free to move about, within certain limits, in their association with the lead nuclei.

Now if an electromagnetic wave such as a red light beam falls upon the face of the lead sheet, common experience tells us it will not go through the lead to continue on the other side. What happens to the beam? The fact that we can see a red spot where the beam falls on the lead is proof that some of the wave's energy is reflected away from the lead to our eyes. A careful measurement of the temperature of the lead shows that some of the energy of the wave is absorbed and degraded to the form of heat.

Why does not part of the wave energy go through the lead sheet? Why does it go through a glass plate? Along the plate surface there are tiny charged particles. If these particles are free to dance to the tune of the incident wave, they will pass the wave along through the material and permit it to radiate from the back side in its original direction. If, however, the charged particles along the wave path through the lead are not free to oscillate according to the frequency of the red beam, the wave is effectively stopped from penetrating by absorption and reflection of its energy in the surface layer of the plate. This simple model so far seems to make sense.

To illustrate this point, tie a string to a rock and then hold the rock up off the ground a few inches. You will find that if you move your hand back and forth horizontally at just the right rate, the rock will swing to and fro in a pendulum motion. Push and pull at any other rate and you get no large pendulum motion for the rock. Why? Under the influence of gravitational force and due to the length of the string, the rock has a certain natural period of oscillation.

Field

Glass, which is transparent to visible light, is opaque to infrared (below red) light. *Transparency* now takes on a new meaning for us under this model. If a substance is transparent, its charged particles are oscillating with the passing wave at or near their natural frequency. Unfortunately, this model runs counter to many experimental facts. It is precisely at certain matching or resonant frequencies that the material most sharply absorbs the incident radiation. Apparently there are atomic and/or molecular processes that are not explained by this simple model. Atomic and molecular excitation call for a more sophisticated model. Hence, we are led to reject the simple Lorentz model and to rely on quantum mechanics for far more comprehensive explanations of observed facts.

Problems
1 Two identical nonconducting bodies of mass 10 kg are situated with their centers 3 m apart. Each has an electric charge of 7.5 C. Assuming they are remote from any other body in space, compare their gravitational and electrical forces.

2 Millikan found that the smallest charge is about 1.6×10^{-19} C. If 1 C of such charges was placed on the surface of a conducting ball of 1-cm radius, about how much area would be associated with each elementary charge?

3 An observer in deep space sees a line of positive charges passing him at the rate of 5 C/s.
   a If the charges are elementary charges, how many pass each second?
   b If the charges are equally spaced, what is their velocity?
   c Will a magnetic compass needle detect any magnetic field?

4 Given the conditions of Prob. 3, if the observer moves along with the charge at the same speed:
   a Will he see any current?
   b Will he be able to detect any magnetic field?
   c Compare this situation with that of Prob. 3.

5 If a particle of charge $q = 6 \times 10^{-5}$ C has its kinetic energy increased by 3×10^{-10} J by an electric force, through what potential difference V has it passed?

6 A particle of charge q whirls in a circle of radius $R = 2 \times 10^{-6}$ m around a central charge that attracts it with a force of 4×10^{-7} N.
   a What is the kinetic energy of the charge q?
   b If R is doubled, how does the kinetic energy change?
   c Plot a graph of kinetic energy vs. R for this situation where R ranges between values of 10^{-7} and 10^{-5} m.

7   Compare the electric potential energy between two point charges with the gravitational potential energy between two spherical masses, both in form and in magnitude.

8   Having now observed two inverse-square force fields, gravitational and electrical, both of which result in systems of bound orbiting bodies, speculate upon the possibility of still further bound-body systems responding to other central force fields.

Harvard Project Physics: Reader No. 4, Holt, New York, 1969.   *Bibliography*

Holton, G. J., and Roller, D. H.: "Foundations of Modern Physical Science," Addison-Wesley, Reading, Mass. 1958.

Physical Science Study Committee: "Physics," 2d ed., Heath, Boston, 1965.

Chapter 8
·
Light: The Window of Life

Galileo with his telescope.

8.1 Wavelengths in the electromagnetic spectrum (see Fig. 8.1 insert) vary
The Enigma from those hundreds of miles long to those so short that thousands can fit comfortably on the point of a pin.

If this tremendous range were scaled down to 1 m in length, the portion of it that is visible to the human eye would be limited to a slit about the width of a pencil line.

Through this tiny slit flows the essence of all life. Sunlight reaching the earth through this narrow window reacts with chlorophyll to forge the first vital link in life's food chain. Widen this range of wavelength only slightly and we find the keys to radiant heat and the energy of excitation of molecules and atoms. The disciplines of biology and chemistry are thus solidly linked by a common dependence upon light.

The study of light is central to the progress of science. It has been the essential and key element in the beginning of many of the major scientific disciplines. All science is able to progress only because men learned to describe light and learned to use it. For example, astronomers require telescopes just as biochemists depend on microscopes and spectrometers.

In this chapter we shall retrace the history of light and see how it relates to the beginnings of the major disciplines of science.

Crude attempts to explain the mysteries of light were made in the Greek period. Pythagoras in 540 B.C. believed that an image is formed in the eye as a result of particles emanating from the objects being viewed. Empedocles, 444 B.C., suggested that the eye is endowed with qualities like those of an octopus—that it has the power to project millions of tiny tentacles that surround an object and cause it to become illuminated. It is obvious that he viewed the eye as the active agent and the object as the passive agent simply responding to the tentacles of the eye.

Plato, in the fourth century B.C., tried to combine these two ideas. He suggested that light and sight result from the collision of the tentacles emanating from the eye and tentacles emanating from the object being viewed. His thought was that an interaction takes place similar to neutralization between electric charges. Somehow this neutralization was supposed to result in the sensation of sight by the formation of an image in the eye of the observer.

Plato was the first to perform and record experiments with light. Light coming through a tiny hole into a dark room was reflected from a polished metal sheet. Experiments using this simple equipment led to his being credited with two of the basic laws of geometric optics: (1) light travels in straight lines, and (2) when light is reflected, the angle of incidence is equal to the angle of reflectance. This means that the angle that a light ray makes when it strikes the flat surface is exactly the same as the angle made by the reflected ray as it leaves the surface.

In 340 B.C., Aristotle believed that luminous bodies are of exactly the same material as the sensations they produce in the eyes. He reasoned thus: "Nothing can be given out of a body unless it is of the same nature as the body."

Lucretius, in the first century B.C., stated that the particles emanating from the objects being viewed unite in the eye to form an exact image of the object from which they are emitted. The idea here is that the object is an active agent emitting something that the eye assembles into an image. Lucretius surmised that the particles emanating from the object are not in the form of the image while traveling through space. These particles can only be reunited by some wonderful process within the eye. He believed that we can see because the eye has this strange power to reconstruct these particles into the image of the original object.

We can see that early investigations of light were based almost entirely on the mentally developed theories of the philosophers of the time. The one exception to this pattern was Plato. He was the first to make a simple attempt at scientific experimentation in order to describe the phenomenology of light.

You may be tempted to regard these early theories as entirely erroneous. However, it is important to see that each of these ideas, in its own way, contained some small part of what we now consider to be the best model for light. For example, the theory of Lucretius states that particles unite with the eye to form an exact image of the body from which they are emitted. Between the body and the eye, the particles are "scrambled" and definitely not in the form of an image. This is not too far from the actual state of affairs. We now know that when light travels from an object to our eye, the energy in the light does, in fact, become scrambled in space. It is most difficult to reconstruct the image without a special device. The device needed is, of course, a lens. While Lucretius was not aware of the lens in the eye or its function in bending the light into an image distribution, his observation that this unscrambling of the light into an image is due to a property of the eye was essentially correct.

You will recall that Ptolemy was best known for his astronomical model of the universe, which put the earth at its center. Ptolemy also wrote a treatise on optics. In it we find the first mention of refraction, the bending of light as it leaves one transparent medium and enters another. Aside from this one major contribution in A.D. 150, with the coming of the Roman Empire the study of optics in Europe completely ceased for approximately one thousand years. The Romans were satisfied with copying the works of the Greeks and the other preceding societies. The Romans must, however, be credited with the recording of many of these earlier works. In addition to recording they made minor progress such as the use of glass lenses for the starting of fires.

8.2 Pre-Newton Ideas

A Persian, Alhazen, around 1000 A.D., carefully described the parts of the human eye. He also demonstrated the formation of an image upon the retina by the eye's lens. Alhazen explained fairly accurately the twilight phenomenon in our atmosphere. Using principles of light, he was able to calculate the depth of the earth's atmosphere at approximately 60 mi.

In the latter part of the thirteenth century, Marco Polo recorded that the Chinese were using lenses. Even though these lenses were crude, they were in common use. Chinese history indicates that lenses were used to magnify images. There is some suggestion that Confucius may have known about spectacles as early as 500 B.C. The Chinese undoubtedly ground simple lenses during the Ming Dynasty, A.D. 1368 to 1644.

Roger Bacon, a well-known British astronomer of the thirteenth century, began the study of optics in order to further his interests in astronomy. He described the possibility of combining lenses and mirrors for better results. Such combinations are now used in telescopes and other optical instruments.

There is an interesting sidelight on the life of Roger Bacon. The studies in which he made use of lenses and other optical devices led directly to his persecution by members of the church. They alleged that he was practicing black magic.

Some historians credit the Italian Salvino Dalmato of Florence with the invention of spectacles in their modern form about the year 1317.

In 1609 Galileo heard of a strange new invention by Hans Lippershey, a crude telescope. Galileo was quick to realize the importance of the instrument. Using the basic principle of Lippershey, he immediately designed a better instrument, which is still called the galilean telescope. With this telescope, he was able to observe for the first time the moons of Jupiter and the rings of Saturn.

This was the first experimental use of a well-designed and well-constructed optical system. It led to his book "Dialogues Concerning Two Chief World Systems: Ptolemaic and Copernican Systems," in which Galileo discussed the problems of both the astronomical models. We find here an experimental verification of astronomical predictions by

Copernicus, and we see simultaneously the beginning of the field of modern astronomy.

For the first time in history Galileo demonstrated clearly the power of experimentation and examination. More than anyone else before him, Galileo Galilei showed the importance of systematic experimentation. From this time forward, scientists would take a more investigative approach to the solving of problems.

Willebrod Snell (1591–1626) is credited with establishing the law of refraction while working at the University of Leyden in Holland. His work was published in 1637 by René Descartes in the book "La Dioprique." Building on earlier work, Snell did considerable experimentation on the velocity of light and developed laws in this area that are still accepted today.

The ray phenomena of light (concerned with light always traveling in straight lines) are reflection and refraction. An understanding of these leads to an understanding of how images are formed in refracting systems. In all the ray discussion we shall be talking about a very thin pencil of light that has its origin in some distant light source.

8.3 Geometric Optics

If a pencil of light falls upon a very smooth reflecting surface, such as a silver mirror or a piece of polished glass, a portion of the incident pencil will be reflected away from the surface, as shown in Fig. 8.2. Both in-

Reflection

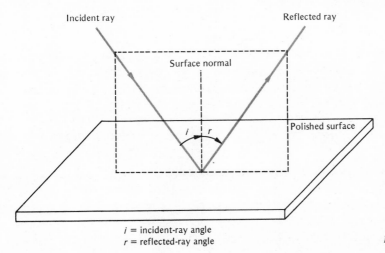

i = incident-ray angle
r = reflected-ray angle

Fig. 8.2

cident pencil and reflected pencil, along with the perpendicular at the point of reflection, lie in the same plane.

If the surface is not smooth, this simple picture is greatly complicated. We must then begin to ask questions about the nature of the surface roughness and about the kind of light in the incident pencil. Clearly this is not a ray problem any longer.

There are other interesting questions about specular reflection, e.g., how much of the energy in the incident pencil shows up in the reflected pencil? This problem involves polarization, which is not a ray phenomenon. In general, the larger the incident angle i, the more energy in the reflected pencil.

Refraction If a pencil of light of one single color falls upon the boundary or interface between two dissimilar transparent materials, such as air and glass, a portion of the energy of the incident pencil will be refracted or bent upon passing into the new medium either toward or away from the perpendicular to the surface, as shown in Fig. 8.3.

A pencil of light incident upon the boundary or interface between two dissimilar transparent media will be partially reflected at the interface as before. A portion of the pencil is, however, transmitted through the inter-

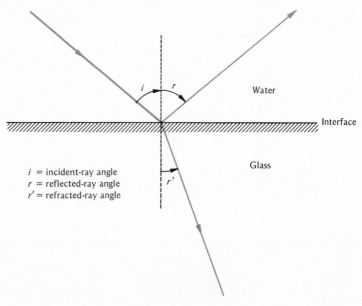

i = incident-ray angle
r = reflected-ray angle
r' = refracted-ray angle

Fig. 8.3

face in a new direction. This change in direction, called *refraction*, was known to the ancients. Alhazen used his knowledge of it to determine the depth of the earth's atmosphere from refraction of the sun's rays.

It was Snell who found the key to the dependence of the angles i and r' of Fig. 8.3 on one another. While observing incident and refracted pencils, he hit on the truth of his experimental observations, finding that a ratio of the sines of i and r' is always constant for any two transparent substances forming a refracting interface.

$$\frac{\sin i}{\sin r'} = n \qquad \text{a constant} \qquad\qquad\qquad [8.1]$$

But why should a different constant n appear experimentally for each new combination of materials? On the surface of the problem we might conclude that some property of the materials themselves is responsible for this. Those who followed in Huygens' footsteps succeeded in showing experimentally that this mysterious constant is just the ratio of the speed of the light waves in the two media. A medium such as air, in which the wave speed is nearly as great as in a vacuum, is said to have a small optical density. A medium such as crown glass, in which the waves travel more slowly, is said to be of greater optical density. When a pencil of light passes an interface into a medium of relatively higher optical density, it is rotated toward the interface normal. For a reverse passage the opposite is true.

For convenience, each substance is assigned its own absolute *index of refraction*, n, which states the speed of light in the medium relative to its speed in vacuum, e.g., in the case of water,

$$n_w = 1.33 = \frac{\text{speed in vacuum, } c}{\text{speed in water, } v_w} \ .$$

Since light is known to travel at nearly 3×10^8 m/s in a vacuum, its speed in water may be found from its index of refraction:

$$v_w = \frac{c}{n_w} = \frac{3 \times 10^8}{1.33}$$
$$\approx 2.3 \times 10^8 \text{ m/s}$$

Snell's law may now be stated in alternate form making use of these indexes of refraction:

$$n_i \sin i = n_{r'} \sin r'$$

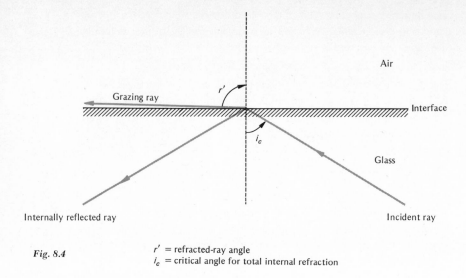

Fig. 8.4

r' = refracted-ray angle
i_c = critical angle for total internal refraction

where n_i and $n_{r'}$ are the indexes of refraction of the incident and the refractive medium, respectively.

A curious fact becomes apparent as this relationship is carefully examined. Suppose that a pencil is incident at angle i from an optically more dense medium. The refracted angle r' is, therefore, larger than i, and there will be some angle i less than 90° for which r' will just be 90°. If the incident pencil makes an angle greater than this critical angle i_c, no energy in the incident pencil passes through the interface; the energy is, instead, totally reflected internally at the interface.

Let us consider a pencil coming from some depth in a smooth pond to the surface where there is a water-air interface. The critical angle of incidence i_c is found by assuming that $r' = 90°$.

$$n_w \sin i_c = n_a \sin r'$$

Now $n_a \approx 1.0$ and the sine of 90° is just 1.0, so

$$n_w \sin i_c = 1.0$$

i_c is found to be that angle whose sine is just 1.0/1.33, or 0.752. What is this angle? If you were sitting at the bottom of a calm pool as a fish might be, looking upward, what would you see?

The phenomenology of refraction can be completely described relying only on the ray optical description. Refraction lenses are simply devices

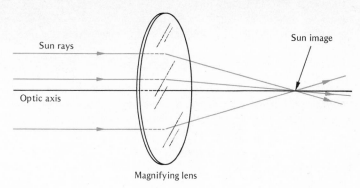

Sun rays

Sun image

Optic axis

Magnifying lens

Fig. 8.5

that take advantage of Snell's law to produce a desired bending of rays. Where rays of light originate, or appear to originate, our eyes see an image. Light rays reflected off our bodies appear to originate at the body surface points, the aggregate of these rays constituting an image for our eyes to see. Similarly we see images any time light rays either converge or appear to converge in space.

This latter idea can best be illustrated by a simple lens example. Nearly everyone has used a magnifying lens to focus the rays of the sun to a point (in reality, a small volume). In this case, the lens is used to create an image of the far distant sun at its focus. Any other distant object will be similarly imaged at the lens focus (see Fig. 8.5). But what about closer objects? They too will be imaged by the lens, though not at its focus. Rays that are incident parallel to the optic axis of the lens are refracted so as to pass through the focal point F upon the opposite side. Similarly, rays that pass through a focus to the lens are all refracted so that they leave the lens parallel to the optic axis. In Fig. 8.6 we use the two focal rays from the head of the object in order to find the image of the object. Where these rays cross to the right of the lens, we find the image point corresponding to the head of the object. The rest of the image may be inferred. Notice that the image is inverted relative to the object in this case. Notice also that

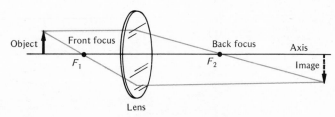

Object

Front focus

Back focus

Axis

F_1

F_2

Image

Lens

Fig. 8.6

light rays actually do intersect at the image, and that the series of intersections of rays is what our eye interprets as an image. This is a *real image*.

We shall look at one more example with this same lens. Now the object O in Fig. 8.7 is placed between the left focal point and the lens. The ray passing from the head of O to the lens in the direction of F_1 is refracted and passes to the right parallel to the optic axis. The focal ray through F_2 diverges away from this focal ray. However, the eye traces these rays backward and infers that they intersected at the head of the image as shown. These rays did not actually converge at the image; hence, we have a *virtual image*, which, incidentally, is not inverted as the real image was.

There are many kinds of lenses, and we might go on indefinitely finding images using focal rays. However, many of these will be left to your newly acquired understanding for solution.

We shall show only one more ray diagram here, for the light microscope, so that you may grasp the concept of image magnification (Fig. 8.8). In this case, two lenses are involved. The first of these, L_1, creates a real image, I_1, which is the object of L_2. Focal rays show the enormous magnification of the virtual image I_2 over the object. How might we build a telescope for magnifying objects at a great distance?

**8.4
Huygens and
Newton**

In the history of the study of light, two names loom as giants. These two people really initiated the science of optics and the thorough and detailed study of light. One of them was Christian Huygens (1629–1695), a Dutch physicist. He published a remarkably conceived wave theory in his famous book "Trete du la Lumier," published in 1690. He proposed the

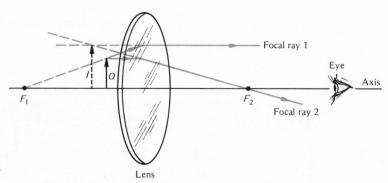

Fig. 8.7

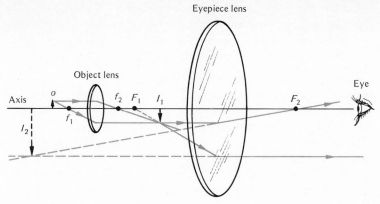

Fig. 8.8

propagation of light energy by wave process. It is a curiosity of history that Christian Huygens, who proposed the wave theory of light, lived out his entire life in the scientific shadow of Isaac Newton, the second man to undertake a thorough study of optics.

Newton's theory was that light consists of particles and that these particles travel through space in perfectly straight lines, as long as that space is homogeneous (all the same). This basic assumption led to the development of the field of optics known today as *geometric* optics. This is the science of light rays dealing with lenses and reflecting devices as already considered.

The wave theory of Christian Huygens led to that field known as *physical* optics. It treats other phenomena of light, such as interference and diffraction. Huygens' wave theory was almost completely ignored during his lifetime due to the fact that Newton was such a popular and powerful figure in those days. Huygens' paper explaining light waves indicated that they travel in a hypothetical medium termed the "luminous ether." He had assumed this to be present in all space. His reasoning was convincing, and his explanations were simple. "Light is made up of waves. And the wave length determines the color," he said. "The longest wave lengths produce the light that we call red, and the shortest, light that we call violet. In between are all the other colors of the visible spectrum." Today we refer to this theory as the *Huygens' wave theory.*

Huygens was also well known as an astronomer and a mathematician. He did a great deal of work in developing new theories in science. He was a physicist by training and also had a mechanical aptitude that served him well. Years of research in optics led him to form his revolutionary theory that explained light as waves. He described its behavior as similar to that found in a pool of water into which a rock has been thrown. Traveling outward in concentric circles, the waves are reflected only when they strike some object. Huygens theorized that light also consists of a vibration that spreads outward from its source.

Newton declared in his corpuscular theory of light that particles of light are given off by all luminous bodies. These emissions consist of tiny particles or "corpuscles" of matter that fall upon any object in their path, bounce off, and are detected when they reflect back to the eye. According to the newtonian view, visual sensations are produced by the impact of these minute corpuscles on the retina of the eye. Newton's particles are supposed to pass freely through transparent substances. When they reach the boundary of an optically denser medium such as glass, they deviate from their straight paths due to the force of attraction by the denser medium. This is how Newton explained refraction.

One of the curious paradoxes of history is the fact that at the very time that Newton announced his corpuscular theory of light, he had already discovered the periodicity of light—i.e., that it consists of waves such as those hypothesized by Huygens. However, Newton made no attempt to develop any hypothesis dealing with waves. Rather, he expounded only the one single corpuscular theory, ignoring his own strong evidence of wavelike behavior.

One of Newton's more familiar experiments (see Fig. 8.9) is the one in which he sent ordinary white light through a prism and found that it dispersed into a spectrum of colors. He concluded, in view of his particle theory, that each color must be a different-size particle that requires a different length of time in which to penetrate the prism. Continuing the experiment, he then recombined these dispersed colors back into white light by passing them through a second prism. Newton's treatise "Opticks" caused a minor disturbance in the scientific world at the time it was published. It was heavily criticized by his contemporaries, and Newton almost withdrew from scientific society because of this criticism.

Thomas Young (1773–1829) was reading at the age of two, could speak and understand Latin at the age of six, and at that same age could read and write seven languages. During his relatively short lifetime, he was the master of everything that he set his mind to, from horsemanship to music. In 1801 he published "The Mechanisms of the Eye." He is responsible for the theory of the wavelength dependence of color in physiological optics, i.e., the color vision and interference phenomena in the human eye. Young showed that two beams of light could combine in such a way that they would completely cancel or annul one another, thereby producing a dark fringe or the total absence of light at certain

Fig. 8.9
Newton's prism
experiment.

places. There was no way that Young could explain this on the basis of Newton's corpuscular theory, but an explanation was possible under the wave theory of Huygens. If at any one place the wave from one beam produces a crest in the wave, and the wave from another beam produces a reverse crest, the sum of the two would be zero, or total darkness. This is a simple explanation of the principle of the superposition of waves, or *interference*, as it is now known. Many examples of this phenomenon of interference are to be found in acoustics, the study of sound waves, and in other wave forms such as those on the surface of water.

Young, accepting the idea that an elastic ether occupies all space, brought the work of Huygens up to date with his experimentation. He started the work that later led Augustin Fresnel to apply the principle of wave motion to the study of optics.

Before going further we should reflect on the work of Anton van Leeuwenhoek (1632–1723). In 1675 Leeuwenhoek, in a paper to the Royal Society, mentioned that he had built by that time 247 microscopes (light instruments designed to greatly magnify small objects). During the ensuing years, Leeuwenhoek sent over 100 letters on microscopic observations to the Royal Society of England and to the French Academy. His work was chiefly responsible for stimulating research in bacteriology and establishing firmly the study of microorganisms in biology.

It is important that we see the work of Leeuwenhoek in its proper perspective to science as a whole. His thorough understanding and application of the principles of light gave the first significant impulse to this scientific area, which had previously been largely descriptive. This work spurred the study of microorganisms.

Augustin Fresnel, a French engineer, refined the wave theory to explain the phenomenon of diffraction, the spreading of light around obstacles. He also explained the polarization of light by adopting the idea that light vibrations are at right angles to the direction of travel of the light. To explain the transmission of light through space, he continued to postulate that all space is filled with ether, which acts as a carrier for light waves. Fresnel did much experimentation to prove the wave theory, and he developed it to such a degree of completeness that it was then assumed to be the final word, even in view of Newton's earlier successes.

In the work of Fresnel and Joseph von Fraunhofer (1787–1826), a contemporary of Young, we find applications of algebraic mathematics to the solution of problems in optics. Fraunhofer did a great deal of work with the phenomenon of diffraction. He showed that the interference rings, first observed by Newton, could be used for testing optical surfaces to a very precise standard. Fraunhofer was the first to notice and measure carefully the absorption lines in the solar spectrum.

Hermann von Helmholtz (1821–1894) was a physician and a physicist. During his lifetime he contributed much to the science of physiology, anatomy, and pathology. His works on physiological optics are the most important ever written in this field. Much of what he wrote stands as perfectly good science today.

Anders Jonas Ångström (1814–1874) was a Swedish physicist who established the international unit now used for the measurement of wavelengths in the visible spectrum. This measurement, called after him an *angstrom unit*, is equal to 10^{-8} centimeters. Because the centimeter is a cumbersome unit of measurement to work with in such minute measurements, the angstrom unit has been adopted and readily accepted for use in discussions of measurements of light in the visible spectrum.

**8.5
Invisible
Radiation**

By the middle of the nineteenth century, it was discovered that the visible portion represents only a small portion of the entire electromagnetic spectrum. Other rays exist beyond both ends of the visible portion, rays that cannot be seen by the human eye.

Sir William Herschel, an English astronomer, in 1800 conducted the experiment that first proved the existence of invisible rays. Herschel put a prism in a beam of sunlight, which split the light into its colors. He then placed a thermometer within each color. He found that red is the hottest. By moving his thermometer below the red, into an area that apparently was not illuminated, he found the temperature higher than it had been in the red color. Thus, he proved the presence of invisible rays, which he called *infrared rays* (*infra* means *below*). These rays are below the visible spectrum in frequency.

Herschel performed other experiments with these infrared rays. He found that they could be reflected by using mirrors and focused with special lens systems. He found that they are emitted by a bed of hot coals and by the sun. As we know, the main characteristic of infrared is heat.

Johan William Ritter, a German physicist, found strange things happening at the other end of the visible spectrum, beyond the violet portion. These short-wavelength rays are capable of producing certain chemical effects, but do not cause heating. Ritter noticed that white silver chloride turns black when exposed to the rays beyond violet light. He had discovered *ultraviolet rays* (*ultra* meaning *beyond*), which are higher than the highest frequencies of visible light waves. Ritter's experiments proved that ultraviolet rays, or UV, can be focused and reflected just like visible rays. He also found that these rays do not penetrate glass very well.

In a series of published papers dealing with the nature of light, James Clerk Maxwell (1831–1879) reported that light energy consists of electromagnetic waves equally divided between an electric field and a magnetic field. These fields are mutally perpendicular, and perpendicular to the direction of propagation. He reached the conclusion that these waves can extend far beyond the infrared. One of his suggestions was that a vibrating electrical charge will set up such waves and that these waves can travel through space at the speed of light. He calculated that speed from his theory at approximately 186,000 mi/s. This was the first indication that there is a definite relationship between all the various radiations known to exist in the electromagnetic spectrum.

Two German physicists, Wilhelm Weber and Frederich Kohlrausch, found that the velocity of an electric current in a perfect conductor is almost the same as the velocity of light. These two related findings were close enough for Maxwell to draw his conclusion: "We can scarcely avoid the inference that light consists in the transverse undulation of the same medium which is the cause of the electric and the magnetic phenomenon." He had correctly identified light waves as electromagnetic waves and had declared that electric current and light waves both travel at the same speed.

A decade later Heinrich Hertz produced electromagnetic waves by purely electrical means. He proved that these waves are similar to light waves: they have the same velocity and can be reflected, refracted, and polarized. The electromagnetic theory, based on this discovery, showed that radiant energies from many different sources can be unified into one single family. The only physical difference is in their wavelength and their frequencies, which vary from zero to infinity.

Wilhelm Röntgen in 1895 discovered mysterious new rays beyond the ultraviolet. These very high-frequency waves pass through material objects such as wood and still cause photographic film emulsion to darken. Röntgen called these mysterious rays *x-rays*. The frequency of x-rays was found to be dependent on the amount of electrical energy used in the generation of the waves. Today we know that there are waves of even higher frequencies that go far beyond the x-ray. We find them associated with nuclear phenomena. We group them together, referring to them simply as *gamma rays*. They are the most energetic of all the known electromagnetic waves.

**8.6
Waves or
Particles?**

All light instruments may be placed into one of two categories: image-forming types and non-image-forming energy-measuring devices. Curiously, the image formers can nearly all be described by assuming that light travels in straight lines, according to the geometric or *ray* optics of Newton. Non-image formers depend for the most part upon interference and diffraction phenomena that defy description under the ray model of light. Those instruments must be described according to a wave interpretation, i.e., *physical* optics as first stated by Huygens.

Here lies one of the great mysteries of our universe. A single entity, light, can be understood only by describing it from two apparently different points of view. So long as we do not confine light by forcing it to pass through small apertures or around small objects, it behaves as if it consists of a stream of tiny particles that carry momentum. Momentum should call to mind the idea of mass, and so we are faced here with trying to visualize particles of light as somehow being associated with a mass. What was historically required was a model that could visualize momentum for a particle that ceases to exist at other than the speed of light. Obviously the model of Newton with its ideas of absolute time and space was hopelessly inadequate for this purpose. A model was soon forthcoming that assumed the equivalence of mass and energy and that was founded on the master assumption that the speed of light is invariant regardless of who measures it (independent of the speed of the source of light or the speed of the observer). The *special theory of relativity* of Albert Einstein asks us to assume this somehow uncomfortable condition on reality — uncomfortable because it seems to disagree with common sense. None can deny, however, that up to now special relativity has been remarkably successful in its explanations of observed phenomena. This is, after all, the only test required of any model. We have good experimental evidence that light does come in small packets and that a stream of such packets exerts a pressure on an interrupting surface.

On the other hand, if we try to force these packets to fly through the tiny spaces between the edges of a slit, the light spreads out into the space behind the slit in a way that we can understand only by assuming that light is a wave.

Curiously, tiny microscopic particles such as the electron behave in just this same way. That is, electrons too behave at times as if they were waves. It is hard to picture this in the mind, and not essential at this point. This paradox of nature has puzzled the best scientific minds of our time. No theoretician has yet produced a satisfying explanation of this paradox in terms of a general model that is easily understood. Instead, men have invented a model that has predictive power for much of the observed phenomena. This model is called *quantum mechanics*.

We have examined in some detail the historical flow that led to the development of two apparently distinct models for light, the corpuscular and the wave models. Which is correct? Both models serve well to describe and account for the phenomenology of light so long as certain physical restrictions are observed in each case.

This is a classic example of two incomplete paradigms that have recently been merged into a single more powerful paradigm, quantum mechanics. The answer to the above question is, of course, that neither the corpuscular nor the wave model is incorrect. Both describe well a certain range of the phenomenology of light and are mutually compatible. Early workers in the field considered these models to be incompatible because they could not conceive of a simple model that would permit light to behave as both particles and waves. The wave-particle duality principle is now a firmly accepted part of the more mature paradigm.

In 1960 a new device called the *laser* provided men with the first source of pure-color light, i.e., a pencil of light all of nearly the same color (wavelength). This one-color light is profoundly interesting, as we shall see.

**8.7
A New Kind of
Light**

The word *laser* is an acronym: *l*ight *a*mplification (by) *s*timulated *e*mission (of) *r*adiation.

Details of what the laser is, how it works, and what it can do in its various forms are best read elsewhere. It will suffice here to say that the laser can produce pencils of light many times brighter than light at the surface of the sun. Focused to a fine point the laser beam can burn holes in diamond. In its most refined form it can carry millions of images in a thin pencil beam between planets.

We spoke earlier of diffraction as the process in which light is dispersed angularly when it passes around sharp edges and small objects and through small apertures. Diffraction does not produce a random smearing of light beyond a small aperture. A definite pattern emerges in the smear of light, a pattern that depends on the physical nature of the aperture and the light coming through and a pattern that is periodic in distribution. The sharpest diffraction patterns result when the light incident on the aperture is very *coherent*. We shall make no attempt to gain a formal understanding of what is meant by *coherent*. We must be content at this point to understand that highly pure, one-color light, such as that produced by a laser, and white light from a very small source at considerable distance are both examples of relatively coherent light.

An idea of the meaning of coherence in light can be gained by considering coherence in a familiar mechanical example. Whenever a platoon of foot soldiers is marched over a suspended footbridge, its commander, if he is wise, will order the men to route-step, i.e., to be certain that they do not walk so that their feet all come down on the bridge at the same time. If they did march in military fashion with all feet striking the bridge at the same instant, time after time, the energies of each of the footfalls would add up exactly and would cause the bridge to deflect downward. At each footfall the elastic motion of the bridge might be increased and an oscillation of the bridge might result. If this were continued, each footfall would further increase the oscillation amplitude (stretching), and the bridge would break under the men. If, on the other hand, the men route-step, their individual footfall energies do not add to one another. Instead they tend to cancel each other out, and no oscillation of the bridge is set up. In military marching the footfalls are coherent and add to one another. In the route-step the footfalls are incoherent and tend to cancel each other out. Laser light is like the military march, i.e., coherent with all wave amplitudes adding exactly for maximum effect. White light is incoherent. Like the steps, some of the waves are long and some short.   Put together they tend to interfere with one another rather than add up their energies.

The laser is, therefore, the ideal source of light with which to examine the phenomenon of diffraction.   We see here in a series of pictures (Fig. 8.10) a number of diffracting apertures and the corresponding laser diffraction patterns.   Note particularly the difference in pattern size as different-colored laser beams illuminate the same aperture.   This size dependence of the pattern upon color can be used to create instruments that separate light of various colors into its color components for analysis.   This is accomplished by passing the light through a special diffraction grating.   These instruments, *spectrometers*, are in general use in astronomy, where astronomers analyze the light from stars, and in chemistry, where chemists analyze the elemental composition of unknown samples.   Such analysis may also go by the names *spectroscopy* and *spectrometry*.

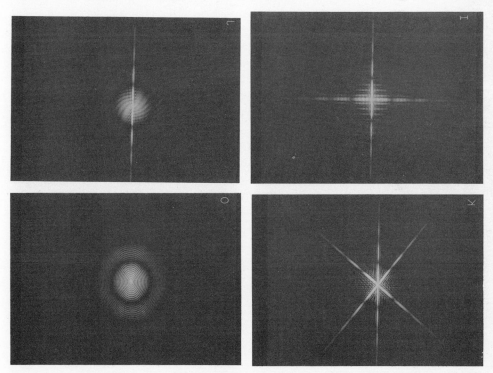

Fig. 8.10   Laser diffraction patterns of the four alphanumeric characters I, J, K, and O.   The characters were cut in opaque material with letter height approximately 25μm.   Note that the distinctly different diffraction patterns may be used to "recognize" these letters any time that they are present in any complicated aperture.

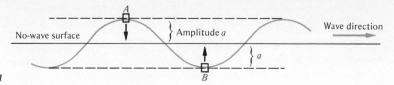

Fig. 8.11

Diffraction cannot be understood using the ray model for light. It is only when we think in terms of waves that diffraction becomes intelligible. Light in this model is assumed to be composed of waves that are electric and magnetic in nature. Since it is the electric field oscillation that gives rise to most effects that we measure, we can confine our discussion to the electric field intensity vector $\vec{E}$.

A charged particle at any point in space will experience an electric field intensity $\vec{E}$ at any given instant as light passes the point. As seen from the particle's point of view, the $\vec{E}$ field oscillates in both direction and amplitude. The rate at which it changes direction and amplitude is far too great for direct measurement. The $\vec{E}$ vector is always perpendicular to the direction in which the light wave is traveling.

Think for a moment about water waves on the surface of a lake or tank. The waves are traveling in one direction parallel to the water's surface, from one side of the lake to the other. Yet the oscillation of the water that makes up the waves is up and down, i.e., perpendicular to the direction the waves are traveling. Corks A and B in Fig. 8.11 bob up and down with amplitude a, as the waves pass. The corks do not travel in the wave direction. Only the wave energy moves in the wave direction. If you doubt that energy is transmitted, watch a boat bob up and down as the waves reach it. This requires that work be done, and the energy comes from the waves themselves. The amplitude is a measure of the energy of the waves (maximum displacement from a relaxed surface, in the case of water waves). Actually the energy of the waves is proportional to the square of the wave amplitude:

Energy $\propto a^2$

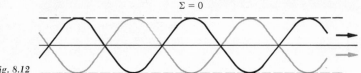

Fig. 8.12

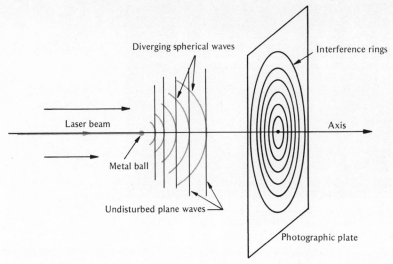

Fig. 8.13

A peculiar behavior of waves is that where they meet in space, they add amplitude algebraically. Thus a water wave with a positive crest meeting another of like amplitude but a negative trough at the point of intersection will add to this second wave at the point so that their sum is momentarily zero (see Fig. 8.12). We see examples of the *superposition* principle of waves often in water waves as well as in other waves.

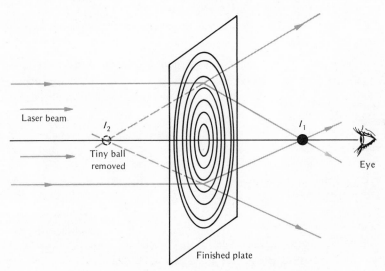

Fig. 8.14

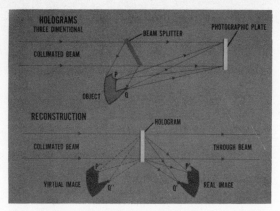

Fig. 8.15 How a three-dimensional hologram is made. The beam from the laser is split into two beams during construction. One beam illuminates the object to be holographed; the other exposes the plate directly. The light reflected off the object interferes at the plate with this direct beam and produces a complicated diffraction grating in the photographic emulsion. The images are shown below reconstructed by illuminating the finished photographic plate by a laser beam.

It is this wave characteristic that accounts for the periodic structure in diffraction patterns. We say that waves of various frequency and amplitude "interfere" with one another through the superposition principle. Light waves behave this way, as do water waves, sound waves, microwaves, etc. Once the principles of wave motion are understood for one kind of wave phenomenon, the same principles can be applied in general to all wave phenomena.

Men have recently learned to use the pure light of the laser and knowledge of diffraction to make a new kind of lens that depends upon bending light by diffraction rather than by refraction. It is not difficult to see how this lens works.

If a tiny metal ball is placed in a collimated laser beam (parallel beam sides), the laser light passes around it, illuminating its surface. If the ball is very tiny, noticeable diffraction occurs in the beam as detected by a photographic plate, as shown in Fig. 8.13. The plate records a definite bull's-eye pattern where it would have been only uniformly blackened by the laser beam alone. This pattern is a permanent record of the intensity of light in the diffraction pattern. The truly marvelous result that we wish to note here is that when the metal ball is removed from the laser beam and the finished photographic plate placed in the beam, two distinct images of the ball may be observed. Diverging rays from the diffracting photo pattern appear to have come from the virtual image I_2. At the same time, real converging rays from the diffraction pattern create a real image at I_1 (Fig. 8.14). Thus, the diffraction pattern created by the beam and ball "remembers" the object that made it, imaging the ball when again flooded by the laser beam. Only a coherent beam will work.

Through a process that is somewhat more refined than this, but nevertheless making use of the same principle, complicated objects can be "remembered" and imaged in three dimensions by complex diffraction plates. Such plates are called *holograms*. Holography, the science of making useful holograms, has advanced rapidly to become a useful tool in research and technology. This is a diffraction process entirely.

Nehrich, Richard B., and Dessel, Voran: "Atomic Light, Lasers, *Bibliography* What They Are and How They Work," Sterling, New York, 1967. **Physical Science Study Committee:** "Physics," Heath, Boston, 1965.

Chapter 9
Scientific Inquiry

The 2-MW
Livermore pool-type
reactor is one of the
major research
instruments at the
Lawrence Livermore
Laboratory,
Livermore,
California. (Courtesy
of the Lawrence
Radiation
Laboratory,
University of
California, Graphic
Arts, Livermore.)

**9.1
A Pattern
Emerges**
You have labored hard thus far to grasp the fundamental ideas of what Thomas S. Kuhn calls the "modern paradigms" of science. These models that men use to describe the world about them are just that—models. There is nothing sacred or eternal about them, even if professional scientists tend to behave as if there were. Kuhn's book, "The Structure of Scientific Revolutions," is excellent reading.

The history of science, excluding the metaphysics of the Greeks, had its real beginning in the lifetime of Galileo Galilei. Beginning at about the time of the Protestant Reformation, science germinated on the foundation of Greek and Moslem natural philosophy. It evolved in a way that was and is profoundly influenced by the whole of human cultural evolution. Its early infancy was set in a framework of religious and social upheaval. This was the period of bold new architecture, magnificent Renaissance art, and serious Elizabethan theater. The infant plant required the power, zeal, and arrogance of a Galileo to thrust it out into the light. It needed the conformation of new instruments born of rising crafts and the acceptance possible only through general communication and publications eagerly read by thirsty scholars. The temporal church, oversensitive from the stings of the Reformation, tried feebly to rout it out, but might as well have tried to shut out the light of the sun. Science had to come. All the facets of culture were ripe for it.

Science did not evolve as a smooth flow of bits and pieces of information that gradually fitted into a single large "puzzle of nature." Its development has been marked by a series of revolutions that have established new paradigms, leaving the old to atrophy and die. These revolutions were sometimes abrupt and unexpected. In other cases, they were more gradual and anticipated by men of vision. One of man's most remarkable characteristics is that of embracing the familiar and rejecting any change. New science paradigms have many times had to wait for general acceptance until adversaries either died or were eclipsed as intellectual powers of science.

The steps that have led, in a typical pattern, to a revolution and a new paradigm are well recognized. In the beginning there are numerous observations of phenomena not adequately explained by the current paradigm. These data may not even be recognized as of fundamental importance because the current model does not deal with them or has set them aside as mere curiosities.

What the scientist sees during a period of observation is largely determined by what his model has led him to expect to see. He is often unprepared for an encounter with new and unexpected phenomena. For hundreds of years before Newton, chemists had known that certain samples of metals gain weight when burned or roasted. Yet this "fact" of observation was not assimilated into a chemical model until the newtonian gravitational model was well established. Until then, the gain of weight had been thought to be unimportant.

The second stage in the process is the attempt by one or more scientists to invent a new model that incorporates everything already known and also explains these troublesome new phenomena. Often the result of these prerevolutionary attempts is a series of partial models, each of which explains some part of the whole, but none of which is completely satisfactory. Nuclear physics is a current example of this stage. Since the beginning of the twentieth century, submicroscopic particles such as protons, neutrons, and neutrinos have been "observed" indirectly through experiments involving macroscopic instrumentation. To date, however, no single model of the nucleus has been successful in "explaining" the full range of observed phenomena.

In the previous example of the weight gained by roasting metal, the assimilation of the newtonian concepts of mass and conservation led Antoine Lavoisier and others to conclude that the metal must be combining with some gas from the air during the roasting. This single realization resulted in the establishment of one of the key concepts of the modern chemical model. Not only do elements such as iron and oxygen combine, but they do so in very precise and predictable ratios of their masses.

The revolution that brings about a new model of science is usually set off by a crisis of persistent unexplained phenomena. Quite often in history the revolution leading to a new model has come about through the efforts of a gifted scientist working outside his own discipline. Perhaps an explanation for this is that a man working in, say, electricity is not inhibited by the restraints and preconceptions of chemists when observing chemical phenomena. This innocence permits a more penetrating examination of a phenomenon with more powerful exercise of imagination than would be possible for a man indoctrinated in the formalism of current chemical theory. The fresh perspective of another discipline is also an asset.

This relatively rare process of mental synthesis leading to new science paradigms is the backbone of science. Revolutionaries such as Galileo, Newton, Dalton, Franklin, Darwin, Maxwell, Descartes, Lavoisier, and Einstein have all made enormous contributions to our current world view.

Thus far we have dealt only with the macroscopic models of the nineteenth century. The twentieth century has been dominated by concern for microscopic phenomena. We shall presently look more closely at this latest phase of science, though not with the same rigor as in the preceding chapters.

During the Renaissance science depended upon new developments in technology. New instruments significantly extended human senses. For example, in the eighteenth century Herschel saw, with the aid of an improved telescope, the planet Uranus, previously thought to be a star. Similarly, the microscopes of Leeuwenhoek established the discipline of microbiology.

At this point, there is a need to distinguish carefully between *science* and *technology*. Science is a methodology that strives to develop and refine natural paradigms. Technology is quite a different matter. Technology deals not with ideas but with processes and devices that are useful to man in a purely mechanical way. Science is a philosophical activity, while technology deals with hardware.

A common misconception represents science as the source of technology. This is not true. Technology has for centuries preceded science, with scientific progress often dependent upon new technological developments. The steam engine had long been in use pumping water from mine shafts before the refinement of thermodynamic theory. The telegraph was a familiar tool long before the electron had been observed and identified.

We should pause now to reflect that science does not deal with "truth" in the sense that religious philosophies do. Science is a fabric of models, none of which are "true" or even unique, but all of which are subject to change as the experimental process continues. Technology is ancient, reaching back into the mists of prehistory. Science is a relative newcomer.

9.2 Hazards of Measurement

Measurement lies at the heart of all science. When a new model is advanced, it invariably makes certain predictions that are subject to experimental verification through careful measurements. As science has become more abstract and its models more esoteric, the problem of measurement has become more complicated. Hence, the evolution of science paradigms has brought an ever-increasing need for greater subtlety in measurements. In many twentieth-century experiments scientists can observe only the simple output of complicated machines and instruments that do the direct microscopic measurements. Thus, the machine or instrument lies between the observer and the phenomenon observed, and no direct human observation is ever possible.

In this typical modern situation, the investigator must consider the intermediate instrument, i.e., what it is telling him and what errors may occur in the data. He must worry about the basic design of his instruments and whether or not he is asking for the right kind of information. Then, too, he carefully evaluates the data. The inexperienced scientist who has not carefully designed his total experiment is likely to wind up with a mountain of meaningless data. An observation is never better than the experimental design. Good design always involves a thorough analysis of the questions to be asked of the phenomenon and of the magnitude and kinds of errors to be expected.

Experimental errors can be of several kinds. These may be grouped as (1) systematic errors due to failure to anticipate and control variables not measured directly, (2) errors built into the instrumentation that may or may not produce random variations in the data, and (3) errors in analyzing and interpreting the data. Your teacher can give you many concrete examples of these kinds of errors if you have not already encountered them in the laboratory. Some errors can be anticipated and kept to a minimum. There will always remain, no matter how good the design, some random errors. The trick is to make this kind of error unimportant by good design.

Part of the evolution of the inquiry process has been an increasing extension of human senses through special instrumentation. The telescope and microscope were at first crude instruments. They have since been refined to the limits of practicality. The 200-in-diameter telescope on Palomar Mountain in California is about as good as a light telescope can get for a number of reasons. Atmospheric distortion makes higher magnification useless in imaging, and structured limitations make a larger size impractical. The 200-in telescope is primarily a device to gather in light from very faint objects so that they may be observed.

9.3 Extending the Senses

The microscope is limited in its magnification by the nature of light itself. Objects smaller than 10 μm (about one-hundredth the diameter of human hair) produce images that are grossly distorted. This is due to diffraction. Electron microscopes, however, operate on a principle that is independent of light. These are used to image objects many times smaller than those resolvable in a light microscope. The electron microscope, too, has its diffraction limit.

The human brain cannot separate events that occur more rapidly than about 100 per second. A variety of instruments is, however, able to do so, presenting easily assimilated data to the human observer. Can you think of any that do so?

What, then, is the limit of what we can know? The nineteenth and twentieth centuries have produced sense-extending instruments that are technological marvels. Electric and magnetic technology has produced a vast array of instruments that are used in measurement in every phase of natural science. Coupled with computers that perform preprogrammed data analysis, these measuring instruments are advancing science and technology so rapidly that human culture has not been able to fully assimilate resulting changes in life. In Chap. 12 we shall discuss some of these instruments.

In summary, instruments have extended the range of human senses far beyond what any man can experience.

**9.4
Current Science
Disciplines**

Physics is the simplest and yet the most esoteric of all the science disciplines. It deals with the most fundamental of natural processes. Its paradigms involve statements about conservation in nature and fundamental relationships between massive particles and energy from the subnuclear level to macroscopic.

Chemistry is probably closer to physics than is biology. Whereas the physicist typically deals with well-defined problems in which events are well ordered, the chemist often deals with a complex problem in which disorder appears to be the rule. Chemistry may be thought of as the detailed study of the elements that comprise the universe, the way in which they combine with one another, and the properties of the many possible combinations. The chemist deals with a large number of particles that assume a wide variety of associations, sizes, shapes, and behavior. He is concerned with those physical states in which matter is organized primarily into molecules, i.e., solids, crystals, liquids, and gases. In this concern, he attempts to find order within the apparent riot of nature.

One phase of chemistry deals with very large *macromolecules* in which carbon atoms are the basic building blocks. The *organic* chemist may be involved in developing strong long-chain molecules such as nylon, or he might be studying the chemistry of life. Magnificent detective work has led to the discovery of proteins, DNA (deoxyribonucleic acid), and other components of living systems. Those interested in this detective work should read "The Double Helix," by J. D. Watson.

The biologist must be both a physicist and a biochemist in a certain sense. He works with the most complex physical systems that exist. Biology deals with the detailed study of living systems. These systems require constant energy input. They cycle the nonliving elements through their systems and are able to reproduce themselves exactly. This study embraces life, its complex internal relationships, and its interactions with the nonliving part of nature. Biologists have made great strides since the middle of the nineteenth century.

Although the science disciplines deal with fundamentals of the total universe, many science areas are inherently interdisciplinary. The best known of these are the environmental sciences: astronomy, which deals with the extraterrestrial part of nature; geology, concerned with the evolution, structure, and processes of the earth; oceanography, which deals with the marine environment; and geophysics, with its concern for the planet earth and its environment in near space. The scientist in these interdisciplinary areas must combine competence in biology, chemistry, and physics to a greater or lesser extent.

The boundaries between science disciplines, although historically well defined, are now largely a matter of formal convenience. More and more scientists are crossing the old boundaries to join hands with colleagues on common problems.

Environmental science problems are usually very complex. Measuring instrumentation often must be placed in a very hostile environment where data must be remotely sensed and relayed on to humans. It is only since 1950 that man has known much about the earth, the moon, and the vast reaches of the hydrosphere. The sheer mass of data collected in these environments since 1950 staggers the mind. It has been reduced and analyzed only with the help of electronic computers. It is clear that the investigator can make measurements in these environments only with wide competence in the basic sciences and a helping boost from technology. Much of man's success so far in these areas has been due to advanced technology in the form of rocket systems, electronics, and deep-submergence systems.

Once again we see the dependence of science upon technology. There is a definite science-technology interplay. The scientific achievements of this century have been primarily the result of technological research and development. Technology has advanced rapidly during this period as a result of the growing economic thrust of society. Hence, science has consistently capitalized on the growth of industrialism.

Technology often cannot be separated from science. This is due to the high order of interdependence of the two. The placing of the first man on the moon was heralded as a great scientific achievement, but there was little science involved. This particular achievement was almost entirely technological. Far more scientific advancement was accomplished by the remote probes that first examined the moon. Those who are asked to pay the bill for these achievements must have this distinction between science and technology clearly in mind. In your judgment, should the technological or the scientific venture have higher priority?

Problems 1   Nobel peace prizes have increasingly gone to those who have designed and built the giant machines that support nuclear scientists. Were these prize winners engaged in science or technology?

2   Can you order and relate to one another the few great revolutions of the physical sciences from the seventeenth century to the beginning of the twentieth century?

3   Pick one historical paradigm revolution in either physics or chemistry and identify events leading up to the revolution according to the outline of stages in this chapter.

4   Identify those properties of science that make it unique in human activity.

5   Debate the following statement with your classmates: "The phrase *social science* is a misnomer since social science is not a science discipline and does not even follow the procedures common to all science."

Bibliography Asimov, Isaac: "Life and Energy," Anchor Science Study Series, Doubleday, Garden City, N.Y., 1965.

Asimov, Isaac: "A Short History of Chemistry," Anchor Science Study Series, Doubleday, Garden City, N.Y., 1965.

Kuhn, Thomas S. "The Structure of Scientific Revolutions," University of Chicago Press, Chicago, 1962.

Watson, J. D.: "The Double Helix," Signet, New York, 1968.

Chapter 10
A Balanced Look at Nature and Science

The 200-in Hale telescope showing observer in prime-focus cage and reflecting surface of 200-in mirror. **(Photograph courtesy of the Hale Observatories.)**

10.1
The Beginning
Where did our universe begin? How old is it? When will it end? How did it get to be the way it is? These are all questions for which we can never find complete answers. Men have only their limited physical senses augmented by sophisticated instruments upon which to rely. All that is possible is a partial answer—actually a speculation based upon fundamental concepts of mass, energy, and motion such as those contained in the first chapters of this book. (In this respect, nuclear physics has contributed heavily to some recent understandings.)

These basic concepts have nonetheless permitted us to speculate with some confidence upon many of the questions. For example, the only information that reaches us from space is in the form of light and other electromagnetic radiation; yet from this meager information, it is possible to say a good deal about stars and other objects in space.

We have been able to measure the distances between the earth and the stars and between the earth and distant clusters of stars called *galaxies*. These distances are measured in light-years, the distance light travels ($c = 3 \times 10^8$ m/s) in one year. An astounding observation has been made and verified: the galaxies are moving outward, away from a point in the universe, at a speed that is roughly proportional to their present distance from that center. This speed is about 3×10^4 m/s per 1 million light-years distance away from center, e.g., a galaxy 1 million light-years from the center today is traveling outward at 3×10^4 m/s speed. A galaxy at a distance of 10 million light-years from center, as seen today, has an outward speed of 10 times the speed of the first galaxy, or 3×10^5 m/s away from center.

At a speed of 3×10^4 m/s, assuming that a galaxy has traveled at this constant speed, the total time of travel would be the distance divided by the velocity.

$$T = \frac{10^6 \text{ light-years}}{3 \times 10^4 \text{ m/s}}$$
$$\approx 10^{10} \text{ years}$$

Thus, we see that any galaxy visible today must have come from a point near this mass center about 10 to 20 billion years ago.

If this extrapolation backward in time is substantially valid, our universe as we now observe it must be about this old. What happened before the galaxies were a concentrated mass at center and what happened to make them explode outward 10 to 20 billion years ago are unknowns. This model is known as the "big bang" theory.

The age of a star can be estimated from the amount and kind of energy it radiates outward to us. The life story of a star is fascinating. The most abundant element in any galaxy is hydrogen, the lightest atom consisting of a single proton nucleus and an orbiting electron. A large fraction of a total galactic mass is hydrogen.

There are other curious objects within sight of our light and radio telescopes besides ordinary stars and galaxies. Quasi-stellar objects (*quasars*) are believed to be the most distant objects we can see. The quasar is a starlike object but much larger and billions of times brighter than a star. Recently a Dutch astronomer working at Palomar Observatory recognized the usual spectrum of an element in light gathered from a distant quasar. This spectrum had been shifted, however, a long way toward the red end of the spectrum. His calculations showed that this quasar is moving away from us at a substantial fraction of the speed of light. The doppler shift noted here in the light from the quasar has a more easily understood parallel in sound. Nearly everyone is familiar with the shift in pitch of an automobile horn as the auto approaches at high speed, passes, and then moves away at high speed. The shift in pitch in this example is analogous to the shift in color of spectral light from the quasar as it moves away from us.

In nearer space there are *pulsars*, stars that are very bright and pulse like a firefly. A very recent discovery by radioastronomers indicates that the pulsar at the core of the Crab Nebula is pulsing 30 times each second (Fig. 10.1). The Crab Nebula is the result of a giant explosion that was visible in broad daylight in the year 1054. Curiously, Europe is the only area that apparently failed to report it. This pulsar has greatly excited the scientific community for reasons that will soon be discussed.

Discoveries in nuclear processes in the twentieth century have permitted a rational description of the life cycle and processes of stars. In interstellar space there are known to be huge clouds of hydrogen with enormous numbers of hydrogen atoms in random motion, e.g., the hydrogen cloud in the constellation Orion. Sooner or later there will occur in such a cloud regions of higher concentration of hydrogen atoms. These regions of higher density will exert a net gravitational force of attraction upon other hydrogen atoms, thus drawing more and more toward the gravitational center. As the balls of hydrogen gas grow, the gravitational force grows and causes a contraction of the ball. The more atoms that are attracted and added to the ball, the more dense the ball becomes and the greater is its gravitational field. As the gravitational force increases, the speed of

10.2
Birth and
Death of a Star

Fig. 10.1 NGC 1952 Crab Nebula in Taurus. Messier 1. Taken in red light. Remains of supernova of A.D. *1054, 200-in photograph.* (**Photograph courtesy of the Hale Observatories.**)

atoms falling toward the center increases. Hence, the mean kinetic energy of atoms in the gas (the temperature) grows as the ball attracts more and more hydrogen and continues to contract.

When the temperature of the ball of gas reaches a certain point, the hydrogen atomic collisions have sufficient energy to cause a quantum excitation of the atoms. As excited hydrogen atoms relax back to ground state, they emit light photons characteristic of hydrogen, and the ball begins to glow with the characteristic hydrogen spectrum. The yellowish color of a sodium lamp is familiar to many, just as the bluish cast of a mercury lamp is common in street lamps. The hydrogen spectrum has a dominant red color. A telescopic view of the cloud in Orion verifies this point.

The contraction continues, and temperatures near the center of the ball reach 10^6 K. Collisions near the ball center are energetic enough to cause the electrons to be torn away from the nuclei, and an ionized gas of hydrogen now glows with photons of all wavelengths emitted. This white light is a much more complicated emission process.

A star is being born. Further gravitational contraction drives the temperature at the center up to 10^7 K. Now the hydrogen nuclei are profoundly influenced, and a nuclear fire starts at the center. In a process termed *fusion*, two protons combine to form a deuteron, one proton decaying to form a neutron. Two deuterons then fuse to form helium nuclei, which are highly stable. The process may be represented thus:

$$2_1H^2 \longrightarrow {}_2He^4 + energy$$

The helium nucleus, also called an *alpha particle*, contains two protons and two neutrons. Its mass, however, is significantly less than the combined masses of its particles. The difference is released in the form of energy according to Einstein's equation that relates mass and energy, $E = mc^2$.

This nuclear fusion releases an enormous amount of energy, which creates a counterpressure outward from the star center. This counterpressure effectively prevents any further gravitational contraction in a kind of tug of war between gravity and nuclear fusion. In this second stabilized state, the star will remain for a long time, probably billions of years. It is

Fig. 10.2 NGC 224 Great Nebula in Andromeda. Messier 31. Satellite nebulae NGC 205 and 221 also shown. 48-in Schmidt photograph. **(Photograph courtesy of the Hale Observatories.)**

a giant furnace manufacturing helium nuclei out of hydrogen nuclei at its center. This process continues until the hydrogen supply near the center is almost exhausted.

When the central hydrogen supply nears exhaustion, the fusion counterpressure begins to drop, thus permitting a continuation of gravitational contraction. The temperature at the center begins again to increase. When it reaches 10^8 K, one of nature's most remarkable processes begins. At these temperatures the helium nuclei fuse to form heavier nuclei. Carbon and oxygen are probably first.

$$3_2He^4 \longrightarrow {}_6C^{12} + energy$$
$$4_2He^4 \longrightarrow {}_8O^{16} + energy$$

As the fusion furnace continues, a huge amount of energy is released. A new counterpressure is established with the result that matter near the star surface is puffed out to form an enormous red star. It is red because the radiation reaching us is due largely to the hydrogen in the outer 10^6 mi of the star. Antares and Arcturus are examples of such red giants. Red supergiants may be hundreds of millions of miles in diameter. Our own sun will some day puff out and engulf the earth.

This third phase of star life does not last long compared to phase 2. As temperatures climb in the star's dense center, the fusion becomes more general, and heavier nuclei are formed, e.g., magnesium, silicon, and sulfur. In this terrible inferno are manufactured most of the lighter nuclei of our familiar family of elements. Free neutrons knocked out by collisions of nuclei are absorbed by other nuclei to form both stable and unstable nuclei. Unstable nuclei decay to more stable forms by emitting both particles and gamma rays.

As the nuclear fuel nears exhaustion, the star center contracts still further. With the counterpressure reduced, the giant red star collapses to a tiny white dwarf of incredible density, resembling a single giant nucleus. It is at this critical stage that a small number of such stars explode (supernovae), hurling their nuclei outward into space, where they contaminate clouds of interstellar hydrogen. From these contaminated clouds of hydrogen new second-generation stars will form, stars that contain heavy nuclei from their beginning. It is likely that our sun is such a second-generation star. It is during the explosion of the dwarf that a number of heavy nuclei such as gold, lead, and uranium are formed. These heavy nuclei cannot be manufactured in the red-star furnace.

The very recent discovery of fast-pulsing pulsars, such as the one in the Crab Nebula, has led to a model that views the residual nucleus of a supernova as a neutron star of very small dimensions—perhaps only a few

Fig. 10.3
NGC 4594 spiral
galaxy in Virgo, seen
edge on. Messier 104.
200-in photograph.
(Photograph
courtesy of
the Hale
Observatories.)

tens of kilometers—and of incredible density. To picture this density, imagine the earth crushed by some giant force to the size of a boulder, yet retaining its original mass. The evidence for this model comes from the conclusion that the body is spinning so fast, as evidenced by its rapid pulse rate of 30 flashes per second. The only object that could spin so fast without disintegrating would be a small body of unbelievable density. The pulsar must be like a giant atomic nucleus. A teaspoonful of its material not only would be impossible to lift, but would sink down through the earth's crust like a hot knife through butter.

Galaxies are not infrequently racked by explosions that hurl great clouds of radiating particles out beyond the boundaries of the galaxy. Were such an event to occur in our Milky Way, all life on earth would be snuffed out. Astronomers are very interested in a thorough study of the "pulse" of our own galaxy.

The star or stars that exploded to furnish the gas cloud that would later be the mother of our solar system probably exploded more than 10 billion years ago. In the clumping of the gas cloud into star masses, an accident occasionally occurs that results in the formation of satellites. Some of the

**10.3
The Solar
System**

smaller clumps containing heavy atoms are not massive enough to be suns themselves. These are the planets and asteroids of our solar system.

The smaller planets, of which our earth is one, contain heavy elements such as silicon and iron, whereas the larger planets contain predominantly lighter elements. Although their gravitational contraction did not make them hot enough to produce fusion, their surface temperatures were undoubtedly too high to retain any hydrogen atmosphere.

The early atmosphere of the earth undoubtedly contained carbon dioxide, methane, and nitrogen, but probably did not contain any oxygen. Oxygen readily forms strong molecular bonds with many elements, and therefore, must be constantly released by some chemical process in order to be present in a planetary atmosphere.

It is a fortunate accident of nature that placed the earth at its present distance from the sun, with surface temperatures ranging generally between 0 and 100°C. In this temperature range water can exist in liquid form. Cooled nuclei in the gas cloud pick up electrons to become atoms, and these atoms enter into association with other kinds of atoms to form molecules and crystals. Thus, this planet, fortunately, came to have a large hydrosphere.

In the earth's primitive atmosphere, solar ultraviolet was able to penetrate easily to the planet's surface. Oxygen in today's atmosphere prevents this. UV photons are chemically active and able to break molecular bonds. The eventual result was a grand proliferation of molecular

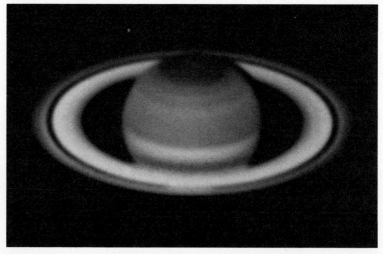

Fig. 10.4
Saturn and ring
system photographed
with 100-in
telescope.
(Photograph courtesy
of the Hale
Observatories.)

species such as sugars, nucleotides, and amino acids necessary in all life forms. These probably evolved from chance associations in the warm primordial seas. With conditions like this existing over long periods of time, the earth became a very favorable incubator for what we know as life. Under current science paradigms, it would be surprising had life never resulted.

Before we discuss the further development of these molecules into life forms, we shall pause long enough to discuss a method of determining the age of the earth and its life forms. Radioactive nuclei decay to stable nuclear forms over a period of time. Given a large number of radioactive nuclei of one kind, such as carbon 14, we can measure that period of time over which one-half will decay to stable form. This period is known as the decay *half-life* for the radioactive nucleus in question. Suppose we have a room containing thousands of time bombs, each set to go off at some time between 0 and 1,000 h. We have no idea which bomb will go off at any particular instant. All we can do is keep track of the explosions and measure the time required for about half of the bombs to explode. This might be 7 h or it might be 383 h. In the former case we would say that this collection of bombs had a relatively short half-life of 7 h. In the latter case they had a long half-life of 383 h. Unstable atomic nuclei are like the time bombs, with each distinct type (*isotope*) having its own characteristic half-life.

There are atoms that have the same chemical properties, i.e., the same number of protons in their nuclei, but have quite different physical properties. Carbon 14 is one example of an isotope that is chemically indistinguishable from the much more abundant carbon 12. In shorthand notation, these two isotopes of carbon are indicated by $_6C^{14}$ and $_6C^{12}$, respectively. The subscript 6 in each case refers to the number of protons in the atomic nucleus and determines the chemical species to which both isotopes belong. The superscripts 14 and 12 indicate the number of nucleons—protons plus neutrons—present in each nucleus.

**10.4
Isotopes,
Half-Lives, and
Radiation
Dating**

The number of neutrons in the nucleus, and more particularly the excess of neutrons over protons, determine the stability of that nucleus. If the neutron excess renders the nucleus unstable, it will decay to a new isotope by emitting energy and mass in the form of gamma photons and particles. The new nucleus may itself be unstable.

During the decay process, the number of protons present in the nucleus may change, hence transforming the nucleus into an isotope of a different chemical species. This depends entirely upon the original nucleus. Several examples that illustrate these processes are shown here.

$$_{92}U^{238} \;--\overset{decay}{------}\; _{90}Th^{234} + \text{alpha particle } (_2He^4) + \text{energy}$$

$$_{90}Th^{234} \;--\overset{decay}{------}\; _{91}Pa^{234} + \text{beta minus (electron)} + \text{antineutrino}$$

$_6C^{14}$ is produced in the earth's atmosphere by cosmic rays from $_6C^{13}$. This latter nucleus is stable. The $_6C^{14}$ is unstable and decays to the stable isotope $_7N^{14}$. What makes this particular process important is the fact that new carbon 14 atoms are manufactured by cosmic rays at very nearly the same rate as they decay to nitrogen 14. Thus the ratio of $_6C^{12}$ atoms to $_6C^{14}$ atoms is nearly constant in time in the air.

When plants take carbon dioxide from the air during photosynthesis, they tie these carbon atoms into their own tissues in just the same ratio as they exist in the air. $_6C^{14}$ is a beta emitter (energetic electron). When the two carbon isotopes are originally tied up in plant tissues, the radioactive carbon 14 emits about 15.3 betas per minute per gram of carbon present on the average. When the plant dies, it no longer brings in carbon, and the $_6C^{14}$ in its cells begins to disappear by emitting betas and transforming to nitrogen.

In 5,760 years one-half of the original $_6C^{14}$ atoms will have decayed to nitrogen. For example, if a gram of carbon taken from a fossil tree limb emits only an average of 3.83 betas per minute, four carbon half-lives of 5,760 years each have gone by since the tree died. The fossil is, therefore, known to be about 22,000 years old. Carbon 14 analysis is an extremely useful way of dating remains of any once-living thing, since all life forms take carbon from their environment and tie it into their tissues while living. It is, however, subject to significant errors in dating, as has been shown by analysis of very old bristle cone pines, which may be accurately dated by ring counting.

Algae have probably existed for more than 6×10^8 years, fish 3×10^8 years, reptiles 2.75×10^8 years, mammals 1.5×10^8 years, and man about 10^6 years. Billions of years were required for man to evolve from the beginnings of life in the primordial seas. The dating of rocks and meteorites by this same method indicates that the earth and the rest of the solar system originated about 4.5 billion years ago.

10.5 Evolution   Charles Darwin, recognized as the father of evolution, was initially influenced by the evolutionary theories proposed by geologists of his day.

James Hutton and Charles Lyell understood the evolutionary process of the earth's nonliving materials to a certain extent. After reading Lyell's "Principles of Geology," Darwin was led to conclude, before mid-nineteenth century, that animals, too, have evolved.

In 1831 Prof. J. S. Henslow of Cambridge University arranged for young Darwin to take passage on *H.M.S. Beagle*, which was to be at sea cruising in southern waters for 5 years. Darwin's careful observation of speciation and location of plants and animals on this journey led to his publication of "On the Origin of Species" on November 24, 1859. The first edition of 1,250 copies was entirely sold out on the first day.

A storm of protest and argument raged at once and led to a popular polarization that still exists today. In *Origin*, Darwin suggested that he would "soon . . . shed light on the origin and history of man." This he did in his "The Descent of Man, and Selection in Relation to Sex." His family's protests notwithstanding, he was laid at death in 1882 beside the remains of Sir Isaac Newton in Westminster Abbey. In Darwin's own words, "ignorance more frequently begets confidence than does knowledge: it is those who know little, and not those who know much, who so positively assert that this or that problem will never be solved by science." Humanity has little else to cling to as we approach the last quarter of the twentieth century.

Darwin's works have led to a new fundamental paradigm in biology. Whether it is "true" or "false" is unimportant, and perhaps even irrelevant. Its usefulness in understanding structure and function in biology is well established. Its impact upon the mainstream of society has been to cause many to regard man as only another animal with certain special characteristics but subject nonetheless to the same natural laws as all other living species.

10.6 Entropy

A word here is necessary as a prerequisite to real understanding of the latter chapters of this book. We have observed the conservation of energy in a simple mechanical sense, but have said little about energy in the real sense of complex nature.

On a macroscopic scale mass and energy together are conserved. We cannot create energy out of nothing, just as we cannot produce mass from nothing. In any system there is always an upper limit to the amount of energy available. Our interest at this point will be to examine what becomes of energy as it performs work in a system.

There are two rules to keep in mind. These are perhaps best stated in gambling terminology:

1 You can't win.
2 You can't even break even.

Starting with a given amount of energy E_o stored in the molecules of gasoline, we set out to do useful work with a gasoline engine. When you are out of gasoline, the work stops. It is not possible to get more work out of the engine than the energy put into it. "You can't win."

When a machine works, a certain amount of energy is irretrievably lost in the process, and hence, is not useful. A gasoline engine creates and loses heat, a form of energy. In animals, also, a certain amount of food energy is lost as heat. "You can't even break even."

These two ideas are enormously important, as we shall soon see. We often speak of the second rule as the law of *entropy*—no system is 100 percent efficient. To a chemist, entropy often is used to describe the amount of disorganization in the organization of matter. To the physicist, entropy means wasted energy. A biologist may use entropy to describe the wasted energy in plants and animals feeding upon one another. Still others may use entropy in a sociological context in describing the output of committees. We may think of it as a sort of disorganization that reduces the availability of useful energy in a system.

**10.7
Great
Principles of
Science**

This is not a textbook of biology, but it is artificial to treat the whole world system without mentioning its living systems. This is not a textbook of social science, but the authors hold that science has much to say to society. There is no intent in the latter chapters to do more than sketch obvious implications of science for mankind and to point out the influences of technology upon the manner and mode of human life patterns.

The great principles of science can be reduced to a relatively few statements that have broad application in all disciplines of science. There are surprisingly few really fundamental ideas underlying all current models. These collectively represent the current paradigm.

1 The universe consists of matter and energy in a dynamic state of change.
2 That which we define as *momentum* is conserved in all isolated systems.

3   In the macroscopic world both matter and energy are conserved; in the microscopic world, they are interchangeable but nevertheless conserved as mass-energy.

4   The physical state of matter is determined by the energy of the system in which it resides. The energy state is best described by temperature, with plasma at the upper extremes and molecular solids at the lowest temperatures.

5   There are at least three natural forces. The weakest is *gravitational* and is expressed as an attraction between large masses. The second, *electrical*, is much stronger and is manifest as the force of attraction or repulsion between electrical charges. The strongest of all, *nuclear*, binds the particles within the atomic nucleus.

6   The entity that we define as *electric charge* is discrete and conserved in nature.

7   At relatively low temperatures, matter arranges itself into regular structures called molecules and crystals, which form the physical substances sensible to man.

8   Radiation is both particulate and wavelike in nature, but always manifest as the transport of energy through space.

9   Life has evolved as a specialized process of macromolecular organization. It possesses the ability to duplicate itself, sometimes with modification, and requires continuous input of energy.

10 The living cell is the basis of structure and function in all living organisms. The genes of its nucleus are the chemical key directing its morphology, its association with other cells to form organs, and the association of organs to form complete organisms. The genes provide the mechanism for reproduction and evolution through natural selection.

11 All natural processes require energy, many of these processes being cyclic in nature. During the process a portion of the energy is always degraded to some lower, unusable form.

1   One gram of carbon extracted from a wooden digging tool found at   *Problems*
    the site of Stonehenge was found to emit on the average 11.7 betas per minute. About how old is this tool?

2   Is the "big bang" theory accepted paradigm or is it a preparadigm model? How do you know this?

3   If the earth were crushed to a 1-m^3 ball without losing any of its mass, what would its density be?

4   Choose any simple mechanical system that you normally use around the house and do a careful analysis of it, showing what happens to energy in all its forms.

5   Debate the statement that Darwin's evolution model produced social effects very similar to those produced by Newton's universal law of gravitation.

Bibliography   **Charon, Jean:** "Cosmology: Theories of the Universe," McGraw-Hill, New York, 1970.

Project Physics: Text, Unit 6, Holt, New York, 1970.

Chapter 11
Technology

Hologram image of the entrance to RCA Laboratories, Princeton, N.J., is read out of lithium niobate crystal, center, by laser beam and projected onto frosted glass screen, lower left. Development may lead to a crystal that stores several hologram images as atomic patterns that can be read out, one by one, by rotation in a laser beam. Such a unit could eventually become a revolutionary document storage system in which files of statistics, architectural drawings, computer data, photographs, maps, and other graphic materials are stored permanently in crystals the size of sugar cubes. (Courtesy of RCA News.)

Technology embraces both man-made devices and any special set of procedures required for man's use. Within this definition, for example, medical technology is distinct from medical science. The former is the actual technical practice of medicine. The latter, dealing with experimental and theoretical synthesis, strives toward a better understanding of the human body and its processes. We should be careful to make a clear distinction between science and technology even though at times it might seem that they are indistinguishable.

**11.1
Technology
Explosion**

For most of the million or more years of man's existence, there is little evidence of a technology beyond a rudimentary level. There are notable exceptions to this rule in examples already mentioned, e.g., the pyramids and observatories of Neolithic times and metallurgy that played so large a role in developing nations. Engineering was in a crude state of development until the Romans built a modern road system, aquaducts, and arches. Many of those structures stand today, after 2,000 years. It is an outstanding fact that the Greeks, who were the first philosophers of merit, developed no significant technology beyond the common arts of shipbuilding, etc. The Romans, on the other hand, who were not philosophically inclined, developed a solid technology in architecture and civil engineering (Fig. 11.1). Medical technology had its beginning in techniques, instrumentation, and drugs developed to a crude state in Egypt and in the Far East.

At the end of the Dark Ages in Europe, when the Germanic states and Italy rose to primacy in Western culture, a new preoccupation with technology developed. This was the beginning of the age of instrument makers, those forerunners of the industrial revolution. Trade guilds sprang up around Europe. Thus, a solid foundation for the technological prominence of Western Europe was established.

Since the eighteenth century, history in Western culture has been dominated by technology. This same period of history is one of great and increasing lust for power, both in technology and in politics. The power derived from man's own body or from beasts of burden was augmented by the windmill. A convenient unit of power was adopted after the development of steam engines in the late eighteenth century. One *horsepower* is the power required to lift a 550-pound weight through a vertical distance of one foot in one second. This is about the limit of what a draft horse could accomplish at that time. One horsepower is equivalent to 746 watts.

*Fig. 11.1 The tomb of Cecilia Matelle on the Appian Way, Rome. It was common for
the wealthy to construct family tombs such as this along the cobbled Appian Way. This
particular site is not far from the Christian burial catacombs, If you could look over
this tomb into the distance, you would see the remains of one of the great Roman
aquaducts that watered the city in the days of the glory of the Roman Empire. You may
still drive your automobile along the Appian Way – but you must be prepared for a teeth-
rattling ride over the cobbles.* (Courtesy of the Italian Government Travel Office.)

Windmills developing 7 or 8 hp were used to pump water and grind
grains, but they were not equal to the task of pumping water from deep
mine shafts. Men had begun to burrow into the ground in their search for
raw materials needed to support growing industries. Textile mills, metal
foundries, and the like were springing up as mechanical inventiveness
became a premium commodity in Europe. Remember that the science of
Galileo and Newton was set early in this same period.

Larger and more dependable power sources were sought. Steam engines
were developed by trial and error in the absence of thermodynamics.

Early models provided a few tens of horsepower. This later rose to thousands of horsepower per engine. As available power increased, industries grew larger, with sweeping social changes following in the wake of their growth.

Men began to exploit deposits of stored fossil fuels in a thirst for power that still prevails today, as we shall see presently. Industrialization brought with it a profound social revolution. This was manifested as political wars, wars of revolution, exploitation of large groups of laboring poor, and sweeping changes in values and life style for all. The word *exploit* is used here in two senses: using without replacing and unethical use of labor force. Both uses involve a lack of concern for conserving a resource. The many wars that raged through Europe, later extending into the colonies of imperial European nations, strongly influenced the technical development of society. It is paradoxical that wars that destroyed so many men and human works also spurred agricultural and medical technology, resulting in an unprecedented growth of human population.

World population doubled from the sixteenth century to the latter nineteenth century. It doubled again from then to the middle twentieth century, and will be redoubled in the 1970s. The current doubling period is longer (65 years in the United States). In some South American nations the doubling period is as short as 20 years and growing shorter. This catastrophic growth of human population has proceeded largely in parallel with growing technology, which in turn has fed to a large extent upon exploitation of fossil fuel reserves. This is a key point that should be kept firmly in mind.

Industrialization, motivated by profit and spurred by competition, has been a powerful impetus to advancing technology. In order to compete, manufacturers must now operate an extensive research and development effort geared to step up the technology and speed up the rate at which natural resources are pulled out of the earth and placed in the consumer-use cycle. Competition has led to a philosophy of obsolescence in which no product endures for long, being rather discarded for new devices long before its useful lifetime is exhausted. Through this process technology has fed upon itself to produce an ever more rapidly advancing technology. To date no political entity has made more than a token effort to control this cycle. In the balance of this text, we shall argue that it is absolutely essential that man begin immediately to develop such control. Large segments of human population are now so completely dependent upon technology that they would perish if denied the support of technology even for a short time. Can you imagine what life in your community would be like if technology were to vanish overnight?

The billion-horsepower rocket motors of the twentieth century are a sub- **11.2** stantial advancement over the hundred-horsepower steam engines of **Unlimited** James Watt. This advancement in power technology has freed large **Power** numbers of men from the necessity to cultivate and harvest their own food. The invention of engines that develop high power per unit of engine weight has made the aviation industry possible. Transportation, both on the surface and in the air, has made possible the distribution of goods and food in ever-increasing volume.

Far too many modern power plants produce their power by breathing large amounts of oxygen and burning it with fossil fuels. These engines spew out large volumes of solid and gaseous wastes, many of which are biologically hazardous. They rely entirely upon the heat produced in

Fig. 11.2 An air view of Kansas City, Kansas, and Kansas City, Missouri, at the confluence of the Kansas (bottom) and Missouri Rivers. The silt-filled Missouri River describes a horseshoe curve at the left, dividing the two cities. Owing to the angle from which this air view was made, the upper branch of the Missouri is flowing eastward toward its confluence with the Mississippi River at St. Louis, after the pollution-laden waters of the Kansas River have joined it from the west (right side of photograph). The downtown district of Kansas City, Missouri, can be seen in the center background; the Kansas City Municipal Airport is the land at upper left, jutting into the Missouri River. Note the outfalls on both banks of the Kansas River, flowing toward the confluence. (Courtesy of Federal Water Pollution Control Administration, U.S. Department of the Interior, Washington, D.C.)

burning for mechanical energy. The process is one of exchanging the chemical potential energy stored in fossil fuels for mechanical energy. Much of this energy is lost as heat to the surroundings.

These thermodynamic, air-breathing engines represent a two-pronged dilemma as they increase in numbers. First, they gulp precious oxygen from the air—oxygen that can be replaced only by green plants. Second, they threaten to poison not only man but all living things with their lead, hydrocarbons, sulfur dioxide, nitrogen compounds, carbon monoxide, and particulate pollution. The machines that exploit fossil fuels must soon be replaced by power sources that derive their energy from relatively clean fuels.

Gravitational energy has not yet been developed fully as a source of useful power. Dams with hydroelectric power plants are common but by no means as numerous as they could be, though full development here would be inadequate for needs. Tidal hydroelectric power plants are very rare. The sun's radiant power drives the weather cycle. Tidal action comes from gravitational energy. These are both excellent potential sources of relatively clean electrical power. Of the 10^{17} W of radiant solar power received by the earth, about 10^{15} W are required to drive the fresh-water pump that distributes waters evaporated from the oceans over the continental land masses.

Nuclear power is still in its infancy. Nuclear fission reactors are now employed on a small scale to generate electricity. Practical containment of the fusion process may be in the immediate future. Controlled matter-antimatter reactions, the ultimate power source, is not within the foreseeable future of human technology. Nuclear power presents the dilemma of radioactive waste disposal, although there seems to be hope that rational and relatively safe procedures may be found for dealing with radioactive wastes. These will, however, be financially expensive.

The world with its current and projected population of tens of billions must ultimately depend entirely on solar energy, gravitational energy, and nuclear energy. If our technology fails or is weakened, large segments of the population must die out in consequence. Paradoxically, the most primitive cultures stand the best chance of surviving such an eventuality. Why?

11.3
Technology and
Inquiry
Men began recording events by scratching with a stone on a cave wall or on another stone. Written languages and mathematics are relatively new tools for recording ideas and events. Man has been able to mechanically reproduce written records for only a few hundred years.

Fig. 11.3 Aerial photograph of an industrial complex illustrating on a small scale how many individual sources combine to create a single volume of polluted air. Meteorologists of the U.S. Department of Commerce pioneered in air-pollution studies 20 years ago and today issue daily pollution forecasts to interested groups.

The rise of that branch of technology known as electronics has brought systems that can store information, reproduce it, or process it in prodigious quantities and with great speed. The entire King James version of the Bible can be recorded on a spot of special tape no larger than a dime and in less time than you took to read this sentence. In the jargon of information theory, technologists refer to the "bit-packing density," the "bit-storage rate," and the "bit-recovery rate." In ordinary English what they are talking about is how tightly we can jam stored information into storage space, how fast it can be packed away in this space, and how fast specific pieces of information can be retrieved from storage. As you see, technology generates its own new language.

Computers have gone through three distinct generations of development in about three decades. A whole new language has grown up with them. The influence of computers upon human life is so profound that it has caused speculation that future generations of computers may replace men as laborers in all but a few technological areas.

Third-generation computers are very small by comparison with first-generation vacuum-tube models. These new microcircuit devices consume a tiny fraction of the power required by their ancestors. The use of special electronic sensors and servomechanical devices with computers has made them almost human, and superior to humans in some ways. Calculations that required the entire productive lifetime of Kepler are now done by third-generation computers with great accuracy in seconds.

The significance for science of this rapid growth in information technology is that it has enormously increased the scope and amount of research that can be done by scientists today as compared to even a few decades ago.

11.4 Technology and the Shape of Higher Education

Technology has brought about fundamental changes in all facets of society, including its institutions of learning. Many educators have embraced the philosophy that schools should sense what kinds of technicians society needs and then turn out graduates, like well-machined parts, to fill these technical needs.

Over the past two centuries colleges and universities have gradually shifted away from liberal arts and normal school curricula toward professional technological curricula. There are relatively few colleges or universities today that do not offer substantial courses of study in the technologies. Many courses of study in the sciences are, in reality, training programs for future technologists. The very concept of the present-day university reflects the extreme technological orientation of society.

The traditional liberal arts subjects, even though their names are still used as window dressing, have subsided to an all too often secondary role in the university. Professional educators now tend to focus their primary concern upon questions such as "What can a graduate do with this degree?" as if the educational process has failed if it does not specifically prepare the graduate for a job within the technology. This new concept of education is a radical departure from the classical liberal arts philosophy of universities.

Along with the technologies in the curriculum has come the rise of disciplines that attempt to deal with the by-products of technology: business management, psychology, sociology, etc. These are separable into two classes: (1) those which prepare the student to go forth and grapple with the technical-industrial world of business and (2) those which try to prepare specialists to deal with the myriad psychosocial problems produced by the crush of technological advancement and the attendant population problem.

Viewed in this frame of reference, it is not difficult to appreciate the many problems that beset institutions of higher learning. These institutions are struggling desperately to protect their detached academic environment, while at the same time striving to deal more directly with the complexities of a technological society. Curiously, the technologists and scientists who have achieved the pinnacle of academic success still insist upon being called "doctors of philosophy." Few of them wear this title with justification in the classical sense. To this extent higher education has been influenced by technology and its child, industrialism.

Technology is a resource that requires constant feeding and care if it is to survive. It feeds upon other resources, such as minerals, power, and human attention. The only care it has received up to now is promotion of its growth by the most rapid possible means. Nobody has yet tried seriously to control it. Indeed, the great masses of humanity seem to be blissfully unaware of any need to control it. Those who do appreciate the need for control are apt to be called doomsdayers. Any who point out the imminent or potential dangers of an uncontrolled technology are likely to be called hysterical by those who profit most as individuals from uncontrolled technology.

**11.5
Servant and
Monster**

There are limits to the food available to man, to the amount of oxygen that can be drained from the atmosphere each day, to the stored energy in fossil fuel, to the amount of toxins and impurities that living things can tolerate in their environment, to the amount of fresh water available, and to the amount of ecological simplification that the biosphere can tolerate. *Ecological simplification*, to be defined more precisely in Chap. 14, is a degenerative process in which long-standing life balances are destroyed. There is also a limit to human population, as we shall soon see.

We can continue to operate a high-level technology only if we realize its hazards and control it to keep it always within the finite limits mentioned above. Technology is now in violation of several of these limits and is threatening to violate others. We shall soon argue that, on the basis of scientific process and logic, human population is already too large. We are already poisoning the biosphere, and we have already simplified world ecology beyond reasonable limits.

The whole fabric of technology is interlocked. It is not enough to produce sufficient food to feed a population. The food must also be distributed in some fashion. Thus, agriculture is linked inescapably with transportation, as well as with the manufacture of machinery and chemicals required to produce the food. If any link of this chain fails, the consumers must go hungry.

Those who derive short-term profits from technology are not inclined to be overly concerned with ecological hazards created by their procedures and products. Thus, technology is a monster in the hands of those who contribute to the violation of our planetary ecological limits willfully or through ignorance or neglect.

Society must very soon find effective ways of controlling technology. The hour is already late. Kept healthy and in control, technology is the key to a richer human experience. Its contribution to science is enormous. If we do not control it, however, it will be the means of our destruction.

Controlled technology implies responsible technology. A responsible technology is not necessarily a sharply curtailed technology, but rather one shaped to exist in harmony with nature. Such a shaping of technology will require the best efforts of scientists who conduct their work with full acceptance of their specific responsibility to the delicate balance of nature.

Science, like society at large, is heavily dependent upon technology to provide its research machinery. It is not the responsibility of science to produce "miracles" that will continually permit technology to grow beyond control, producing as it grows more problems that require more miracles to solve. Rather, there must be a balance between science and technology that permits both to grow in excellence and scope without destroying the balance of nature.

Problems 1 Debate the following statements with fellow students:
  a The structure of society is almost wholly dictated by technology. In this sense, we are all slaves to it.
  b By the year 2050 technology either will be highly refined from present forms or will not exist at all.
  c Only the most remote aboriginal tribes will survive the next two centuries intact.
  d Technology and science will be able to supply solutions to human problems indefinitely.

2 What would happen in your community if all transportation broke down and then ceased to exist (*a*) overnight? (*b*) over a period of several months?

3 What does the corporate manager really mean when he announces

publicly that he cannot clean up the processing of his product?

4   What measures do you believe are absolutely required for the control of technology?

Science, Man and Conflict: Reprinted from *Scientific American,* ***Bibliography*** Freeman, San Francisco, 1970.

Scientific American: September 1970.

Chapter 12
The State of Technology

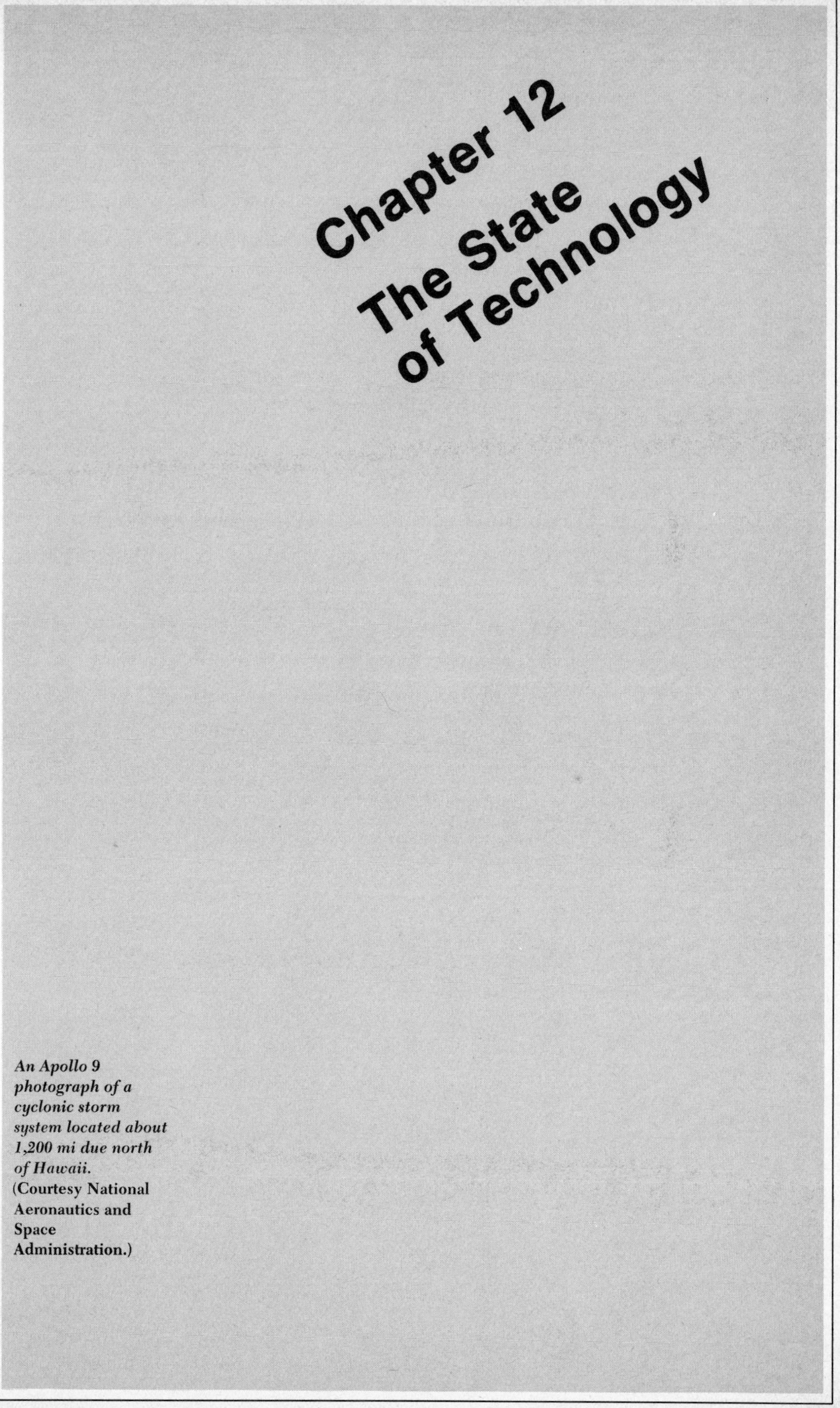

An Apollo 9
photograph of a
cyclonic storm
system located about
1,200 mi due north
of Hawaii.
(Courtesy National
Aeronautics and
Space
Administration.)

If we would control technology, we must first understand it. We need also to be aware of the extent of its influence upon society and its effect upon the advancement of science.

In twentieth-century Western civilization one of the strongest motive influences has been and continues to be economic profit motive. This culture is permeated by a series of shortsighted economic assumptions that have become accepted as universal truths. Some of these are as follows:

1   There will always be more of every resource needed for expanding technology.

2   Progress demands an ever-growing economic output in which obsolescence is an acceptable philosophy of operation.

3   Any action may be justified if the profits are high enough.

4   The ecosystem in which we live exists solely for man's benefit and is capable of absorbing unlimited insults.

5   If troubles do arise, science and technology will always be able to solve any problem that threatens us.

6   Because the above are true, human population can go on expanding indefinitely.

The absurdity of some of these assumptions is apparent to even the casual reader on the basis of common sense. Much of the balance of this book will deal with a thorough examination of these ideas from the point of view of science paradigm. We shall begin, however, by examining current technology.

12.1 Electronics: A Modern Genie

Almost all technological areas have enjoyed the substantial and even essential support of electronic black boxes. The surgeon depends upon oscilloscopes and other measuring equipment in nearly all procedures. The space program would be totally impossible without electronics. Our transportation system is wholly dependent upon electronics. These dependencies range from the switching of traffic lights to the complex automatic systems of a jet transport.

To a large extent the progress of electronic devices through several distinct generations has been a history of the development of new materials and material handling techniques. The vacuum tube circuits of World War II were replaced by semiconductor diode and transistor circuits in the 1950s. Transistors made possible much more compact circuits operating on a fraction of the power required for vacuum tube circuits (Fig. 12.1).

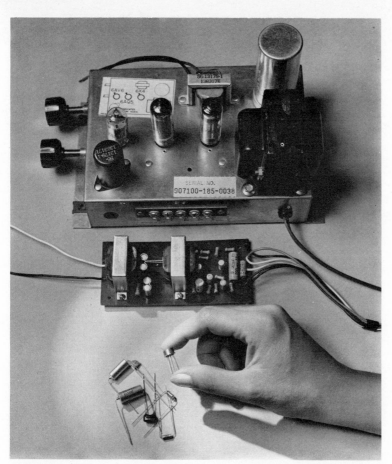

Fig. 12.1 These three generations of phonograph amplifiers demonstrate the "yester-day, today, and tomorrow" of electronics for the home. The tiny amplifier held between two fingers (bottom) contains a speck-size integrated circuit, developed by the molecular electronics division of Westinghouse Electric Corporation, Elkridge, Mary-land, which performs essentially all the functions of the transistorized amplifier (center) and the vacuum tube amplifier (top). The additional components are capa-citors, used to shape the output of the integrated circuit amplifier for best sound reproduction. A small battery is being used to power it.

The space program brought with it still further requirements for com-pact and lightweight circuits of ever higher durability and reliability. The 1960s saw the development of microcircuits so small that a micro-scope is necessary to see some of the components. These tiny circuits can be packaged for flight aboard a satellite at a minimum of weight and bulk.

This evolution in electronic technology has been so swift that nearly everyone has observed or owned electronic products that have quickly become obsolete. Radios, televisions, and tape recorders are common examples illustrating this point.

The first scientific and business computers required rooms filled with racks of vacuum tubes. These were the giant machines often pictured in cartoons. Third-generation computers are a startling contrast. Often they are completely contained in a relatively small, free-standing cabinet with various accessory cabinets nearby. After the cartoons, one almost feels cheated that there is not more to the fabled computer.

Computers keep records, mail letters, print checks, control machines, solve complicated problems for scientists, and intimidate the man on the street. They sense temperature and pressure and meter fuel to an engine accordingly. There seems no limit to practical applications of computers in technology. Even the least expensive of them can do certain kinds of calculations in microseconds.

The coming decades will see the general use of third-generation electronics—molecular electronics. A teaspoonful of speck-size components

Fig. 12.2 Sophisticated manufacturing devices equipped with microscopes enable Westinghouse Electric Corporation employees to handle products of almost microscopic size called integrated circuits. The photo was taken in one of the clean rooms of the company's molecular electronics division facility. The tiny products of this relatively new technology are capable of performing the same electronic functions within a tiny silicon chip that would require 50 or more conventional components.

can be welded together in a solid matrix to form a single complete integrated circuit. Such a circuit has the strength and rigidity of a solid block of germanium or silicon. Modern electronics manufacturing firms have "clean rooms" in which sterile practice rivals that found in a surgical operating theater. Such rooms must be perfectly free of dust and lint and contain microscopes and micromanipulators for handling tiny circuit elements.

Electronic circuits are the backbone of many areas of scientific research. They power the giant linear accelerators and control the particle beam for a number of simultaneous experiments. It is in such areas as this that the distinction between technology and science may be difficult. Keep in mind that if it is a machine performing a predetermined operation, it is technology.

Because the laser beam is almost perfectly single-colored, it is being used for a host of new technological applications, from surgery to communications. Scientists are using it to investigate how molecules are constituted and how coherent radiation interacts with matter. Lasers are of several different types, each with its own range of properties and uses. The gas atomic and molecular lasers, e.g., helium-neon, argon, and carbon dioxide, are usually continuous-beam (CW) lasers used where high-beam coherence is desired. Carbon dioxide laser beams, operating in the subvisible (infrared) may, however, be powerful enough to soften rocks for easier drilling. Solid crystal lasers, e.g., ruby crystal and neodymium-glass lasers, are most often single-pulse-type beams delivering great power for welding, cutting, vaporizing, etc. These may be focused to tiny spots that are many orders of magnitude hotter than the surface of the sun.

Laser development has already produced a large family of technological devices for use in industry, science, and medical practice. Laser television may be commercially available in the near future. Space satellites are already using laser scanning systems for basic measurements such as mapping. The laser gyroscope, a nonmechanical guidance system, has the appearance of a small lighted crystal ball. It may be the heart of our future navigation systems.

Electronics development has permitted the building of a neutron gun that fires a stream of these tiny chargeless particles. Neutron activation of atomic nuclei in a sample of material detects atoms that are present in incredibly small numbers. The presence of atoms of arsenic in the remains of Napoleon Bonaparte has led to the current suspicion that he died as a result of this poison. Criminologists are making increasing use of activation analysis.

Fig. 12.3 An integrated circuit chip of 55 NOR circuits fabricated from masks generated in the experimental automated process. The circuit chip, containing 207 field-effect devices, is compared in size to crystals of common table salt.

A beam of neutrons fired into a sample produces a stream of gamma photons from activated atomic nuclei present in the sample. These gamma photons, being of characteristic energies depending upon the active nucleus emitting them, constitute a kind of "fingerprint" that identifies the source nucleus. A careful analysis of the stream of gamma photons yields both the kind and quantity of nuclei present in the sample. An element may be detected even if only one-billionth of a gram is present.

**12.2
History of
Biomedical
Technology** Before man became an urban creature, health problems were thought to be due to a lack of something the body needed or the presence of some evil agent. Dietary deficiencies, for example, were probably recognized early, through trial and error, as contributing causes of poor health. The

problems of health were no doubt closely associated with religious beliefs and superstitions. Early remedies consisted of a mixture of useful materials, procedures, and superstitious hocus-pocus. We now realize, of course, that the hocus-pocus, where the patient had solid faith in the healer, may have been as effective as the application of medicants. The gyrating medicine man of early tribes was, in a way, the forerunner of the modern psychiatrist.

Many natural drugs, e.g., opium, ephedrine, caffeine, cascara, digitalis, and perhaps even penicillin, were long ago prepared from herbs. Many such medicines are the basis of present-day primitive culture practice.

The early Chinese practiced acupuncture. Acupuncture derives from early Taoist philosophy, which held that the body is normally in a kind of equilibrium between plus and minus forces. Certain areas of the body were supposed to be the flow points of life forces. By puncturing the skin with needles at these flow points, the balance of life could be restored to the patient's body. Elaborate charts located these points for Chinese physicians, who punched away at their patients. Acupuncture is still used in modern China with remarkable results.

At the same time, Egyptian physicians adhered to a rigidly standardized medical practice. In addition to the usual natural remedies, they held that health is much influenced by the signs of the cosmos. The Egyptians apparently did recognize the value of good diet and hygienic practice. They also seem to have made use of hypnosis in their treatments.

These early Egyptian healers were quite aware of the advantages of banding together with a single corporate mind. Their rigid control of many drugs and standardization of rules of practice illustrate this point. Easily obtainable herbs were disguised by adding a variety of foul ingredients that rendered the remedy most obnoxious and most impressive. A required part of every treatment was always a prescribed incantation.

With the Greek culture came a trend away from medical sorcery. Hippocrates initiated the systematic study of medicine and human physiology. He recorded many of the practices and ideas of his contemporaries. After the classical period of Greek and Roman culture, the practice of medicine died out in most of Europe, with the medical sciences being carried forward almost exclusively by the Moslems. The decline of the Roman Empire and the Dark Ages of Europe brought a continuous round of plagues and epidemics that ran their course, decimating whole segments of the population.

The Age of Enlightenment in Europe is already a familiar story. However, biomedical science and technology remained in a remarkably primitive state until the twentieth century.

**12.3
Biomedical
Technology**

Human life has been considerably extended in its average span of years. Medicine has enlarged into a number of highly specialized fields of practice. Medical science has become closely allied with biochemistry and biology, with research confined largely to centers of biomedical science. The practicing physician may participate in scientific research, but on the whole he rarely initiates and carries out scientific research. He is, rather, a highly skilled, and in Western culture a highly paid, technician. With rare exceptions he still belongs to a closed society with a single corporate mind much like his Egyptian forebears.

Electronics has contributed heavily to the advancement of both medical science and medical technology. X-rays, mannequins that respond like human patients, and a spectrum of measuring devices, lasers, and other black boxes are standard tools of the practitioner and training centers. The real science of medicine, however, takes shape in the biochemistry and pathology laboratories where scientists search for new knowledge. They are aided in this search by electron microscopes, spectrometers, and other electronic equipment. It now appears that the negative electric potential of the cell wall is directly linked to the process in which some cells become cancerous, reproducing rapidly and behaving as if they cannot sense their environment. Hence, a thorough knowledge of the biochem-

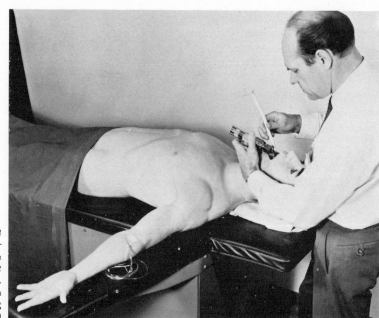

*Fig. 12.4
A human simulator
in use to train
student
anesthesiologists.
(Courtesy of Sierra
Engineering
Company.)*

ical-bioelectrical nature of cells is required if we are to stop cancer. The mechanisms of living tissues are still poorly understood.

One of the evil demons of the ancient sorcerer has turned out to be a family of microorganisms called virus. Somehow these organisms are able to get inside living cells and use these cells to their own ends with results destructive to the host organism. Much needs to be learned about viruses.

Biochemistry has undergone a revolution that has yielded practically everything we now know about the physiology of living things—all within a few decades. Most drugs now prescribed routinely were unknown 20 years ago. Biochemical imbalances have recently been recognized as contributing agents in human mental aberrations. Oral contraceptives have placed in the hands of man, for the first time, a reliable means with which to limit his reproduction. We shall have much to say on this subject later.

Sulfa drugs and penicillin brought a dramatic reduction in some illnesses that had kept human population in check for thousands of years. Meningitis, pneumonia, and gangrene, long the scourge of armies in wartimes, were effectively knocked out during World War II.

Biochemistry has identified the all-important cycles of elements through living organisms and back to the nonliving environment, establishing the importance and subtle mechanisms of such elements as phosphorus, iron, iodine, potassium, calcium, and nitrogen in life processes. These discoveries, along with major breakthroughs in genetics, made possible a similar revolution in agriculture.

Much, though not nearly enough, is already known about the virus. The nucleic acids, DNA and RNA, are the core of the virus. A new vaccine appears to be effective against the epidemic rubella virus, which causes German measles. A protein called *interferon* produces a natural immunity by inhibiting viral reproduction in cells. Interferon production in the human body can be stimulated by a certain double-stranded ribonucleic acid.

Biochemists have now succeeded in creating, by purely chemical techniques, the first man-made gene. The gene is the complex molecular structure within any living cell that determines cell reproduction and the destiny of any particular cell. At reproduction it is the genes of the parents that combine in a process known as *meiosis* to determine the genetic structure of the new individual.

At the present state of the science of genetics, many scientists are confident that we shall soon be able to manipulate genes to eradicate genetic diseases such as hemophilia and diabetes. The temptation to "improve" the species is great. For the moment, however, people do not seem to be able to agree on what constitutes improvement. A careful examination of this question illustrates the seriousness and potential threat of genetic manipulation in humans.

Deoxyribonucleic acid (DNA) specifies in the genes of chromosomes the complete chemical details of the enzymes required for the machinery and fabric of the living cell. One gene is a stretch of DNA that contains perhaps a thousand building blocks.

And so the biochemical story goes on and on in incredible complexity. We have barely scratched the surface.

**12.4
Spare Parts and
Preventive
Medicine**
Implants, transplants, grafts, and the like have become quite common. The problem of rejection by the body of foreign objects or tissues has refocused attention of scientists on the total chemistry of foreign-protein rejection. Unmatched transplants, for example, are more often than not "recognized" by lymphocytes as "foreign," and the foreign cells are then attacked and destroyed.

Hearts, bone marrow, kidneys, eyes, and arteries have been transplanted in dramatic team surgery. Silicone plastics have been found to be inert in the body, and hence are being used as blood vessels, drains, and artificial tendons. Recently, a fluorocarbon, liquid Teflon, has been used as an experimental substitute for blood in small animals. One envisions a man living to a ripe old age and going to his final rest with, like an old automobile, only a fraction of his original parts.

Rather than waiting until a body malfunction is manifestly obvious in a suffering patient, it would seem a wise procedure to detect any malfunction at the earliest possible moment and correct it. This indeed is a concise statement of an emerging medical philosophy. The rapid increase in the sophistication of medical electronics makes it reasonable to expect that routine diagnosis of malfunctions in the body will soon be fast and accurate. The gas-liquid chromatograph, for example, rapidly identifies optically not only the bacterial species involved in an infection, but also many of the strains within each species.

Electronic analysis of brain waves of a patient undergoing vision tests identifies vision problems even when the patient cannot communicate. Thus, vision defects in small children may be detected and dealt with before further damage occurs.

Ironically, man is entering a new era of human medical practice at just the time that his polluting technology and numbers threaten his existence. We may soon have biologically clean hospitals and surgical theaters in the weightless environment of an orbiting satellite, a boon to patients with cardiovascular disorders. Genetic manipulation and genetic surgery may eliminate many of man's oldest enemies. We may reasonably look forward to better understanding and effective treatment of mental disorders.

It is hoped we shall also make progress in our knowledge and application of the human relationship to the total environment. Without this, the rest is merely impressive futility.

1 Discuss with your classmates the obvious social implications of **Problems** human genetic manipulation.
2 Write a short critique of the six "universal truths" listed in the chapter introduction.

Any standard history of medical science.   *Bibliography*

Nehrich, Richard B., Jr., and Dessel, Voran: "Atomic Light: Lasers, What They Are and How They Work," Sterling, New York, 1967.

Gibbon, Edward: "Decline and Fall of the Roman Empire," Great Books of the Western World, Modern Library, New York, n.d. (suggested source).

Chapter 13
Probing the Hostile Environments

A smog's eye view of
New York, taken
October 27, 1963.
(Courtesy of
National Air
Pollution Control
Administration, U.S.
Department of the
Interior,
Washington, D.C.)

In the final chapters of this book we shall concentrate on attempting to understand something of the total relationship of man to his environment. All that has gone before is necessary for a fuller understanding of this most important relationship. In these chapters we shall make use of the great principles of modern science.

13.1
First Ventures
into Unnatural
Environments

It was inevitable that men should eventually come to the point where their curiosity concerning the hostile environments would push them into these environments. The great seas of the earth have fascinated men for thousands of years. The air-water interface has provided a path to adventure and commerce all through recorded history. Fishermen have taken the contents of the seas without understanding much about that world below, a world in which unadorned man must quickly perish.

The lack of oxygen in breathable form and the great pressures even at relatively shallow depths were insurmountable barriers until the twentieth century. In deliberately entering this environment with the aid of advancing technology, we have learned and continue to learn a great deal about man himself.

We have already developed the basis of human thought about the space environment. As a hostile environment, space begins at about 15,000 ft above the planet surface, where human respiration becomes nearly impossible. The upper portion of the troposphere, the stratosphere, the ionosphere, and the exosphere are part of the earth environment but these layers are hostile to man.

All life on this planet exists in a confined envelope bounded by rock on one side and by the upper atmosphere on the other. This envelope is a very thin "orange-peel" volume at the surface of earth. This volume is about 3 billion km^3, only $\frac{1}{3}$ of 1 percent of the volume of the earth. If we could stack people side by side and one on top of the other, how many would fit in this orange-peel volume? This is, of course, an absurd prospect.

This orange-peel volume provides about 1 km^3 of space for each man, woman, and child in our present population. Of course, a portion of this space is water, and a rather large portion at that.

A more realistic problem may be the following: If the surface area of dry land is about 2×10^8 km^2, how many people can we stack side by side on it? At the present rate of human reproduction, assuming that such a thing were otherwise possible, we would reach this population by the year 2400.

The point of all this is that all life lives in a volume that has definite physical boundaries. Man can move beyond these finite limits only through the technology of artificial life-support systems. The crush of human population may force a movement into hostile environments for the purpose of colonization, though such efforts may be abortive considering the problems that must be overcome.

Man in space and man in the oceans is a new experience for us all. We shall not be concerned with the nonscientific motivations that have served to drive the space and oceanographic efforts thus far. We shall be content for the moment to examine these very interesting, partially scientific ventures with a scientific perspective.

Tyros, Syncom, Mariner, and Apollo are familiar terms, though many will have difficulty associating the term with the correct venture into the space environment. The scientist has many excellent reasons for exploring this environment. Our ventures so far have demonstrated the usefulness of newtonian mechanics and have added a wealth of information concerning the earth and its near neighborhood.

13.2
Why Space?

By moving away from the earth and looking back at it with keen instrumentation, we have learned much that was previously impossible to observe. Space is there, and so we have reached out for it. The expansion of our knowledge in just two decades of space research has put a sharper edge on human intellect. This advancement has fostered a rapid growth in the general appreciation of man's place in the universe.

In 1967 alone there were more than 120 earth satellites launched successfully—primarily by the United States and the U.S.S.R. These and many others prepared the way for astronauts to visit the moon. This achievement, however, was primarily one of technology and was proportionately very expensive. The presence of man in a spacecraft is a heavy burden and places insurmountable obstacles in the way of advanced and efficient scientific research. Well-designed instrument packages can be placed where man will probably never be able to go or where man can go only at terrible cost to the mission's scientific capacity.

Man-in-space experiments are nonetheless producing a wealth of physiological information about the human body and its reactions to environmental changes. Confinement, weightlessness, and the problems of a closed ecosystem on shipboard are a few areas already intensely researched.

For the most part, we have sought experimental data concerning the structure and processes of the earth's gaseous envelope and radiation belts.

We have probed the moon and our other near neighbors in space, Mars and Venus.

**13.3
An Orientation
to Space**

The sun contains most of the mass of the solar system, while the earth is a mere pebble in its orbit around this monster. The small inner planets, Mercury, Venus, Earth, and Mars, along with the asteroids, are specks plowing through a sea of particles flooding outward from the sun. Jupiter is huge by comparison with these dwarfs, being about one-thousandth as massive as the sun. Its surface is shrouded to a depth of thousands of miles by dense liquids and gases.

Beyond Jupiter are the giants Saturn, Neptune, and Uranus. The incredibly cold rock we call Pluto orbits the sun at so great a distance that an observer on its surface would see the sun only as another bright star in the heavens.

Beyond Pluto the distances are so vast that it would take spaceships years to reach the nearest star system even traveling at nearly the speed of light.

Fig. 13.1 Apollo 10 view of earth rise, looking west in the direction of travel. The lunar module at the time the picture was taken was located above the lunar farside highlands at approximately 105 degrees east longitude. **(Courtesy of NASA.)**

It is clear from this that man's initial probes into space must be confined to his near neighborhood.

The planets and their moons plow through the solar particles, pushing a bow wave of particles forward and streaming a wake behind. Every 11 years or so the sun is seized by a violent inner fury. Great tongues millions of miles long leap from its surface, releasing rush after rush of particle clouds, mostly protons and electrons, which swarm outward into planetary space. Dark spots appear on the solar surface, and the storming fills the planetary space. The earth's atmosphere protects its living creatures from this storm, and because of the protective atmosphere of the earth, man sees evidence of these storms mostly in magnetic disturbances, intense auroral displays, radio and television disturbances, and other, more subtle effects measured by scientists. The unprotected astronaut caught beyond the earth's atmosphere during a solar storm would almost certainly die from exposure to radiation.

The moon lies some 30 earth diameters away from the earth and travels at about 2,300 mi/h in its 27+ day orbit around the earth. Its diameter is just over 2,000 mi, and its surface area is about one-quarter that of the earth. All this was well-known before the space explorations began.

We would not expect a body the size and mass of the moon to have much of an atmosphere. Its surface temperatures on the side facing the sun ensure the escape of most gas molecules into space, since their energy exceeds gravitational binding energy.

Through the data returned by Ranger, Surveyor, and Apollo space probes, we know that the moon is volcanically active and that some sort of surface erosion is in operation. Soft lunar landings of manned spacecraft have paved the way for much closer observation of this body.

Mars has been observed by Mariner spacecraft to be much like the moon. Its surface is pockmarked with impact craters up to 75 mi in diameter. Its famed canals appear to be nothing constructed by living organisms, intelligent or otherwise. Mars does, however, appear to undergo seasonal surface changes. Its surface temperatures do not preclude the possibility of earth-type life forms. Mars appears not to have a molten core, and no magnetic field was measured at the 6,118-mi closest approach of *Mariner*. Its atmospheric pressure is about one-hundredth that of the earth. The whitish polar caps are real and appear to be chiefly CO_2.

Earth passes within 26 million miles of Venus, but that planet remains largely a mystery. It is shrouded by an unbroken mantle of dense clouds that hides its surface. Evidence thus far from United States and U.S.S.R. space probes is partially contradictory and inconclusive regarding its atmosphere and surface. The Venusian day is about 112 earth days long, and its atmosphere about 30 times as dense as the earth's. These two facts argue for large temperature differences at its surface and violent storms carrying surface particles at high velocity.

Earth satellites have already provided remarkably accurate data on our home planet. Its shape and topography and the constitution and dynamic properties of its atmosphere are now much better known. Weather information, for example, is now prepared for public use directly from weather satellites, which record all major weather systems.

13.4 Man in Space

Man's brain is subject to many poorly understood problems that make it, in some ways, vastly inferior to electronic computers, but the human brain is still the only minicomputer that can extensively learn from experience. We analyze complex phenomena and react on the basis of something often as vague as a hunch. Machines can only measure and analyze in ways previously programmed by men. For this reason, it is sometimes a scientific advantage to have highly trained humans immediately involved in space research.

Human curiosity would drive man into space even if better-than-human machines existed, and the problems of his artificial environment in space are formidable. He must breathe a special mixture of gases, eat specially prepared foods, and eliminate toxic waste products. For example, carbon dioxide, exhaled in all animal respiration, must be chemically removed from the atmosphere and then separated into oxygen and carbon. The carbon may be used for radiation shielding and the oxygen recycled for breathing. Water vapor exhaled (a pint or more each 24 h) must be recovered, broken down into its elements, and reused. Because the artificial atmosphere is rich in oxygen, fire is a constant hazard in space. Severe weight restrictions mean that the whole system must be maximumly efficient with frequent recycling and reuse of key elements.

If colonies are to be established in hostile space, there will have to be self-sustaining ecosystems with provisions for utilizing energy for continuous manufacture of food and for maintenance of temperature and elemental balances. Plants and other animals must be included in the system. Absence of significant gravitational force in space is known to produce severe cardiovascular problems in time. Artificial gravity can, however, be produced by spinning the spacecraft. The psychological and psychophysical stresses of such a system are only poorly understood at this time.

Major advances in materials chemistry have already come about as a direct result of space research. Industrial nations are now commonly benefited by space technology. Power technology, electronics, and ceramics are three prime examples of such technological "fallout."

Fig. 13.2   Astronaut Edwin E. Aldrin, Jr., lunar module pilot, preparing to deploy the Early Apollo Scientific Experiments Package (EASEP) on the surface of the moon during the Apollo 11 extravehicular activity.   (Courtesy of NASA.)

There are awesome canyons in the sea floor that would swallow up Mt. Everest with thousands of feet to spare.   There are great rivers that flow through the ocean mass, gouging out canyons of their own and modifying weather the world over.   Volcanic eruptions raise great mountain peaks toward the surface.

**13.5
The Marine
Environment**

The ancient mother of all life has long fascinated man.   It is, therefore, remarkable that so little is known of the oceans even today.   Some of the marine life forms evolved special mechanisms for life on land.   Some, having developed this land specialization, returned to the sea.   Mammalian blood still has much in common with sea water.

The seas are home to a large fraction of all living organisms.   They provide most of the earth's fresh water and atmospheric oxygen.   Paradoxically, the same rains that nurture land life relentlessly wash away the essential life-sustaining elements to the sea.

Fig. 13.3
*Souse coupe diving
saucer at Dana
Point.* (Official
photograph, U.S.
Navy.)

Water covers about 71 percent of the earth's surface and reaches depths of 37,500 ft. Light, essential to photosynthetic organisms, penetrates no more than a few hundred feet below the sea surface. All marine life, therefore, is dependent upon the food-manufacturing autotrophs that must be maintained in this surface film. The mean ocean depth is about 12,500 ft, with pressure increasing 1 atm for every 33 ft down from the surface. Bottom (benthal) living organisms must be adapted to life at perhaps 17,000 pounds per square inch pressure. This tremendous pressure is a key problem confronting scientists who wish to carry out research at depth.

Special vehicles such as *Deep Star* and *Deep Quest* have made it possible for man to travel routinely at intermediate depths of a few thousand feet. These vehicles have been equipped with cameras and special manipulators to permit some research on the site. Tools used at depth must be specially designed to operate in this environment.

**13.6
Science of the
Sea**   *H.M.S. Challenger*, the famous British marine research vessel, cruised 68,900 mi between 1872 and 1876. Her data filled 50 volumes and still occupies the energies of scientists. *Challenger* methods were a bit crude

by modern standards, but her crew made a magnificent contribution to science. Modern electronic devices and mechanical monsters have taken up the task where she left off. Unknown a century ago, today there are great institutes of oceanography that carry on the scientific investigation of our nearby but poorly understood environment, the oceans.

Oceanography can be divided for convenience into four major areas of discipline: (1) physical properties of the water mass itself, (2) the water

Fig. 13.4 Atlantic red hake and finished fish protein concentrate product. Six pounds of fish will produce one pound of fish protein concentrate. (**Courtesy of Bureau of Commercial Fisheries, U.S. Department of the Interior, Washington, D.C.**)

mass as an environment for life, (3) detailed investigation of living forms in the marine environment, and (4) geological study of the ocean floor and continental shelf areas. These are obviously not independent areas of study. Indeed, the key to the nature of the scientific investigation of any environment is interdependence. Still, the above major areas help to define oceanographic problems.

Many kinds of scientific background are required in environmental research, whether the environment be space or ocean. The oceanographer is apt to be a geologist, botanist, zoologist, chemist, physicist, or even a research psychologist or pharmacologist. Often he combines several of these areas of competence. Physical oceanographers are concerned with wave action, tides, currents, turbulence and upwelling, and air-sea interface physics and chemistry. They have generated such useful concepts as characteristic water-mass types defined according to temperature, salinity, mineral content, and chemical components, and transmission and absorption characteristics of light and sound.

Marine geologists have discussed evidence that the continents are drifting and that the sea floor is spreading. They have amassed considerable data on the geology of the ocean floor and have advanced the *regional tectonic plate* theory, which attempts to explain such things as central ocean ridges, deep crescent trenching in its floor, floor sifting and faulting, and mountain formation. The overall scheme of this model is that material in the earth's crust is forced up at the mid-ocean ridges continuously, so that if flows away from the ridges along the ocean floor toward the continents. Upon reaching continental boundaries, it is forced down and under the continental mass to begin its cycle over again. Geological dating of patches of ocean floor tends to substantiate this model.

It is odd to think of something as solid as the earth as a plastic mass that is constantly changing. It will help to remember that these motions are very gradual, with floor movement of a few feet requiring thousands of years. We have barely scratched the surface of this exciting area of research. You may wish to pursue this further.

Marine biologists have discovered that only certain rather well-defined regions of the ocean mass are suitable for the support of life. In order for a good chain to become established, plants must receive proper support from the environment. First there must be currents and upwelling, which serve to keep the heavier-than-water plants at or near the surface, and this same water transport must supply a steady stream of required mineral nutrients. The other physical characteristics of the water, such as temperature and salinity, must be within acceptable bounds. All this serves to illustrate that the seas are definitely not one vast pantry of food only waiting for man to come and help himself. Marine life is abundant both in numbers of species and numbers of individuals, but it is certainly limited and subject to modification or destruction at the hands of exploiting human practice. Ecological disasters in the marine environment are almost exclusively man-made and are coming along with a most alarming increase in both frequency and severity.

It has been estimated that 50 percent of the world human population lives in countries in which the average diet contains less than 10 g of animal protein per day. Protein is essential to the building of human tissue, including brain cells. Protein starvation—now embracing perhaps 500 million humans at mid-twentieth century—is, therefore, a major concern. Paradoxically, populations that suffer most from protein malnutrition are near rich sources of fish protein. Marine protein is now being harvested by industrial nations at about the maximum sustainable rate and fed, in part, to agricultural animals and house pets. The seas, while they might seem a limitless source of protein, are actually quite limited in their productivity of this precious commodity. Many species of food fish, to make matters far worse, are being systematically driven to extinction by overfishing. Herring, salmon, and whales fall into this category.

Exploitation of ocean resources is proceeding at a frightening rate and threatens to upset the delicate balance of marine ecosystems. There is a clear danger that exploitation will engulf the whole of the marine environment. All creatures have an affinity for trace elements. The teeth of some snails are nearly half manganese, which is essential to the manufacture of steel. Certain plankton concentrate iron. Oysters concentrate copper and zinc. Kelp assimilates iodine. Are we to decimate these populations, as we have others, for their mineral content?

Unhappily, many of these same organisms also concentrate pesticides, mercury, and lead washed down to the sea through rivers and estuaries. Each time a predator or scavenger consumes a concentrator organism, the concentration of the toxin is further increased. The ultimate consumer, which may well be man, further concentrates the toxins to dangerous or even fatal levels.

DDT has been detected in fish taken far at sea in concentrations of over 300 parts per million (ppm). This is 45 times the legal maximum limit for human consumption. Strontium 90 is chemically similar to calcium, and atmospheric atomic detonations have sprinkled the ocean surfaces with this deadly radioactive isotope. Fallout on land is consumed by dairy cattle and other grazers or washes down to the sea. Either way, the strontium 90 is concentrated by living organisms selectively. When man consumes it, the strontium is metabolized like calcium, tucked away in ever-increasing concentrations in bone marrow, where it stays indefinitely and irradiates surrounding tissue and blood cells.

The sunrise found my son and I nine miles from shore riding a sea still choppy from yesterday's storm. We had out over seven hundred feet of line hoping to catch a meal of rock codfish. Suddenly a gull swooped in low and landed on the stern of the small fiberglass boat within a few feet of us. The little craft was pitching heavily and his feet slipped this way and that but he made no move to leave. We thought at first that he was interested in our pail of anchovy bait, but then we noted that his breast feathers were covered with oil tar. He simple wanted to rest for a while and we made him as comfortable as we could. This small gesture was a poor attempt to correct the wrong that man had done him. We wondered if the fish we caught were not full of lead, DDT and mercury. Our trip home was silent and a little sad.

Chapter 14
Spaceship Earth

Whooping crane.
(Courtesy Allan D.
Cruickshank, from
National Audubon
Society.)

It just happens that the earth travels in its orbit around the sun at a distance that makes possible the existence of a liquid hydrosphere, with earth surface temperatures ranging roughly between 0 and 100°C. A little closer to the sun or farther away from it, the earth might not have a hydrosphere of any significance. The earth rotates on its own axis once every 24 h, which is convenient for a variety of reasons that have to do with photoperiod available to plants, existence of our tidal motions, etc. Can you add to the list of happy circumstances that have made life possible on the earth?

Our planet's mass is about 6×10^{24} kg. It is not exactly a sphere, but the radius of a sphere with the same volume would be about 6.37×10^6 m. Its total surface area is just over 5×10^8 km², with about 71 percent of this water and 29 percent land. If we were to travel away from the earth into space and look back at it, we would see a circle of area 1.275×10^{14} m². This is a key number, and we shall want to refer to it later.

Our natural home is so familiar to us that it hardly seems necessary to describe its gross features. One useful way of thinking of it, however, is to consider that it divided into a solid *lithosphere*, a liquid *hydrosphere*, a gaseous *atmosphere*, and a rather well-defined *biosphere*. The living organisms we divide for convenience into species, of which man is only one of millions. These are all confined for the most part to the thin mantle of soil, relatively shallow waters, and the lower layer of the atmosphere known as the troposphere. A few hardy species may exist in small numbers beyond these bounds, but the biosphere is, for the most part, well confined to these regions. The imprisoning walls of the biosphere are formed of the boundaries of hostile environments — environments that lack something essential to life or whose physical characteristics are too harsh for life.

The relatively small biosphere of earth is characterized by numerous interfaces between solid, liquid, and gas. These interfaces are of great interest, since it is here that life tends to congregate. Fish tend to live near the water-air interface, not in the ocean depths. Birds stay close to the soil-air or water-air interface, for it is here that they find their food. Major life limiters are water in the deserts and the availability of certain mineral nutrients in the soil and water. For example, iron exists in the seas and oceans in only trace amounts, yet it is absolutely essential to life there. Phosphorus is in very short supply on land, yet it too is essential to the pyramid of life. Where these two elements are not available, we can count on finding little life.

If we were to fill a bowl with water and sprinkle a fine powder in it to form a mixture, and then leave the bowl undisturbed for several days, we would see that in the quiet water the fine grains, heavier than the water, settle out and form a deposit on the bottom of the bowl. In this same way the tiny living organisms in the seas would sink away from the water-air interface to settle on the bottom were it not for the constant agitation of the water by tides, currents, and wave action. Where land forms are sustained by legs and roots, microorganisms in the sea are absolutely dependent upon turbulent mixing to keep them near the sunlight, which is the ultimate source of the energy needed to power life. It is indeed fortunate that we have tides and weather disturbances, for the first parent cells were probably evolved in water.

The lithosphere is about 60 percent oxygen, 20 percent silicon, 6 percent aluminum, and the rest small amounts of hydrogen, sodium, iron, calcium, magnesium, potassium, and elements existing in trace amounts (by relative numbers of atoms). The hydrosphere, of course, is mostly water, with hydrogen 66 percent and oxygen 33 percent. It also contains chlorine, sodium, magnesium, sulfur, and many other elements in traces, among these iron. The atmosphere is about 78 percent nitrogen, 21 percent oxygen, 1 percent argon, and the rest trace gases. Note here that nitrogen, so essential to life, is extremely abundant but in a form that is not directly useful in biological processes. Nitrogen must first be *fixed* by living microorganisms in a special chemical form before plants can use it.

The biosphere incorporates within it at any given moment a variety of elements. Some of these elements—hydrogen, oxygen, carbon, nitrogen, phosphorus, and sulfur—are absolute requirements for life. Others, such as calcium, potassium, silicon, magnesium, and aluminum, are also involved but to a lesser extent. It is of the utmost importance that we recognize at this point that living organisms cannot use these elements only once and then discard them at the bottom of the sea. The same atoms must be cycled again and again through organisms, whether man or tree, bird or fungus. If these materials were to wash down to the sea and settle out onto the bottom, the biosphere would be drastically altered, if not finally destroyed. One of the great thrusts of the life evolutionary process has been to develop highly efficient mechanisms that prevent this ultimate erosion of vital elements. In the mature or *climax* community of plants and animals, this recycling of elements is highly efficient. Root systems hold the soil, and cyclic processes of life and death return the elements to the soil again and again. Man's agriculture has been a major destroyer of climax communities and their efficient systems for recycling elements. *Ecological simplification* is any process that destroys the mature balance of the climax community.

**14.1
Earth Energy
Systems**
It is a common belief that the energy and power available to man and to the earth's many energy systems are limitless. We shall examine this belief in the light of our understanding of the principles of science.

We can begin by thinking of the earth as a big machine. In accordance with the laws of thermodynamics, it receives energy at a certain rate from the sun in the form of radiation, uses some of it to drive its systems, and returns the rest to space directly. Since the earth is neither heating up nor cooling down significantly, we know that the rate at which energy is received (incoming power) is just balanced by the rate at which it is radiated into space (outgoing power). The portion of the incoming power

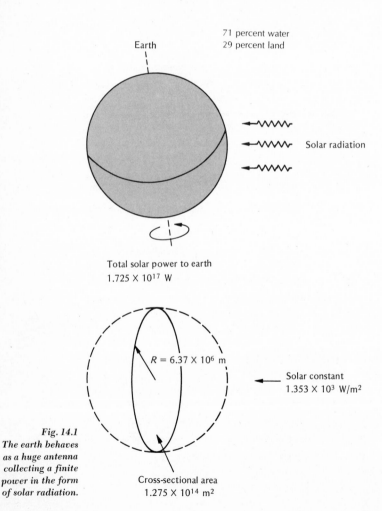

Earth

71 percent water
29 percent land

Solar radiation

Total solar power to earth
1.725×10^{17} W

$R = 6.37 \times 10^6$ m

Solar constant
1.353×10^3 W/m^2

*Fig. 14.1
The earth behaves
as a huge antenna
collecting a finite
power in the form
of solar radiation.*

Cross-sectional area
1.275×10^{14} m^2

that drives earth energy systems is eventually degraded to heat and radiated away at much longer wavelengths than incoming solar radiation. Stated another way, the sun is a relatively hot radiator (6000 K), and the earth a relatively cool one (250 K). Should anything significantly upset the balance between incoming and outgoing power, the earth would begin to either heat up or cool down. In either case the biosphere might be unable to adjust fast enough to compensate for the change.

Now let us look at the use the earth makes of solar energy (Fig. 14.1). The earth receives energy from the sun at the rate of about 1.353×10^3 watts per square meter of area normal to the sun direction. More simply, the total incoming radiant power is about 1.725×10^{17} W with a sharp energy peak in the visible and infrared region of the spectrum. Of this amount, 30 percent is immediately scattered or reflected back into space by the atmosphere and clouds; thus, the earth is quite bright when viewed from near space. Another 50 percent reaches the surface and is absorbed in the atmosphere by gases, clouds, and dust. Nearly all the wavelengths from blue-green to red make it through to the surface, but of this energy only $\frac{1}{10}$ percent is fixed by plants through photosynthesis.

Photosynthesis is the ultimate source of all food, and food is the source of chemical potential energy required to drive all heterotrophs (life forms that do not manufacture their own food). Hence, the limit of availability of food for life is rigidly set by the amount of solar energy fixed by photosynthesis. This amounts to about 1.7×10^{14} W of power. A glance at the exponent here is sufficient to convince even the most optimistic dreamer that man will not in the near future significantly increase the amount. There is also the problem of getting man-produced power into a form useful in photosynthesis.

Photosynthesis is a process in which solar energy is partially stored as chemical potential energy in sugars and carbohydrates. It requires much more than just energy, of course, but energy is at present our primary concern. We shall presently follow this line of discussion to its logical conclusion, i.e., how large a human population the earth can sustain.

The evaporation of water at the earth's surface and subsequent condensation of the vapor in clouds to rain is the mechanism that keeps the surface cooled and the adjacent atmosphere heated. Without this energy cycle, the surface would become very hot and the atmosphere very cold. The Arctic and Antarctic regions are relatively cold, and equatorial regions quite hot, for reasons already apparent. This global temperature difference is the cause of major weather patterns. As a mental exercise, let us try to follow what *might* happen if something were to increase this temperature difference by, say, 10°C. In general, the greater the tempera-

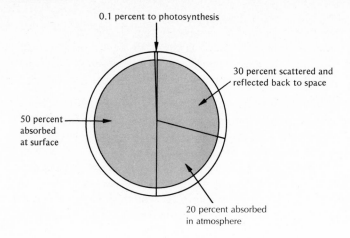

Earth power budget

0.1 percent to photosynthesis

30 percent scattered and reflected back to space

50 percent absorbed at surface

20 percent absorbed in atmosphere

~10^{14} W fixed by photosynthesis

1. *You can't use more power than the amount available!*
2. *You can't even use what is available!!*

Fig. 14.2 Out of the 10^{17} W of power received by the earth from the sun, only 10^{14} W is available to life—and even this amount is subject to the severe restrictive losses in the system.

ture difference, the more violent the weather disturbances. More cloud mass would cover the planetary surface, and more of the sun's radiant energy would be reflected back into space. Under this influence the mean surface temperature might tend to cool, which in turn would influence further formation of cloud masses. It is not too difficult to see that an oscillating pattern of reactions in the weather would result from any such primary disturbance.

The formation of large deposits of fossil fuels was in a way an accident of nature. At a time in the evolution of life when species were proliferating and expanding their populations rapidly, large quantities of organic matter with its stored energy were unused in the life process and deposited in such a way that its stored energy was not available to life until man began using it. Coal, oil, and natural gas are burned by industrial society at such an enormous rate that a few centuries of burning will totally exploit the nonrenewable reserves. It took millions upon millions of years to create these deposits. It is perhaps most instructive to view fossil fuels as stored solar energy kept in a bank for millions of years. That bank will one day close its doors with no chance of reopening them. At the present time all organic matter produced by photosynthesis is used up for its energy. Ultimately, the biosphere, too, gives up its energy as heat. A mature community makes the best possible use of this energy before giving it up as heat. A simplified community, one of the most abundant

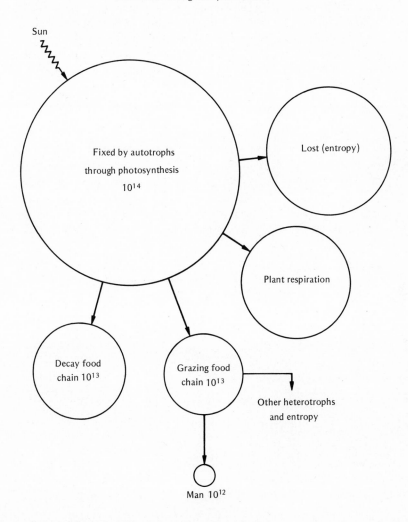

Power flow through biosphere (watts)

Each man requires a minimum of 10^2 W

Fig. 14.3

products of man's tampering, is very wasteful of energy. Simplified communities tend to consist of smaller, more hardy individuals in both plants and animals. Far fewer species are represented, and large numbers within a single species are the rule.

In summary, the earth as a machine is driven by about 10^{17} W of radiant power from the sun. Only a tiny fraction of this goes to power life systems of the biosphere, about 10^{14} W. The availability of key elements in the biosphere may locally adjust the use of solar energy in photosynthesis downward. Climax communities tend to make maximum use of available energy, whereas simplified communities make much less efficient use of it. The tides and weather patterns are absolutely required for the maintenance of the earth's temperature structure, for the mixing of marine organisms and the distribution of life-giving elements. What would be the ultimate effect of these same influences, i.e., tides and weather, if the biosphere ceased to exist?

14.2 Photosynthesis Photosynthesis is the process whereby green plants and blue-green algae fix a portion of the solar radiation in the form of chemical potential energy stored in sugars and carbohydrates (Fig. 14.4). Light of the right wavelength is essential, but in addition carbon dioxide, fixed nitrogen, phosphorus, water, and a variety of minerals are all required raw materials for photosynthesis. We have already mentioned that iron and phosphorus by

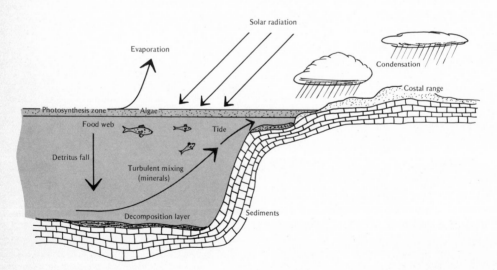

Fig. 14.4 Photosynthesis, the key to biosphere energy, depends on solar energy, upwelling of minerals, and fresh-water cycle.

their scarcity limit the process even more than the availability of sunlight in some places. Oxygen is released in the process of photosynthesis. This is a vital feature of the process, since oxygen, chemically very active, would soon disappear from the atmosphere were it not for its continual replenishment by photosynthesis.

Out of the total energy received by plants, only about 10 percent is available to the grazing food chain which includes man. Another 10 to 20 percent goes to the decay food chain. The rest of the energy goes toward plant respiration and heat. Just as gasoline engines are far less than 100 percent efficient, so photosynthesis leads to wasted energy. (See Fig. 14.3.)

Best estimates indicate that the 10^{14} W of power that drives photosynthesis produce an annual amount of about 10^{11} metric tons of dry organic material. At the very best only 10^{13} W is available to power the whole of the grazing food chain. Of this amount, only about 5 percent is available to man through agriculture. Hence, a maximum of about 10^{12} W is available to power man — a very generous portion of the pie.

Within the grazing food chain there are herbivores, which directly consume the producing plants (autotrophs). Herbivores thus lie at the first trophic (feeding) level above green plants. Carnivores feed upon the herbivores (trophic level 2), and carnivores upon carnivores (trophic level 3), and so forth. At each of these trophic levels there is additional loss due to animal respiration and entropy. The *rule of ten* states that at each successive level only 10 percent of the total energy is available to the consumer. Hence, it is clear that animals that are feeders solely on trophic level 3 and higher can exist in only small numbers due to the lack of energy available to them. Herbivores, on the other hand, operate at level 1, where energy is relatively abundant. Man is sufficiently adaptable to subsist at any of the consumer levels, though in areas of high standards of living he prefers to spice his diet at level 2 and higher.

It is important to recognize that a desire to continue feeding at the higher trophic levels can be satisfied only by sharply restricting the numbers of individuals in the population. Unfortunately, there is no way around this purely thermodynamic barrier. In areas of high human population density, the population (excluding industrial urban centers) tends to feed directly upon producing plants. It is obvious now why these people have no choice but to do exactly this. One curious anomaly in this picture is the Indian subcontinent, where huge populations of herbivores (cattle and monkeys) exist but are not used for food.

The agricultural practices of man will be discussed more fully in Chap. 15. However, it needs to be stated here that one significant influence of agriculture is the driving of more and more of the energy available

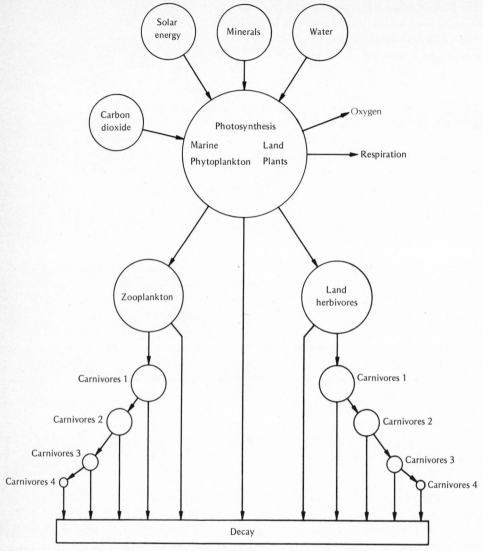

Fig. 14.5 *A simplified flow of energy and materials through marine and land food webs ending in decay. The process is actually cyclic (not shown). At each level, energy is lost through respiration, etc.*

from photosynthesis into the decay food chain. For example, *eutrophication* is a process in which lakes and streams are flooded with mineral nutrients through runoff from agriculture or industry or both. With the abundance of mineral nutrients, life explodes in the water. Decay feeders such as bacteria and fungus multiply rapidly. Eventually the supply of oxygen is squeezed out and the community becomes a stinking mass producing methane gas, alcohols, aminos, sulfurous gas, and partially decayed organic mass. Lake Erie is a prime example of this process. (See Fig. 14.6.)

Because all living organisms require constant energy input, and because there is a finite amount of power available, a fundamental problem of life is competition for available energy. The kind of sharing that goes on among species is a part of the larger study of ecology.

14.3 Human Population vs. Energy Available

Since the time that man ceased to hunt and gather his food in favor of farming, he has been about the business of simplifying one ecosystem after another. When man plows up a climax community and plants rice or wheat where it stood, he renders the community highly unstable. Let us return for a moment to a number developed earlier. Man has a useful limit of 10^{12} W with which to power his species.

Human machinery requires an average power of 10^2 watts per person for proper operation. Much of this energy is dissipated as heat or goes to evaporate water. Some of it goes to physical work such as walking or lifting, and some to maintain the body in its many functions. If each human requires 10^2 W continuously and only 10^{12} W of power is available, then we begin to see the basis for arguing that human population either must be voluntarily limited or will be limited by nature directly.

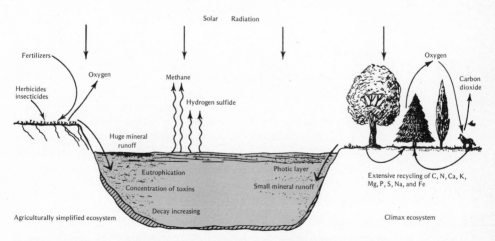

Fig. 14.6 The climax ecosystem is tending toward ever more efficient conservation of minerals and energy. The agriculturally simplified ecosystem is highly unstable and inefficient in retaining and recycling required minerals, water, and energy. Overfertilization of water leads to choking of this system by eutrophication.

If we make the obvious calculation, we see that 10^{10} (10 billion) is the upper limit of sustainable human population, at least at present and for the foreseeable future. This number assumes that a large portion of human population subsists at trophic level 1. Subpopulations that enjoy subsistence at higher trophic levels place an additional burden on the power budget. How many people could the earth support if they all were to subsist solely at trophic level 3?

The implication of these facts is inescapable. Nature will move very swiftly now to limit human population. Either man will find an effective way to accomplish this voluntarily and without delay, or a natural mechanism will once again bring the death rate up to the birth rate. The most probable mechanism seems to be a combination of events such as nuclear war, famine, epidemic, and environmental poisoning. Failing in voluntary control of population, we can only hope that nature will not judge us unfit to survive as a species. If the crisis comes to the worst, it is not beyond the realm of possibility that man, in his struggle to survive the mechanism, may push the whole of life balance beyond the compensation point. It seems more likely, however, that what will occur will be a painful period of population adjustment leading to a stable population of closer to 10^9 or even 10^8 individuals.

The populations of the United States and some European nations average an overall technological power consumption of about 10^4 watts per person. Much of this is supplied by exploitative burning of fossil fuels. In many locations the distribution of food, for example, is entirely dependent upon energy derived from fossil fuels. Unfortunately, there is little general appreciation of the severity of these problems — problems that are undeniably real and will not go away no matter how hard man might wish it. Even if the figures in this chapter were off by one order of magnitude, the problem would be unchanged, being only offset in time by a few more generations.

On this finite planet with its finite supply of power and delicately balanced biosphere, man threatens to destroy the balance through his failure to recognize the effect of his own increasing numbers. He cannot apply too much pressure on other living things by indiscriminate reproduction without paying the forfeit of his own well-being. No technological wonder or scientific breakthrough will change the picture even by the smallest bit. We do not know how to increase significantly the productivity of photosynthesis, and even if we did, there is no source of power available with which to drive the increased productivity.

Humanitarian zeal, idealism, and political-economic considerations have led the United States to export millions of tons of food in past decades to underdeveloped and starving nations. From 1954 to 1965 the United

States shipped some 3 million tons of nitrogen, 1.2 million tons of phosphorus, and 1.5 million tons of potassium in the form of food to these nations. These elements represent a national resource more precious than gold, since they deplete United States soils of precisely those minerals required for continued productivity. India alone continues to receive over a million tons of food per month from the United States. What has historically happened is that nations such as India have used this food to further expand their already disastrously huge populations to the same state of personal misery that existed before shipments started. It is the authors' opinion, after considerable soul-searching, that some nations must be written off as beyond this type of assistance, if the United States is truly to assist those nations that have reasonable prospects for improvement. The concept of the United States as a land of infinite plenty is myopic in the extreme. This concept must give way to hard-headed realism in the interest of salvageable segments of human population.

We already have a rough listing of the elemental composition of the four spheres of earth. We have looked in some detail into which elements are vital for life processes. Man in his new industrialized life style, however, has subscribed so far to a philosophy of mineral exploitation. This philosophy reaches its ultimate form in the economic principle of obsolescence. This philosophy will very quickly bring him to the end of the practical availability of many elements now in common use. Table 14.1 shows the estimated dates of exhaustion of some important elements. These es-

**14.4
Limited
Materials**

ELEMENT	ESTIMATED YEAR OF EXHAUSTION
Fe	2500
Mn	2100
Cr	2500
Co	2120
Al	2130
Ni	2080
Mo	2060
Tu	2020
Cu	2010
Sn	1990
Au	1989
Ag	1988
Zn	1988
Pb	1987

*Table 14.1
Estimated Dates
(Year) of Exhaustion of Ready
Supplies of Elements, Based on
Current Rates of
Use and Probable
Future Use in
Technological
Societies*

* *Scientific American*, pp. 205, September 1970.

timates are based on prospect of future use that seem most reasonable.

One would think that the iron smelted each year would be mostly returned to the furnaces for reuse. In reality only about one-third is reused. In the United States alone 6×10^2 kg of new steel per capita is consumed annually. Two-thirds of this amount is ultimately cast aside to rust.

Prior to the eighteenth century no society was ever able to concentrate enough power to build significant heavy industry. Great tracts of forest land were cleared to obtain charcoal for smelting of metals. The trees were cut far faster than they were able to replace themselves. As we have already seen, the development of the steam engine in the late eighteenth century, coupled with a type of coal effective in iron smelting, ushered in the age of heavy industry.

The electronics industry has brought heavy demands on copper, silver, gold, and other metals. The silver in United States coins has been replaced by less critical nickel and copper. It is true that plastics have been added as a major substitute for metal in many applications. This plastic, however, is derived from fossil fuels. At present and projected rates of use of fossil fuels, most investigators agree that the bulk of the deposits will be exhausted by the twenty-third century.

From now on it will become more and more difficult to extract metals from their ores, since the percentage of metal content in available ores will continue to drop. The obvious extension of this trend into the future results in a picture in which man must pulverize mountains of granite in order to feed industry. The 300 million tons of solid waste dumped in the United States yearly may well increase almost in direct proportion to population increase and the rate of power usage. The world has already reached the point where solid refuse must be dumped at the expense of a nearby neighbor. The seemingly infinite reservoir of space has disappeared. When man throws his trash "away" from now on, it will most often be on his neighbor's head, or worse, on one of those precious few remaining unspoiled ecosystems.

Problems 1   In what ways does the earth biosphere differ from a laboratory culture?

2   A series of natural accidents made possible the evolution of life on earth. Some were mentioned in this chapter. Can you add to the list of these accidents?

3   Debate the thesis of this chapter with a peer group that does not accept it as valid.

Chapter 15
How Limited Is "Finite"?

We shall now go just a bit deeper into the problems raised in the last chapter. It is not enough for man to live for himself only. Some have charged that religious ethics have fostered the human idea that this life is a transient phase of existence and, therefore, of little importance. Others believe that it is the nature of man to grasp all within reach and bend it to his purpose regardless of consequence. Whatever our belief, the fact remains that humanity has exploited and plundered the environment with only the small twinges of conscience and regret expressed by poets and philosophers.

We have continued to use the land, for example, as personal property, regarded as chattel and abused in whatever manner the owner sees fit. This concept of land has been extended to include the entire continental land masses of the earth and now is being extended to the ocean and its bottom as well. The principle of exploitation is so widely accepted as the normal code of behavior regarding real estate that man is now in danger of simplifying even the last remaining ecosystems of the earth. Who has not seen or heard an advertisement proclaiming that a new remote area of great natural beauty is to be opened up for urban settlement?

But let us pause now to lay a proper foundation before we continue.

15.1
Ecosystems and
Evolution

Ecology is the scientific study of the myriad interdependencies that exist between species in a community and between the living community and its nonliving environment. We have already traced the power used in the biosphere as an example. And yet the definition of ecology must be expanded still further. The dependence of one species on another and its relationship with the environment need not be either complete or passive, but, as we have shown, absolute interdependence is the key to all living communities.

Recent evidence lends a great deal of weight to the point of view that life must almost certainly exist wherever physical conditions will permit. Amino acids of a type unlike any on the earth have been found in a meteorite. The early hydrosphere and atmosphere of the earth provided the environment and raw materials necessary for the production of amino acids and their evolution into organisms that displayed those properties we call life. Just as there must have been a grand proliferation of molecules, so also there must have been a grand proliferation of organisms that possessed the biochemical means to adapt their energy processes and physical structures to exist and reproduce in their environment. The cells of these organisms contained the genetic keys both for cell duplication through mitosis and for organism reproduction through meiosis. *Mitosis*

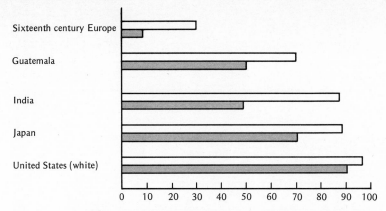

Fig. 15.1 Percentage of individuals in the population of sixteenth-century Europe versus selected populations of mid-twentieth-century nations that survived to age twenty (open bar) and to age fifty (dark bar).

is the process in which the nucleus of the cells of an organism duplicate themselves in growth and replacement. *Meiosis* is the process in which the nuclei of reproductive cells (gametes) from parents fuse and combine genetically to form a new individual. The end of the former is to reproduce cells within an individual; the end of the latter is to fuse gametes to produce a new individual. These early organisms had to be able to adapt to environmental changes in order to survive. One of the chief adaptive mechanisms developed by both plants and animals is mobility. The legs of a horse, wings of a bird, and wind-blown seeds of a tree are all examples of this mechanism. How many other examples can you think of?

We have ample fossil evidence of many species that failed to survive due to inability to adapt rapidly enough to changes in their ecosystem. These may have been forced out of the food chain by other species in competition. They may have fallen victims of weather or other environmental patterns, or they may have gone down under predation of other species ranging from bacteria to wolves. In cases of many extinct species, we shall never be quite certain as to the actual causes involved. In other cases we can construct reasonable models from fossil evidence, and for some recently extinct species we have all the evidence necessary for certain knowledge of underlying causes.

There is a thread that runs through all life evolution. Species tend to diversify through adaptation and natural selection always toward organisms that are more able to function efficiently in the ecosystem. Only man deliberately selects against natural selection by ensuring that the physically and genetically inferior members of the species survive.

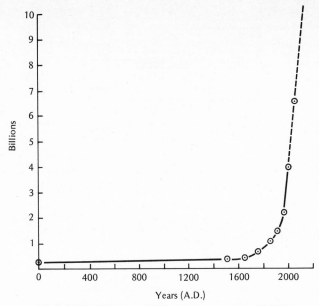

Fig. 15.2 *Worldwide human population over the past 2,000 years.
Note the nearly stable population up to the beginning of the sixteenth
century. Dotted curve is an extrapolation based on current doubling
rate. At current rate of increase, population could reach a trillion by
the year 2240. At this level, each person would have less than 30 m² of
space.*

As human society has advanced, e.g., intensifying industrial urbanization
and power utilization, those factors that have survival value in human
genetic makeup have changed. An extreme example of such change
might be an increased tolerance to carbon monoxide in the air we
breathe. We might also become more tolerant of high noise levels, or
might even come to require high noise levels (noise being any unwanted
sound and the level of toleration differing from individual to individual).
Such modification would actually work against those individuals who are
poisoned easily by carbon monoxide and those whose systems are trau-
matized by high noise levels.

In nature, natural selection eliminates the inferior strains. In the human
population, tampering with natural selection is leading to a proportionately greater fraction of weak and genetically inferior individuals. For example, medical science has found a way for hemophiliacs to live on into
the age of reproduction. Women and men who are known carriers of
recessive undesirable genes go right on reproducing and spreading these

genes further in the human genetic pool. This story is far too long to recount here, but you may want to read it in detail elsewhere.

The natural climax of evolution of the species in ecological relationship with other species and their environment is the mature ecosystem. The major earth ecosystems can be broken down into forests, grasslands, deserts, tundra, and marine communities. In general the equatorial and very warm bordering regions where plenty of fresh water is available are centers of lush communities in which large numbers of both plant and animal species are represented, but in very limited numbers of individuals in each of the species. The tropical rain forests are prime examples of this type of community. The cold polar regions and regions where water is in short supply tend to support less stable populations in which there are far fewer species represented but larger numbers within a given species. The stability of the ecosystem is of key importance here. The greatly simplified ecosystem is one in which even slight environmental changes, or slight changes in species interrelationships, can have a

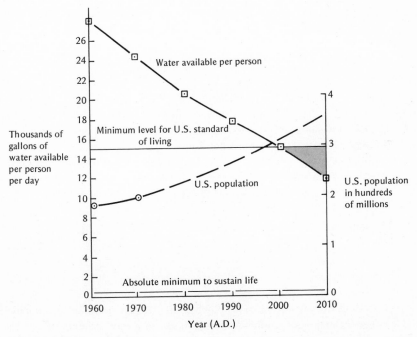

Fig. 15.3 Gallons of fresh water available per person in the United States assuming a total average rainfall of 5,000 billion gallons per day. Dotted curve represents best estimate of United States population to the year 2010. Note that after the year 2000, there will not be sufficient fresh water per person to maintain the desired United States standard of living. (**After** Bradley, Science, vol. 138, pp. 489-491, 1962.)

catastrophic influence upon the populations. The interdependence of the few species is rendered critical because alternative dependencies do not exist. Once simplified, a community is extremely vulnerable to attack from a hardy species that suddenly finds itself with no limitations on food and no natural enemies to hold it in check.

**15.2
Agriculture**
With only 10^{12} W of power available to support human population, a human population of 10 to 40 billion is the maximum sustainable. It is necessary, therefore, that our current population be supported by a highly efficient agriculture and agriculture-support system. It is of the greatest importance that agriculture be seen in the light of two quite different societies. On the one hand there are the so-called backward societies in which the population is largely tied to farming, with the farmers providing for their families directly from their own soil and the energy of themselves and their beasts of burden. On the other hand the industrialized societies typically have a small fraction of their population involved in farming. The few farmers provide food for the nonfarming masses. This latter system absolutely requires huge power inputs to build farm machinery, operate the engines required in the farming operation, and build and operate the fleet of transporters required to distribute the food to the consumers.

Industrialized societies with large populations are possible only through the continuous exploitation of fossil fuels for power. The food on the urban dweller's table comes indirectly from solar energy stored millions of years ago as well as from recent sunlight. Any prolonged interruption of this flow of energy must send the urban dweller into the fields and forests in search of food—an enterprise for which he is remarkably poorly prepared. At best only a few individuals would survive such a catastrophe.

In his farming history man has systematically torn up and simplified one community after another. His search for fuel has deforested great tracts of land, just as his plow has torn the precious topsoil and permitted the wind and rain to carry it down to the sea. Wherever the plow has gone, the rivers have run dark with their heavy burden of soil. It is no accident that the sites of ancient civilizations now have been reduced to nearly useless deserts. In his lust for hides nineteenth-century man reduced a population of millions of North American bison to a few pathetic individuals. The grasslands the bison once roamed have largely fallen victim to the plow. Wheat, corn, and oats have replaced most of the original species. But hardy weeds have moved in, and insect pests have swarmed in by the billions to ravage the simplified community. Poisons have to be used to

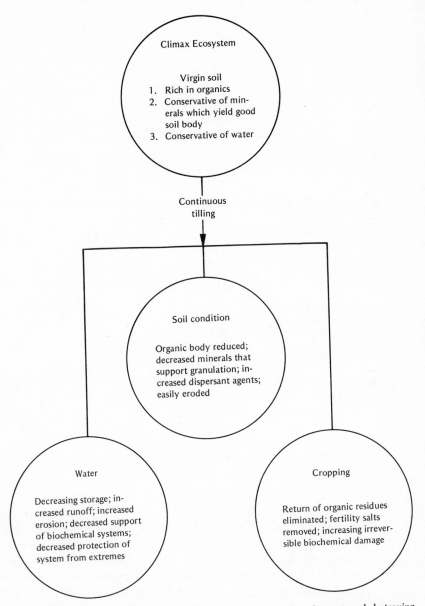

Climax Ecosystem

Virgin soil
1. Rich in organics
2. Conservative of minerals which yield good soil body
3. Conservative of water

Continuous tilling

Soil condition

Organic body reduced; decreased minerals that support granulation; increased dispersant agents; easily eroded

Water

Decreasing storage; increased runoff; increased erosion; decreased support of biochemical systems; decreased protection of system from extremes

Cropping

Return of organic residues eliminated; fertility salts removed; increasing irreversible biochemical damage

Fig. 15.4 For perhaps 40,000 years, man's agricultural activities have been at work destroying climax ecosystems. Shown here are some of the immediate and long-range effects of tilling good soil continually. From Mesopotamia to the American Midwest, these practices have rendered climatic extremes more and more serious and finally devastating to the soil.

control the pests, both insect and plant. And when the soil becomes depleted by generations of exploitative harvesting, nitrogen and phosphorus have to be dumped on it.

Much has been said about the tremendous reserves of food left to man in the oceans. In reality it is highly improbable that more than 10^8 metric tons of fish per year can be provided by the seas. The simple fact is that the oceans, on the whole, are not very productive.

Any tampering with aquatic ecosystems, e.g., temperature change, leads to the same sort of ecological simplification as on land. A few hardy species take over the community, and the percentage of energy diverted to the decay food chain is increased. The most tragic consequence of man's simplification of ecosystems is that in many cases the changes are irreversible. The seas and their creatures have been profoundly influenced by the industrial and agricultural activities of man. DDT and mercury poisoning are fast rendering some species of food fish unfit for human consumption. A number of species of aquatic birds are near extinction as a result of long-lasting poisons that attack both the individual and its ability to produce viable offspring.

The thing to remember about human agriculture, whether on land or in the marine environment, is that it can be carried out only at the expense of ecosystems that are simplified in the process. This is not in itself a major danger, if it is rigidly limited both in scope and in its methodology so as to produce the smallest harm to earth ecology as a whole. Too much agriculture or a continuation of the exploitative practices of the past must necessarily place too much strain on the balance of the total ecosystem. The trick is knowing how much is too much and developing social and economic mechanisms that keep human agriculture within acceptable bounds. We do not yet know what this limit is, but it seems likely, from the boundless evidence of ecological damage already done, that the practical limit has already been exceeded.

15.3 Demography

In the light of the certain knowledge that human population cannot continue to grow, we shall turn now to consider the population at present. Changes in human population are the result of two factors considered simultaneously—birth rate and death rate. If the birth rate exceeds the death rate, then population increases. At the present time the world population doubling period is between 30 and 40 years. That is, we can reasonably expect a population of some 7 or 8 billion people by the end of the twentieth century. This assumes that no major adjustment of current population trends occurs during this period. If, for example, large masses

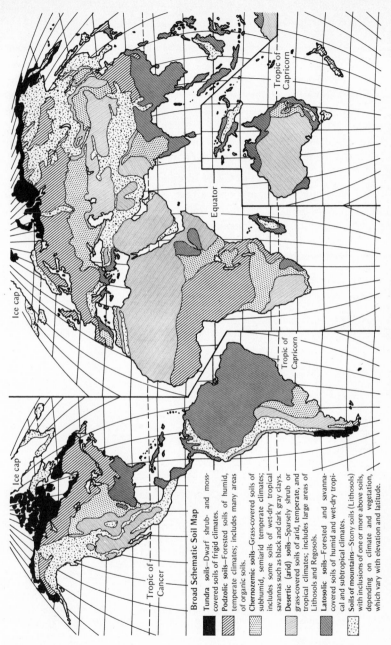

Broad Schematic Soil Map

Tundra soils—Dwarf shrub- and moss-covered soils of frigid climates.

Podzolic soils—Forested soils of humid, temperate climates; includes many areas of organic soils.

Chernozemic soils—Grass-covered soils of subhumid, semiarid temperate climates; includes some soils of wet-dry tropical savannas such as black and dark gray clays.

Desertic (arid) soils—Sparsely shrub or grass-covered soils of arid, temperate, and tropical climates; includes large areas of Lithosols and Regosols.

Latosolic soils—Forested and savanna-covered soils of humid and wet-dry tropical and subtropical climates.

Soils of mountains—Stony soils (Lithosols) with inclusions of one or more above soils, depending on climate and vegetation, which vary with elevation and latitude.

Fig. 15.5 World map of broad soil types. (From Konrad Krauskopf and Arthur Beiser, "Fundamentals of Physical Science," 6th ed., McGraw-Hill, New York, 1971.)

of adults were to become incapable of reproduction due to accumulations of some poison, this projection would be offset accordingly.

Medical science has both prolonged life and greatly reduced infant mortality. This has had the effect of slowing the death rate while ensuring a higher viable birth rate. Medical science has also provided excellent mechanisms for preventing conception. While this holds great promise as a control on birth rate, the existence of such control measures is far from a complete solution to the birth-rate problem. There are numerous cultural problems that so far have made exercise of birth-rate control virtually impossible. These will be discussed further in Chap. 16.

We must avoid the pitfall of blaming science for the troubles that beset humanity. Science is only a tool, and is in itself neither good nor evil. Science has provided many solutions to physical problems that lie astride the path of human development. It has undoubtedly contributed indirectly to the creation of other problems. However, it is a willing tool in the hands of enlightened men who are more and more turning their atten-

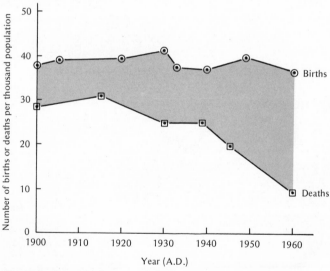

Fig. 15.6 Annual birth rate and death rate per thousand population for Ceylon from the years 1900 to 1960. Note that whereas the birth rate has remained fairly stable, the death rate has declined precipitously. The shaded area between curves represents the net growth of population; for example, in 1960, Ceylon had a net growth rate of 27 individuals per thousand. This picture is common in recent times in nations that have benefited from improved medical practice and use of pesticides. (After Science, Conflict and Society, Readings from Scientific American," Freeman, San Francisco, 1969.)

tions toward problems of human population and earth ecology. There are many scientists who can speak with excellent authority on the subject of the human demographic equation. There are numerous others who, for various reasons, find it convenient to attack the credibility of the scientists. Too often these reasons have little to do with objective evidence and a great deal to do with ignorance, superstition, and vested interests in no way related to the good of the ecosystem.

There is one aspect of demography that deserves further illumination. If all couples of reproductive age were to agree simultaneously to have no more than two children, it would still take a period of some 70 years before the population would stabilize, i.e., cease to grow. During this period the birth rate would still exceed the death rate, with the death rate catching up only very slowly. Japan, which is a good example of a nation that has had some success in adjusting the demographic balance, has a population that is still slowly growing even though several years have passed since initiation of control measures.

It seems clear, in light of this population overrun period, that human population is destined to rise to perhaps 15 billion even with immediate control measures. This number is uncomfortably large and will result in heavy stress on the already heavily burdened earth ecosystem. If human reproduction continues unchecked, however, the results are certain to be catastrophic—for man certainly, and perhaps for the whole ecosystem.

If the material of this chapter seems harsh and negative, it is because the evidence renders it thus. It is only by careful consideration of all the evidence that proper corrective action can be taken. The greatest danger at this time is that, having examined the evidence, the individuals of society will be discouraged from taking any action in the face of the enormity of the problems involved. Chapter 16 deals with a few of the major problems and suggests some broad directions for action by individuals and groups toward more responsible behavior. In so doing the chapter will just touch on some of the cultural issues involved.

Bresler, Jack B.: "Environments of Man," Addison-Wesley, Reading, Mass., 1968.

Detwyler, Thomas R.: "Man's Impact on Environment," McGraw-Hill, New York, 1971.

Revelle, Roger, et al. (eds.): "The Survival Equation," Houghton Mifflin, Boston, 1971.

Shepard, Paul, and McKinley, Daniel: "The Subversive Science," Houghton Mifflin, Boston, 1971.

Walker, Charles R.: "Technology, Industry and Man," McGraw-Hill, New York, 1968.

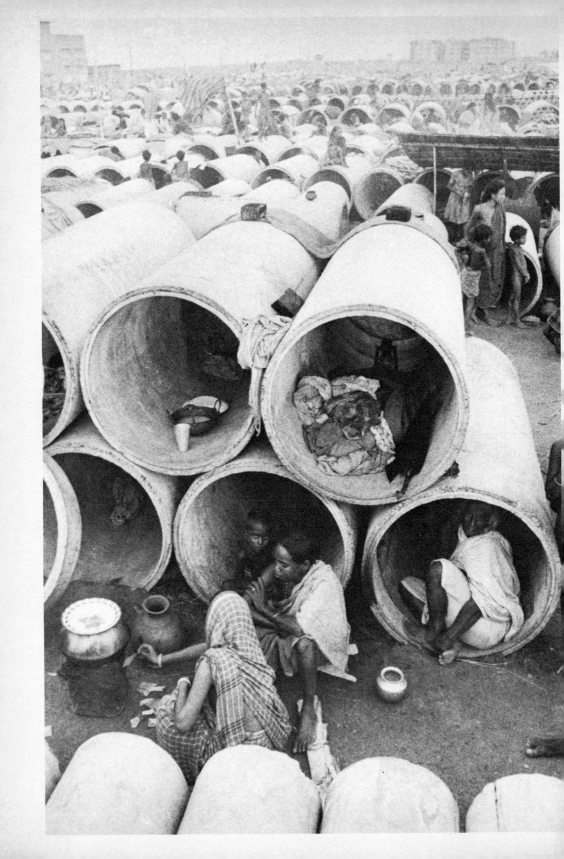

Chapter 16
The Quality of Life

During the author's visit to Calcutta in 1965, these people would have been classified fortunate indeed to have some cover from the elements. Most of the poor observed at that time were sleeping body to body on the bare sidewalks with no shelter at all. It is not possible to comprehend fully the depth of this human misery without experiencing it with all the senses. The result of such experience on people from advanced nations is often severe mental and physical shock. (Courtesy of Bruno Burbez Magnum.)

The quality of life on earth increasingly depends upon the behavior of man as a species. In this chapter we shall discuss the nature of some of man's broad behavioral problems with an eye toward possible remedies. We shall examine some of the cultural aspects of the problems in the hope that this will help to establish the relevance of science and scientists to culture as a whole.

16.1 Pollution

Basically, the excessive human population is the greatest pollution of our ecosystem. In this sense pollution is anything in the environment that contributes to the degrading of the ecosystem. This is quite different from the popular interpretation of pollution as change in the environment that adversely and immediately affects man. People have been quick to recognize raw sewage and garbage heaps as pollution, but society has only recently realized that mercury dumped into rivers and coastal waters has a profound effect upon the ecosystem. The mercury is now finding its way back to man. Several of the heavily used food fishes have been recently found to contain concentrations of the poison too high for safe human consumption.

Agriculture, through advances in industrialism, has been responsible both for the huge increase in population of the last century and for many of the pollutions that now threaten the very systems required to support that population. Nonagricultural industry has, through the burning of fossil fuels for power, polluted the atmosphere with hydrocarbons, lead, carbon monoxide, nitrogen compounds, sulfur compounds, and other noxious substances. The extent of atmospheric pollution has now reached and surpassed critical levels in many localities. The problem is so serious that residents of some urban areas have been advised by medical authorities to move away if they possibly can. Smog alerts are common in many of the larger cities.

Transportation is the chief offender in atmospheric pollution, with public power companies and private industry also contributing heavily. The popular literature is replete with references and analyses of atmospheric pollution. Atmospheric pollution has brought about an era of unprecedented increase in both mortality and morbidity from respiratory disorders such as emphysema and bronchitis. In addition, evidence is mounting to show that smog is also a killer of many other species, both plant and animal.

Immediate action is necessary to stop the destructive interaction between agriculture practices, industrial practices, and the ecosystems. Chlorinated hydrocarbons such as DDT have been extensively used to control

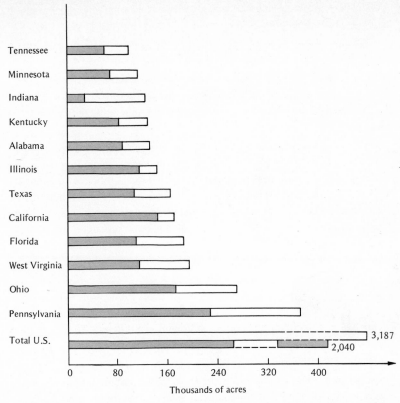

Fig. 16.1 *Bar graph showing the total land area disrupted in each of a sampling of states by strip and surface mining operations, and for the United States as a whole. The dark portion of the bars shows the land areas that must be reclaimed by deliberate conservation action. Land disruption by strip and surface mining is increasing sharply as metals and bulk materials are increasingly required in the economy.* (**After T. R. Detwyler, "Man's Impact on Environment," McGraw-Hill, New York, 1971.**)

pest species in agriculture and in medical eradication of disease-carrying species in local areas. DDT is now distributed throughout the world, even in areas where it has never been used. Several species of birds, e.g., the brown pelican, are virtually extinct because of DDT, which interferes with their calcium metabolism and prevents them from laying viable eggs. Virtually 100 percent of the fragile eggs break before hatching.

We are just beginning to understand the physiology of DDT. Humans collect it in their fat in ever-increasing concentrations. It is generally agreed that it attacks the soft organs such as the liver and brain. Some biologists fear that it may already be too late to save many species from extinction and large numbers of individuals from mortality and morbidity due to DDT. (See Fig. 16.2.)

Eutrophication has already been mentioned as the result of overfertilization. As in the case of all other pollutants, the result is the same. Sensitive species in the ecosystem are forced out, to be replaced by more hardy species that may not be acceptable as food for herbivores. The number of grazers is reduced, and the share of energy going to the decay feeders is increased.

In summary, nearly everything a blundering, self-serving population of humans does has the direct result of simplifying and degrading the world ecosystem. These insults might be tolerated if the number of humans was small. As human population grows beyond all reasonable bounds, its crushing pressure on the world ecosystem increases geometrically. The only way out of this dilemma is through scientific research, and perhaps most important, political-social reform that will ensure that humanity behaves intelligently.

16.2 Laws in Collision

The twentieth-century economic paradigms are already in catastrophic collision with the laws of nature. The examples of this are so common that we need mention only two here.

The scientific basis for a nearly "clean" transportation system has been laid down, yet automobile manufacturers insist that they cannot make the necessary revisions in power plants and equipment design. The reason nearly always given is prohibitive costs of changes. Corporations say that they cannot "afford" to change. The economic establishment, with its short-range profit motive, cannot be permitted to continue to dictate an inferior quality of life.

The petrochemical corporations manufacture toxins that they sell at considerable profit. This continues essentially unchanged in the face of certain ecological disaster. Corrective measures have nearly always been too little, too soft, and too late where they have been attempted at all.

In short, where scientific reason and economic purpose have collided, economic purpose has most often been permitted to have its way. Scientists who warn of dangers are, in nearly all cases, simply ignored. Where scientists have persisted in missionary efforts to inform the public of dangers, their efforts have been countered by advertising campaigns that discredit their arguments in the eyes of the public—a public often not equipped to recognize half-truths and imperfect logic. The tragic result of this irresponsibility must be a series of extremely painful lessons at the

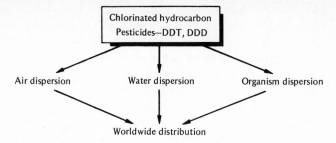

(Organisms concentrate to levels 1 million times environment)

Marine effects	Land organisms	Carnivorous birds
1. Fresh-water salmon and trout fry mortality—DDT in egg yolk	1. Soil organisms contaminated	1. Bermuda petrel,* robins, osprey, peregrine falcon, bald eagle, herring gulls, brown pelican threatened
2. Disturbed insect ecology—resistant species swarm while food species die out	2. Carnivores concentrate to dangerous or lethal levels	
3. Evidence of widespread reproductive failure in food fish, contaminated algae	3. Human concentrations from milk, water, and improperly cleaned foods	2. General failure of calcium metabolism in egg production
		3. Lethal concentrations in individuals common cause of mass kills

DDT poisoning leads to

1. Excitability increase
2. Abnormal reproductive processes and behavior
3. Decreased resistance to extremes and infections
4. Increased oxygen consumption
5. Reduced coordination
6. Tremors and death

*The petrel is a solely aquatic bird. The involvement of this species probably indicates widespread involvement of total marine ecosystem.

Fig. 16.2   Chlorinated hydrocarbons have been distributed worldwide and may already have produced profound harm to the world ecosystem as a whole. Many species face extinction or considerable danger because of these toxins. Use should be discontinued immediately.

hands of nature, which cares little for economic gains. The tragicomedy is that corporations, insisting that they cannot afford to change, have spent millions in counterscience advertising.

When one considers the awful dilemma of ever-increasing human population, including the probable consequences, it is tempting to despair of any solution. Yet we do know some things that may, when analyzed, provide the keys to effective control of population.

*16.3
Population
Control*

Most human babies are born as the result of a conscious decision on the part of married parents. A huge number are, of course, outside this classification, but such births are beginning to decline proportionately due to increasingly effective birth-control measures. The decision to conceive a child has been nicely analyzed by Heer and others, who report that it is the result of a consideration of three factors that relate to the condition of the prospective parents: (1) the value that the parents place on having the child in light of those goals that the parents might achieve without the child; (2) the monetary, emotional, and physical costs of the child compared with the cost of achieving other goals were the child not to be born; and (3) those resources which must be invested in the child, e.g., monetary, time, energy, and emotional input, on an absolute basis. A con-

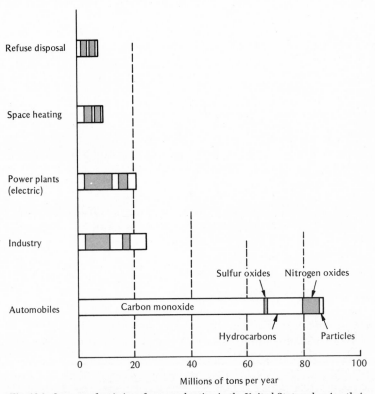

Fig. 16.3 Sources of emissions from combustion in the United States, showing their relative importance and absolute levels per year in producing air pollution. The automobile is clearly the chief source overall as well as the primary source of carbon monoxide, hydrocarbons, and oxides of nitrogen. Emissions from electric-power generating stations and industry contain large amounts of sulfur oxides. (From Singer, Scientific American, pp. 175–189, September 1970.)

scious *yes* decision is always the result of a favorable balance of these three factors for any given parents.

Many social and economic variables function within these factors. A few are somewhat obvious, while others are subtle and a bit surprising. Industrialization in the developed countries has produced sweeping changes in these factors. Although per capita income and free time are known to have significantly increased (factor 3), factors 1 and 2 have combined to produce an overall decline in fertility in females of the developed nations. In the United States the mean life expectancy rose from 47.3 years in 1900 to 70.2 years in 1964. With a tremendous reduction in infant and child mortality, parents can put their faith in the very high expectancy that their children will all survive to maturity. It is, therefore, not necessary to play the odds by hoping that a few out of a large number of births, perhaps 10 or 12, will survive to maturity. As mortality has declined in developed nations, parents have invested increasing emotional energy in fewer children who they feel certain will survive.

Prior to child labor laws and compulsory education laws, it was profitable to have larger numbers of children as an investment toward support. These two types of legislation have killed this incentive in advanced nations except for certain notorious aberrations within welfare legislation and practice. In the poorly developed nations a large number of children, particularly sons, ensures the aged parents of support when they are no longer able to manage for themselves. By contrast, the social legislation in advanced countries that has increasingly provided care for the aged has greatly reduced this incentive.

Education is itself an interesting variable. In the advanced nations where rapidly advancing technology is the accepted mode, the span of school years required to achieve acceptable position and status has continued to increase. The various costs of this increasingly costly investment have no doubt discouraged births, especially within urban families. Urban or suburban families are singled out here because the high cost of education combines with increasing costs of housing space and increasing complexity and intensity of social stress to further limit numbers of births per family. The increasing social and scientific awareness inherent in education has tended to promote negative social regard for large families. Thus the previous social rewards for large families in the agricultural societies that preceded industrialization no longer exist except in underdeveloped nations and states.

As status by birth has given way to status through position and conspicuous consumption, parents have been less willing to make the necessary investments in child supervision and care. These investments are not all monetary. Many women feel that they do not have the required emo-

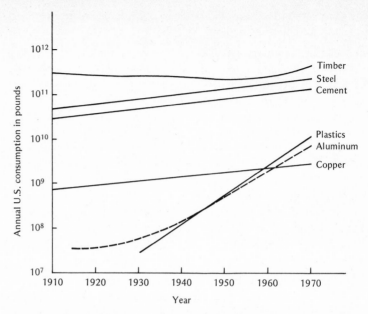

Fig. 16.4 *The trend in consumption of key materials is shown for the period 1910–1970 for the United States. Units of consumption per year are in pounds. Note that this scale increases by order of magnitude. These are smooth curves not intended to show short-term variations in consumption.* (**After Brown, Scientific American, pp. 195–207, September 1970.**)

tional and physical energy to suffer through another birth and infancy period, especially if there are already other infants requiring constant care.

If the developed nations enjoy a general decline in fertility that tends to stabilize the population, the poorly developed nations just as surely suffer from a too frequent *yes* decision based on the same factors. The real problem faced by underdeveloped nations is whether or not they can adjust the three factors for their parents to modify fertility downward. Perhaps this is really a question of industrialization, technological maturity, and achievement of at least a minimum acceptable economic growth. If the population of these underdeveloped nations grows so fast as to preclude the possibilities for such economic growth, a general lowering of standard of living will operate through these factors to produce a population crisis in such nations. This crisis will certainly be manifest as a dramatic increase in mortality. Unhappily, a number of nations now fall squarely within this crisis category.

No solutions to the problem of population control will be found by appointing committees or conducting abstract research in the laboratory. There is no easy way to solutions, just as there is no single action formula that will be effective worldwide.

Family planning has been the only significant action program to date. Although basically effective as a partial plan, it must be combined with other measures in an overall plan of action that will ensure an individual parent's *no* decision to more children on the basis of the three factors listed in Sec. 16.3. Family planning without a complete plan is roughly equivalent to applying a topical dressing to a cancer. In India there has already

	Number of species
Mammals extinct since 1600	36
Probable cause	
Nonhuman	9
Hunting	12
Introduced predators	6
Introduced competitors	2
Habitat disruption	7
Mammals now in serious danger	120
Probable cause	
Nonhuman	17
Hunting	52
Introduced predators	10
Introduced competitors	7
Habitat disruption	34
Birds extinct since 1600	94
Probable cause	
Nonhuman	22
Hunting	39
Introduced predators	14
Introduced competitors	4
Habitat disruption	15
Birds now in serious danger	187
Probable cause	
Nonhuman	60
Hunting	45
Introduced predators	21
Introduced competitors	5
Habitat disruption	56

Fig. 16.5 The mammal and bird species (by number) that have suffered extinction or are now facing extinction from both natural causes (nonhuman) and from purely human causes (all the rest). Note that hunting, very little of which was for food, and disruption of the natural habitat have accounted for a large fraction of these species. (**After T. R. Detwyler, "Man's Impact on Environment," McGraw-Hill, New York, 1971.**)

been some experimentation with incentives combined with family planning. The author personally witnessed one of these experiments in the State of Bihar. Its success was greatly limited by the presence of a holy man who spoke out against it on moral and religious grounds. Obviously, the plan of action there was far from comprehensive.

Good ideas have existed for some time, but leaders of social and political groups have thus far not recognized the population problem as critical. Too many of these leaders have been unwilling, therefore, to invest properly in specific comprehensive measures that already exist in the planning stage. Leadership must be educated to recognize the problem as a critical one. Without this, no measure can succeed.

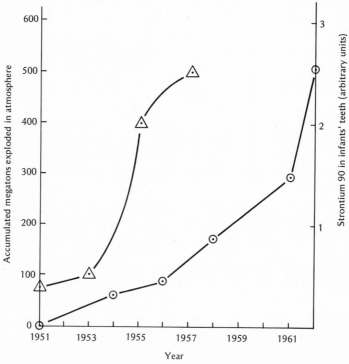

Fig. 16.6 *The accumulation of atmospheric nuclear explosions in megatons for the period 1951–1962. For a portion of this same period, the strontium 90 found in the teeth of infants (110,000 teeth) is shown to correspond directly with these explosions. Sr*[90] *is a particularly dangerous radioactive isotope because, like calcium, it is a bone seeker that remains in the tissue for a long time, continuing to accumulate over the lifetime of the individual. Increasing contamination is thought to be directly responsible for corresponding increase in incidence of leukemia.*

The governments of nations and states have evolved thus far to a point where economic considerations are preeminent. Those involved in representative governments are too often illiterate in science. Senators and other representatives of the people are placed in office as the result of campaigns funded by economic interests. These campaigns have little to do with establishing the qualifications of the candidates to make rational judgments on scientific issues.

Voters tend to mistrust those with too much education. Perhaps this is understandable, but knowledge of science and its relationships to the whole of culture is now absolutely required for survival. Voters in free societies must begin to insist on not only science literacy in their candidates, but also demonstrated willingness to use their knowledge for the long-range good of humanity and the biosphere as a whole.

The fundamental problem is one of alteration of deep-seated values that have been embraced by both management and workers. Bigger is not better. Smaller may have far greater virtue for man. Resources are sharply limited, and any economic system that exploits resources in order to feed an ever-growing productivity must ultimately fail.

Profits alone cannot justify actions that adversely affect world ecology. The profit motive has to be controlled, however this is accomplished. The profit motive is not in itself an ecological danger, but its excesses cannot be tolerated.

The ecosystem of which we are a part must be respected and treated accordingly. Man has only begun to behave intelligently in this regard. The seventh decade of the twentieth century must bring a renaissance of values. The new values must accept man's proper place as only one of nature's creations. They must embrace a kind of reverence of nature, giving up past egocentricity with its endless insults to nature.

Science and technology will not pull any miracles out of the hat to save humanity from the judgment of nature. Some beginnings have already been made toward cleaning up technology, but these beginnings must be carefully cultivated by unstinting use of human resources. In order to act properly, we must first know. Nothing is as important as knowledge. Hence, education that seeks not so much to serve technology and economics but to understand and control them is the first requirement for survival.

The problems of change are many and formidable. Their solutions will require sacrifices from all individuals. Solutions will come only if the masses of humanity are conscious of the need for solutions.

**16.5
Ecology-conscious
Society**

The magnitude of the problems is so great that effective solutions are possible only through a political and social unity that men have so far been unable to achieve. If ever a universal threat to the well-being of all men everywhere existed, it is now.

Individuals who do know and want to help are often frustrated by the sheer magnitude of the problems. Renaissances begin with a few, however, and grow from small centers of genuine concern. The place to start is at home, where immediate revisions of policy and legal structure are possible. Already such centers of concern exist. Their influence is being felt at higher organizational levels, with resulting legislation designed to protect the ecosystem. Do not make the fatal error of withdrawing from the task because of apathy or frustration. Important and often painful decisions must be made, and they can come only as a result of the demonstrated concern of all the citizens in an ecology-conscious society.

Just as one community becomes the example that encourages another community to act, so also one nation or state can become the example for other nations and states.

The right to dissent is fundamental in all free societies, but dissent must be accompanied by thoughtful and constructive alternatives. Dissent without reasonable alternatives is a destructive process and unworthy of those who claim the rights of free citizenship. Hence, it follows that dissenters must be armed with knowledge that is sure and has the strength to survive the subtle efforts of those who will always be opposed to change. Education, not indoctrination or propaganda, is the only path to such knowledge.

The lower schools should teach the fundamentals of ecology right along with mathematics and language. Ecology should not, however, be compartmentalized as an independent subject. It should always be studied in the context of problems of society, even though it searches the depths of scientific paradigms. This is probably the most important issue ever to face educators responsible for curricula in the schools. Treated as "just another fad" or in some other cavalier fashion, ecology education will certainly fail in its important mission.

The terrible price of failing in all this is judgment at the hands of nature. In the event that we do fail, nature may ultimately find that Homo sapiens, the wise man, is unfit to survive. Can any other issue be as important as this?

It is fitting that this text should close with a warning to the reader. There will be many politicians in offices both high and low who will outwardly pretend to embrace sound scientific thinking and good ecological management, but who will secretly serve a different master. Corporate clusters, conglomerates, and cartels, concerned with concentration of economic and political power, are very unlikely to have any real concern for preservation of the ecosystem unless they can derive their real goals from ecological management. These same concerns will always be able to produce highly respected "scientists" who willingly deal in half-truths and misinformation in order to produce at least confusion in the voter's mind.

The voter must be prepared to read and to listen with deep comprehension, just as he must demand to know the facts as they exist. He must exercise a knowledge of basic principles of science for himself, and avoid acting on the basis of the unquestioned authority of any specialist. That means that this text should be only the beginning of life-long study of culturally relevant principles of science.

1   On what basis could birth control be made available to those who are fertile but do not wish to reproduce? In the United States? Worldwide?

2   Identify the major social hurdles that lie in the way of voluntary birth control.

Appendix A

Table of Sines, Cosines, and Tangents; Mathematical Formulas

Table of Sines, Cosines, and Tangents

ANGLE	SINE	COSINE	TANGENT	ANGLE	SINE	COSINE	TANGENT
0°	.0000	1.0000	.0000	46°	.7193	.6947	1.0355
1°	.0175	.9998	.0175	47°	.7314	.6820	1.0724
2°	.0349	.9994	.0349	48°	.7431	.6691	1.1106
3°	.0523	.9986	.0524	49°	.7547	.6561	1.1504
4°	.0698	.9976	.0699	50°	.7660	.6428	1.1918
5°	.0872	.9962	.0875	51°	.7771	.6293	1.2349
6°	.1045	.9945	.1051	52°	.7880	.6157	1.2799
7°	.1219	.9925	.1228	53°	.7986	.6018	1.3270
8°	.1392	.9903	.1405	54°	.8090	.5878	1.3764
9°	.1564	.9877	.1584	55°	.8192	.5736	1.4281
10°	.1736	.9848	.1763	56°	.8290	.5592	1.4826
11°	.1908	.9816	.1944	57°	.8387	.5446	1.5399
12°	.2079	.9781	.2126	58°	.8480	.5299	1.6003
13°	.2250	.9744	.2309	59°	.8572	.5150	1.6643
14°	.2419	.9703	.2493	60°	.8660	.5000	1.7321
15°	.2588	.9659	.2679	61°	.8746	.4848	1.8040
16°	.2756	.9613	.2867	62°	.8829	.4695	1.8807
17°	.2924	.9563	.3057	63°	.8910	.4540	1.9626
18°	.3090	.9511	.3249	64°	.8988	.4384	2.0503
19°	.3256	.9455	.3443	65°	.9063	.4226	2.1445
20°	.3420	.9397	.3640	66°	.9135	.4067	2.2460
21°	.3584	.9336	.3839	67°	.9205	.3907	2.3559
22°	.3746	.9272	.4040	68°	.9272	.3746	2.4751
23°	.3907	.9205	.4245	69°	.9336	.3584	2.6051
24°	.4067	.9135	.4452	70°	.9397	.3420	2.7475
25°	.4226	.9063	.4663	71°	.9455	.3256	2.9042
26°	.4384	.8988	.4877	72°	.9511	.3090	3.0777
27°	.4540	.8910	.5095	73°	.9563	.2924	3.2709
28°	.4695	.8829	.5317	74°	.9613	.2756	3.4874
29°	.4848	.8746	.5543	75°	.9659	.2588	3.7321
30°	.5000	.8660	.5774	76°	.9703	.2419	4.0108
31°	.5150	.8572	.6009	77°	.9744	.2250	4.3315
32°	.5299	.8480	.6249	78°	.9781	.2079	4.7046
33°	.5446	.8387	.6494	79°	.9816	.1908	5.1446
34°	.5592	.8290	.6745	80°	.9848	.1736	5.6713
35°	.5736	.8192	.7002	81°	.9877	.1564	6.3138
36°	.5878	.8090	.7265	82°	.9903	.1392	7.1154
37°	.6018	.7986	.7536	83°	.9925	.1219	8.1443
38°	.6157	.7880	.7813	84°	.9945	.1045	9.5144
39°	.6293	.7771	.8098	85°	.9962	.0872	11.4301
40°	.6428	.7660	.8391	86°	.9976	.0698	14.3007
41°	.6561	.7547	.8693	87°	.9986	.0523	19.0811
42°	.6691	.7431	.9004	88°	.9994	.0349	28.6363
43°	.6820	.7314	.9325	89°	.9998	.0175	57.2900
44°	.6947	.7193	.9657	90°	1.0000	.0000	
45°	.7071	.7071	1.0000				

Mathematical Formulas

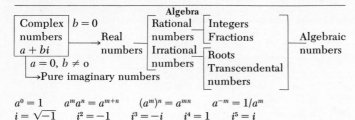

$a^0 = 1 \quad a^m a^n = a^{m+n} \quad (a^m)^n = a^{mn} \quad a^{-m} = 1/a^m$

$i = \sqrt{-1} \quad i^2 = -1 \quad i^3 = -i \quad i^4 = 1 \quad i^5 = i$

Logarithms

When $a^y = x$, then $y = \log_a x$; $\log_a a = 1$; $\log 1 = 0$; $\log xy = \log x = \log y$; $\log x/y = \log x = \log y$; $\log x^n = n \log x$; $\ln x = \log_e x = (\log_e 10)(\log_{10} x) = 2.3026 \log_{10} x$

Arithmetic progression

$S_n = a + (a + d) + (a + 2d) + \cdots + [a + (n-1)d] = n/2 \times \{a + [a + (n-1)]d\}$

Geometric progression

$S_n = a + ar + ar^2 + \cdots + ar^{n-2} + ar^{n-1} = a(1 - r^n)/(1 - r)$, when $r \neq 1$; if $|r| < 1$, $\lim_{n \to \infty} S_n = a/(1 - r)$

Binomial formula

$(x + y)^n = x^n + nx^{n-1}y + \cdots + [n(n-1) \cdots (n-r+2)]/(r-1)! \times x^{n-r+1}y^{r-1} + \cdots + nxy^{n-1} + y^n$, where r indicates rth term

Compound interest

P = principal, r = annual interest rate, A_n = accumulated amount for n years compounded q times per year: $A_n = P(1 + r/q)^{nq}$

Quadratic equations

$ax^2 + bx + c = 0 \qquad x = (-b \pm \sqrt{b^2 - 4ac})/2a$

When $b^2 - 4ac > 0$ roots are real and unequal
When $b^2 - 4ac = 0$ roots are real and equal
When $b^2 - 4ac < 0$ roots are conjugate component pairs

$\sin \alpha = x/r \qquad \csc \alpha = 1/\sin \alpha = r/y$
$\cos \alpha = x/r \qquad \sec \alpha = 1/\cos \alpha = r/x$
$\tan \alpha = y/x \qquad \cot \alpha = 1/\tan \alpha = x/y$

Trigonometry

Fundamental identities

Function of acute angle = cofunction of complementary angle

$\tan \alpha = \sin \alpha/\cos \alpha \qquad 1 + \tan^2 \alpha = \sec^2 \alpha$

$\sin^2 \alpha + \cos^2 \alpha = 1 \qquad 1 + \cot^2 \alpha = \csc^2 \alpha$

$\sin (\alpha \pm \beta) = \sin \alpha \cos \beta \pm \cos \alpha \sin \beta$

$\cos (\alpha + \beta) = \cos \alpha \cos \beta \pm \sin \alpha \sin \beta$

$\tan (\alpha \pm \beta) = (\tan \alpha \pm \tan \beta)/(1 \pm \tan \alpha \tan \beta)$

$\sin \alpha/2 = \pm\sqrt{(1 - \cos \alpha/2)}$

$\cos \alpha/2 = \pm\sqrt{(1 + \cos \alpha/2)}$

$\tan \alpha/2 = \pm\sqrt{(1 - \cos \alpha)/(1 + \cos \alpha)}$

Sine law: $a/\sin \alpha = b/\sin \beta = c/\sin \gamma$

Cosine law: $c^2 = a^2 + b^2 - 2ab \cos \gamma$

Functions of common angles

DEGREE:	0	30	45	60	90	180	270	360	
RADIAN:	0	$\pi/6$	$\pi/4$	$\pi/3$	$\pi/2$	π	$3\pi/2$	2π	QUADRANT
sin	0	1/2	$\sqrt{2}/2$	$\sqrt{3}/2$	1	0	−1	0	I, II
cos	1	$\sqrt{3}/2$	$\sqrt{2}/2$	1/2	0	−1	0	1	I, IV
tan	0	$\sqrt{3}/3$	1	$\sqrt{3}$	∞	0	∞	0	I, III
cot	∞	3	1	$\sqrt{3}/3$	0	∞	0	∞	I, III
sec	1	$2\sqrt{3}/3$	$\sqrt{2}$	2	∞	−1	∞	1	I, IV
csc	∞	2	$\sqrt{2}$	$2\sqrt{3}/3$	1	∞	−1	∞	I, II

Geometry

Triangle: area = $bc (\sin \alpha)/2$

Parallelogram:

  area = $ah = ab \sin \alpha$

Trapezoid:

  area = $h(a + b)/2$

Ellipse: area = πab

Parabola: area = $2ld/3$

Circle, α = central angle in radians:

  circumference = $2\pi r = \pi D$; $s = r\alpha$; area (circle) = πr^2; area (sector) = $rs/2 = r^2 \alpha/2$; area (segment) = $r^2 (\alpha - \sin \alpha)/2$

Sphere: area = $4\pi r^2$; volume = $(4/3)\pi r^3$

Prism or cylinder: volume = (area of base) (altitude)

Pyramid or cone: volume = (1/3) (area of base) (altitude)

Analytic Geometry

Points: distance between = $\sqrt{(x_2 - x_1)^2 + (y_2 - y_1)^2}$

Slope: $m = (y_2 - y_1)/(x_2 - x_1)$

Straight line, b = intercept on y axis: $y = mx + b$

Circle, center at (h,k): $(x - h)^2 + (y - k)^2 = r^2$

Parabola, a = distance from vertex to focus, vertical at (h,k):

  $(y - k)^2 = 4a (x - h)$, axis $\parallel x$ axis

  $(x - h)^2 = 4a (y - k)$, axis $\parallel y$ axis

Ellipse, center at (h,k) major axis = $2a$, minor axis = $2b$:

  $(x - h)^2/a^2 + (y - k)^2/b^2 = 1$, major axis $\parallel x$ axis

  $(y - k)^2/a^2 + (x - h)^2/b^2 = 1$, major axis $\parallel y$ axis

Hyperbola, center at (h,k),

transverse axis $= 2a$, conjugate axis $= 2b$:

$(x - h)^2/a^2 = (y = k)^2/b^2 = 1$, transverse axis $\parallel$ x axis

$(y - k)^2/a^2 = (x - h)^2/b^2 = 1$, transverse axis $\parallel$ y axis

Physical Constants and Formulas

Physical constants

Speed of light: $c = 2.998 \times 10^8$ m/s

Gravitational constant: 6.67×10^{-11} m^3/kg·s$^2 = G$

Coulomb's law constant: $k = 8.988 \times 10^9$ N·m^2/C^2

Boltzmann's constant: $k = 1.38 \times 10^{-23}$ J/°K

Planck's constant: $h = 6.626 \times 10^{-34}$ J·s

1 amu $= 1.66 \times 10^{-27}$ kg

1 C $= 6.242 \times 10^{18}$ el chg

1 eV $= 1.6 \times 10^{-19}$ J

Formulas

Gravitational force: $F_g = Gm_1m_2/R^2$

Electrical force between point charges: $F_e = kq_1q_2/R^2$

Centripetal force: $F_c = mv^2/R = 4mR/T^2$

Radioactive decay: $N/N_0 = e^{-0.693t/t_{half-life}}$

Carbon dated age: $t = -(t_{half-life} [\log (N/N_0)]/0.693 \log e$

$\qquad t = 5760y \times \log (N/N_0)/0.3$

Area of a circle: $A = r^2$

Surface area of a sphere: $A = 3/4r^2$

Volume of a sphere: $V = 4/3r^3$

Constant accelerated motion: $a = $ constant

$\qquad v = at + v_0$

$\qquad d = 1/2at^2 + v_0t + d_0$

Astronomical Data

BODY	MASS (kg)	MEAN RADIUS (m)	SPIN ROTATIONAL PERIOD (s)	MEAN ORBITAL RADIUS (m)
Sun	1.98×10^{30}	6.95×10^8	2.14×10^6	
Mercury	3.28×10^{23}	2.57×10^6	7.60×10^6	5.79×10^{10}
Venus	4.83×10^{24}	6.31×10^6	2.6×10^6	1.08×10^{11}
Earth	5.98×10^{24}	6.38×10^6	8.61×10^4	1.49×10^{11}
Mars	6.37×10^{23}	3.43×10^6	8.85×10^4	2.28×10^{11}
Jupiter	1.90×10^{27}	7.18×10^7	3.54×10^4	7.78×10^{11}
Saturn	5.67×10^{26}	6.03×10^7	3.60×10^4	1.43×10^{12}
Uranus	8.80×10^{25}	2.67×10^7	3.88×10^4	2.87×10^{12}
Neptune	1.03×10^{26}	2.48×10^7	5.69×10^4	4.50×10^{12}
Pluto	?	?	?	5.9×10^{12}
Earth moon	7.34×10^{22}	1.74×10^6	2.36×10^6	3.8×10^8

Kepler's constant: $K = R^3/T^2 = 3.35 \times 10^{18}$ m^3/s^2

Appendix B
Periodic Table of the Elements

Periodic Table of the Elements

$s(l=0)$ $d(l=2)$ s $p(l=1)$

n	I_A	II_A	III_B	IV_B	V_B	VI_B	VII_B	VIII			I_B	II_B	III_A	IV_A	V_A	VI_A	VII_A	INERT GASES
1	1 H 1.00797	2 He 4.0026																2 He 4.0026
2	3 Li 6.939	4 Be 9.0122											5 B 10.811	6 C 12.011	7 N 14.0067	8 O 15.9994	9 F 18.998	10 Ne 20.183
3	11 Na 22.990	12 Mg 24.312											13 Al 26.982	14 Si 28.086	15 P 30.974	16 S 32.064	17 Cl 35.453	18 Ar 39.948
4	19 K 39.102	20 Ca 40.08	21 Sc 44.956	22 Ti 47.90	23 V 50.942	24 Cr 51.996	25 Mn 54.938	26 Fe 55.847	27 Co 58.933	28 Ni 58.71	29 Cu 63.54	30 Zn 65.37	31 Ga 69.72	32 Ge 72.59	33 As 74.922	34 Se 78.96	35 Br 79.909	36 Kr 83.80
5	37 Rb 85.47	38 Sr 87.62	39 Y 88.905	40 Zr 91.22	41 Nb 92.906	42 Mo 95.94	43 Tc (99)	44 Ru 101.07	45 Rh 102.91	46 Pd 106.4	47 Ag 107.870	48 Cd 112.40	49 In 114.82	50 Sn 118.69	51 Sb 121.75	52 Te 127.60	53 I 126.90	54 Xe 131.30
6	55 Cs 132.91	56 Ba 137.34	†	72 Hf 178.49	73 Ta 180.95	74 W 183.85	75 Re 186.2	76 Os 192.2	77 Ir 192.2	78 Pt 195.09	79 Au 196.97	80 Hg 200.59	81 Tl 204.37	82 Pb 207.19	83 Bi 208.98	84 Po (210)	85 At (210)	86 Rn (222)
7	87 Fr (223)	88 Ra (226)	‡															

TRANSITION ELEMENTS

$f(l=3)$

d †

57 La 138.91	58 Ce 140.12	59 Pr 140.91	60 Nd 144.24	61 Pm (147)	62 Sm 150.35	63 Eu 151.96	64 Gd 157.25	65 Tb 158.92	66 Dy 162.50	67 Ho 164.93	68 Er 167.26	69 Tm 168.93	70 Yb 173.04	71 Lu 174.97
89 Ac (227)	90 Th 232.04	91 Pa (231)	92 U 238.03	93 Np (237)	94 Pu (244)	95 Am (243)	96 Cm (247)	97 Bk (247)	98 Cf (251)	99 Es (254)	100 Fm (253)	101 Md (256)	102 No (254)	103 Lw (257)

* Based on carbon-12 as 12.00000.
† Lanthanide series (rare earths).
‡ Actinide series.

Ac	Actinium	
Ag	Silver	
Al	Aluminum	
Am	Americium	
Ar	Argon	
As	Arsenic	
At	Astatine	
Au	Gold	
B	Boron	
Ba	Barium	
Be	Beryllium	
Bi	Bismuth	
Bk	Berkelium	
Br	Bromine	
C	Carbon	
Ca	Calcium	
Cd	Cadmium	
Ce	Cerium	
Cf	Californium	
Cl	Chlorine	
Cm	Curium	
Co	Cobalt	
Cr	Chromium	
Cs	Cesium	
Cu	Copper	
Dy	Dysprosium	
Er	Erbium	
Es	Einsteinium	
Eu	Europium	
F	Fluorine	
Fe	Iron	
Fm	Fermium	
Fr	Francium	
Ga	Gallium	
Gd	Gadolinium	
Ge	Germanium	
H	Hydrogen	
Ha	Hahnium	
He	Helium	
Hf	Hafnium	
Hg	Mercury	
Ho	Holmium	
I	Iodine	
In	Indium	
Ir	Iridium	
K	Potassium	
Kr	Krypton	
Ku	Kuchatovium	
La	Lanthanum	
Li	Lithium	
Lr	Lawrencium	
Lu	Lutetium	
Md	Mendelevium	
Mg	Magnesium	
Mn	Manganese	
Mo	Molybdenum	
N	Nitrogen	
Na	Sodium	
Nb	Niobium	
Nd	Neodymium	
Ne	Neon	
Ni	Nickel	
No	Nobelium	
Np	Neptunium	
O	Oxygen	
Os	Osmium	
P	Phosphorus	
Pa	Protactinium	
Pb	Lead	
Pd	Palladium	
Pm	Promethium	
Po	Polonium	
Pr	Praseodymium	
Pt	Platinum	
Pu	Plutonium	
Ra	Radium	
Rb	Rubidium	
Re	Rhenium	
Rh	Rhodium	
Rn	Radon	
Ru	Ruthenium	
S	Sulfur	
Sb	Antimony	
Sc	Scandium	
Se	Selenium	
Si	Silicon	
Sm	Samarium	
Sn	Tin	
Sr	Strontium	
Ta	Tantalum	
Tb	Terbium	
Tc	Technetium	
Te	Tellurium	
Th	Thorium	
Ti	Titanium	
Tl	Thallium	
Tm	Thulium	
U	Uranium	
V	Vanadium	
W	Tungsten	
Xe	Xenon	
Y	Yttrium	
Yb	Ytterbium	
Zn	Zinc	
Zr	Zirconium	

Appendix C
Metric Tables

Metric Tables

Unit Conversions

Length

FROM \ TO	cm	m	km	in	ft	mi
Cm	1	0.01	1×10^{-5}	0.3937	0.03281	6.21×10^{-6}
m	100	1	0.001	39.37	3.281	6.21×10^{-4}
km	1×10^{5}	1,000	1	3.94×10^{4}	3,281	0.6214
in	2.54	0.0254	2.54×10^{-5}	1	0.08333	1.58×10^{-5}
ft	30.48	0.3048	3.05×10^{-4}	12	1	1.89×10^{-4}
mi	1.61×10^{5}	1,609	1.609	6.34×10^{4}	5,280	1

Area

FROM \ TO	cm²	m²	km²	in²	ft²	mi²
cm²	1	0.0001	1×10^{-10}	0.1550	0.00108	3.86×10^{-11}
m²	1×10^{4}	1	1×10^{-6}	1,550	10.76	3.86×10^{-7}
km²	1×10^{10}	1×10^{6}	1	1.55×10^{9}	1.08×10^{7}	0.3861
in²	6.452	6.45×10^{-4}	6.45×10^{-10}	1	0.00694	2.49×10^{-10}
ft²	929.0	0.09290	9.29×10^{-8}	144	1	3.59×10^{-8}
mi²	2.59×10^{10}	2.59×10^{6}	2.590	4.01×10^{9}	2.79×10^{7}	1

Volume

FROM \ TO	cm³	l	in³	ft³	gal
cm³	1	0.001	0.06102	3.53×10^{-5}	2.64×10^{-4}
l	1,000	1	61.02	0.03532	0.2642
in³	16.39	0.01639	1	5.79×10^{-4}	0.00433
ft³	2.83×10^{4}	28.32	1,728	1	7.481
gal	3,785	3.785	231.0	0.1337	1

Energy

FROM \ TO	Btu	cal	J	hph	kWh
Btu	1	252.0	1,055	3.93×10^{-4}	2.93×10^{-4}
cal	0.00397	1	4.186	1.56×10^{-6}	1.16×10^{-6}
J	9.48×10^{-4}	0.2889	1	3.73×10^{-7}	2.78×10^{-7}
hph	2,545	6.41×10^{5}	2.68×10^{6}	1	0.7457
kWh	3,418	8.60×10^{5}	8.60×10^{6}	1.341	1

Power

FROM \ TO	W	hp	Btu/min	ft·lb$_f$/s	ft·lb$_f$/min
W	1	0.00134	0.05688	0.7376	44.25
hp	745.7	1	42.42	550	3.30×10^4
Btu/min	17.58	0.02358	1	12.97	778.0
ft · lb$_f$/s	1.356	0.00182	0.07712	1	60
ft · lb$_f$/min	0.02260	3.03×10^{-5}	0.00129	0.01667	1

Velocity

FROM \ TO	cm/s	km/h	in/s	ft/s	ft/min	mi/h
cm/s	1	0.03600	0.3937	0.03281	1.968	0.02237
km/h	27.78	1	10.94	0.9113	54.68	0.6214
in/s	2.540	0.09143	1	0.08333	5	0.05682
ft/s	30.48	1.097	12	1	60	0.6818
ft/m	0.5080	0.01829	0.2000	0.01667	1	0.01136
mi/h	44.70	1.609	17.60	1.467	88	1

Force

Unit Conversions

FROM \ TO	g	kg	oz	lb$_m$
g	1	0.001	0.03527	0.00220
kg	1,000	1	35.27	2.205
oz	28.35	0.02835	1	0.0625
lb$_m$	453.6	0.4536	16	1

$1 \text{ A} = 1 \times 10^{-6} \text{ cm}$
$1 \text{ um} = 1 \times 10^{-3} \text{ m}$
$1 \text{ W} = 1 \text{ J/s}$
$1 \text{ kW} = 1,000 \text{ W}$

Chemical and Physical Data

1 atomic mass unit (amu) $= 1.66 \times 10^{-27}$ kg
1 calendar year $= 365$ days (d) $= 3.154 \times 10^{7}$ s
1 coulomb (C) $= 6.242 \times 10^{18}$ elementary charge (elem. ch.)
$c = 2.998$ m/s $= 186,272$ mi/s
Sound velocity (20°C), 1 atm
  Air: 344 m/s $= 769.5$ mi/h
  Water: 1,470 m/s $= 3,288$ mi/h
  Steel: 5,000 m/s $= 11,180$ mi/h
Earth
  Equatorial radius $= 6,378$ km $= 3,963$ mi
  Polar radius $= 6,357$ km $= 3,950$ mi
  Mass $= 5.983 \times 10^{24}$ kg $= 6.595 \times 10^{21}$ tons
Moon
  Radius $= 1,740$ km
  Mass $= 7.34 \times 10^{22}$ kg
Sun
  Radius $= 695,000$ km
  Mass $= 1.98 \times 10^{30}$ kg
Electron charge-to-mass ratio $= e/m_e = 1.759 \times 10^{11}$ C/kg
$G =$ gravitational constant $= 6.670 \times 10^{-11}$ m³/(kg)(s²)
$g_0 =$ gravitational acceleration $= 9.807$ m/s² $= 32.17$ ft/s²
$h =$ Planck's constant $= 6.626 \times 10^{-34}$ J · s
$k =$ Boltzmann's constant $= 1.3805 \times 10^{-23}$ J/°K
$k =$ Coulomb law constant $= 8.988 \times 10^{9}$ N · m²/C²
$N_A =$ Avogadro's number $= 6.023 \times 10^{23}$ molecules/g · mol
$R = 1$ radian (rad) $= 57.3$ deg; 1 deg $= 0.01745$ rad
Rest masses
  Electron $= 1$ $m_e = 9.109 \times 10^{-31}$ kg $= 5.486 \times 10^{-4}$ amu
  Proton $= 1$ $m_p = 1.673 \times 10^{-27}$ kg $= 1.007$ amu
  Neutron $= 1$ $m_n = 1.675 \times 10^{-27}$ kg $= 1.009$ amu
Water data
  Density (20°C): 1 gal $= 8.331$ lb$_m$; 1 ft³ $= 62.32$ lb$_m$
  Heat of fusion (0°C) $= 79.67$ cal/g $= 143.4$ Btu/lb$_m$
  Heat of vapor (100°C) $= 539.6$ cal/g $= 971.2$ Btu/lb$_m$
$\pi = 3.14159$
$\sigma =$ Stefan-Boltzmann constant $= 5.670 \times 10^{-8}$ W/(m²)(°K)⁴

Appendix D

Journey to an Asteroid

Between the orbits of Mars and Jupiter there is a band that contains thousands of bodies from the size of dust grains to asteroids miles in diameter. Nobody is quite sure where these came from, but their origin is not the problem here.

We have identified one in particular, which we shall call *asteroid alpha*. We shall abbreviate this to the symbol α in our discussion. α has an optically measured radius of 8.6 km and is nearly spherical in shape. It has also been observed to spin on an internal axis, like our earth, at a rate of one revolution every six hours relative to the star background. α has a mean orbital radius of 3 astronomical units, or 3 au (the earth's mean orbital radius of 92.9 million miles is taken to be one astronomical unit), but its mass is not exactly known. From preliminary observations of its orbit there seems to be some evidence that its density is significantly greater than that of the earth.

All other asteroids near it are of insignificant mass by comparison and rather far away from it. It appears that a trip to α is both feasible and desirable. We have plotted a trip from the earth to α and the return in such a way that Mars will be far away on both legs of the journey. α is suspected to be 1.2 times as dense as the earth, so this figure must be adjusted to an estimate of 2.2×10^{16} kg. For planning purposes, we shall assume a mass for α of

$$M_\alpha \approx 2.2 = 10^{16} \text{ kg} \qquad \text{(about the mass of a mountain)}$$

Though tiny by earth standards, α is still quite a massive bit of matter circling about the sun. A more precise knowledge of the density of α will tell us a good deal about the dominant elements in its makeup.

How much energy will be required to make a round trip between the earth and α, assuming that this is a surface-to-surface visit? Our spaceship has a mass m of 10^5 kg, and a negligible amount of this mass will be expended as fuel.

We shall approach the problem by considering a series of questions in the order in which they would occur in planning the flight. Only those tools that we already have at hand will be used.

This looks like a very complicated problem, but it can be greatly simplified. We shall first neglect the earth's moon in the problem and consider the earth to be a lone body in space. Further, we shall assume that the trip from α back to the earth will require only escape energy from α, since the earth's atmosphere can be used as a brake to reduce approach velocity of the ship.

It is possible to gain some energy before the ship even leaves the earth's surface. Since the earth spins on its internal axis a period of one day, a ship resting on the equator will travel one earth circumference each day. It will, thus, have a velocity of

$$v_0 = \frac{\text{circumference}}{T_e}$$

$$= \frac{2\pi R_e}{T_e}$$

$$\approx \frac{37.7 \times 10^6}{8.64 \times 10^4}$$

$$\approx 4.4 \times 10^2 \text{ m/s}$$

Hence, it will already have a kinetic energy of

$$\text{KE} = \frac{mv_0^2}{2}$$

$$\approx \frac{10^5 \times (4.4 \times 10^2)^2}{2}$$

$$\approx 9.7 \times 10^9 \text{ J}$$

This energy can be used to good advantage to gain stable earth orbit. Now let us break the energy problem down into subdivisions of requirements so that the sum of these will be the total energy requirement.

1   Energy required to achieve a grazing orbit about the earth

2   Energy needed to travel to α from the grazing earth orbit, arriving at α with near zero velocity

3   Energy necessary to change to a higher orbit in the sun's gravitational field

4   Energy required to escape α from its surface

Recall now all the pertinent data in the problem. We shall use only approximate numbers in order to keep the arithmetic to a minimum.

$R_e \equiv$ earth radius
    $\approx 6 \times 10^6$ m

$M_e \equiv$ earth mass
    $\approx 6.4 \times 10^{24}$ kg

$m \equiv$ spaceship mass
    $\approx 10^5$ kg

$r_\alpha \equiv \alpha$ radius
    $= 8.6$ km

$M_\alpha \equiv$ estimated α mass
    $= 2.2 \times 10^{16}$ kg

1   The energy required to put our ship into grazing earth orbit is the total "stable orbit" energy near the surface of the planet *less* the kinetic energy already gained from the earth's rotation at the equator. It is vital to note that R in the problem does not change significantly, since the ship will only circle the earth near its surface. Orbital energy will be

$$E_{\text{total}} = -U + \text{KE}$$

as before. We know this to be

$$E_T = -\frac{GM_e m}{2R_e}$$

Hence, in order to achieve this orbit we must raise the surface KE to this value. The change in energy ΔE_1 will be

$$\Delta E_1 = |E_T| - \text{KE at rest on the surface}$$
$$= \frac{GM_e m}{2R_e} - \text{KE}_{\text{equator}}$$

where $G \approx 6.7 \times 10^{-11}$. Thus

$$\Delta E_1 = \frac{6.7 \times 10^{-11} \times 6.4 \times 10^{24} \times 10^5}{2 \times 6 \times 10^6} - 9.7 \times 10^9$$
$$\approx 3.6 \times 10^{12} - 9.7 \times 10^9$$
$$\approx 3.6 \times 10^{12} \text{ J}$$

It is clear from this that the KE gained by taking off from the equator, while large enough to be economically important, does not significantly alter the total energy requirement.

Alternate Method of Calculation   This same problem can be greatly simplified by recognizing that no change in gravitational potential occurs. All we wish to do is to get going fast enough to establish orbit. We can calculate the kinetic energy necessary to do this from the expression for centripetal force as follows:

$$F_c = \frac{mv^2}{R_e}$$
$$= \frac{Mv^2}{2} \times \frac{2}{Re} \qquad\qquad\qquad\text{[D.1]}$$

Also $F_c = mg$ $\qquad\qquad\qquad\qquad\qquad\qquad\text{[D.2]}$

where g is the surface acceleration of gravity. Setting Eqs. [D.1] and [D.2] equal to one another,

$$mg = \frac{mv^2}{2} \times \frac{2}{R_e} \qquad\qquad\qquad [D.3]$$

and multiplying and solving for $\frac{mv^2}{2}$,

$$\frac{mv^2}{2} = \frac{mgR_e}{2} \qquad\qquad\qquad [D.4]$$

So the total energy requirement is

$$\Delta E_1 = \frac{mgR_e}{2} - \text{KE equator}$$

$$\approx \frac{10^5 \times 10 \times 6 \times 10^6}{2} - 9.7 \times 10^9$$

$$\approx 3 \times 10^{12} \text{ J} \qquad\qquad\qquad [D.5]$$

This result is similar to the previous one.

2 Now we need to go from earth grazing orbit to α, which is 2 au away. This distance corresponds to about

$$2 \times 1.5 \times 10^{11} = 3 \times 10^{11} \text{ m}$$

Since we wish to do this in such a way that final velocity relative to the earth is nearly zero, we need calculate only the change assuming final KE = 0.

$$\Delta E_2 = E_{\text{final}} - E_{\text{initial}} \qquad\qquad\qquad [D.6]$$

Now

$$E_{\text{final}} = -\frac{GM_e m}{R}$$

where $R = 2$ au, and we know that

$$E_{\text{initial}} = -\frac{GM_e m}{2R_e}$$

Therefore,

$$\Delta E_2 = -\frac{GM_e m}{R} - \left(-\frac{GM_e m}{2R_e}\right)$$

$$= GM_2 m \left(\frac{1}{2R_e} - \frac{1}{R}\right)$$

$$\approx 6.7 \times 10^{-11} \times 6.4 \times 10^{24} \times 10^5 \left(\frac{1}{2 \times 6 \times 10^6} - \frac{1}{3 \times 10^{11}}\right)$$

For the sake of approximation, $1/(3 \times 10^{11})$ is very nearly zero, so

$$\Delta E_2 \approx \frac{6.7 \times 10^{-11} \times 6.4 \times 10^{24} \times 10^5}{12 \times 10^6}$$

$$\approx 3.6 \times 10^{12} \text{ J}$$

Now note that this result is the same as the energy required to establish the grazing orbit around the earth. Is this just coincidence, or is there something more fundamental here?

Any planet of spherical shape, of radius R_p and of mass M_p, can be considered. In summary, the energy to establish a grazing orbit from the planetary surface was

$$E_{\text{grazing}} = \frac{GM_p m}{2R_p}$$

Total energy required to go from this grazing orbit to an infinite distance away arriving at zero velocity relative to the planet (remember we took $1/R \sim 0$ in the case of α) was

$$E_{\text{grazing} \to \infty} = \frac{GM_p m}{2R_p}$$

So it is not a coincidence after all. The total energy required to go from a planetary surface to ∞ is just

$$E_{\to \infty} = 2 \times \frac{GM_p m}{2R_p} = \frac{GM_p m}{R_p}$$

That is, it is just equal in magnitude to the gravitational potential energy at the planet surface. Is this reasonable?

There is another, perhaps more subtle, result here that we can make good use of. If the ship is already in a stable orbit at some radius R_0, the energy required for it to escape from this orbit to ∞ from the planet is just equal to its KE in the orbit:

$$E_{\to\infty} = \frac{GM_pm}{2R_0}$$

Let us summarize these results before going on:

Energy of escape from planetary surface $= U_3 = \dfrac{GM_pm}{R_p}$

Energy of escape from stable orbit $= KE_0 = \dfrac{GM_pm}{R_0}$

We shall make considerable use of these observations.

3   Now we shall have to consider the energy required to move out to α away from the sun. At rest on the earth the ship is in stable orbit about the sun along with the earth. Its gravitational energy is, therefore,

$$E_e = -\frac{GM_sm}{2R_e(1 \text{ au})} \qquad \text{with respect to the sun}$$

Now the total change in energy relative to the sun will be

$$\begin{aligned}
\Delta E_{\text{sun}} &= -\frac{GM_sm}{2R} - \left(-\frac{GM_sm}{2R_2}\right) \\
&= \frac{GM_sm}{2}\left(\frac{1}{R_e} - \frac{1}{R_\alpha}\right) \\
&= 6.7 \times 10^{-11} \times 2 \times 10^5 \left(\frac{1}{1.5 \times 10^{11}} - \frac{1}{4.5 \times 10^{11}}\right) \\
&= 6.7 \times 10^{24} \times (0.67 \times 10^{-11} - 0.22 \times 10^{-11}) \\
&\approx 3 \times 10^{13} \text{ J}
\end{aligned}$$

So we see that it is more costly by one order of magnitude to change our orbit relative to the sun's gravitational force than to escape the earth's surface. From parts 1, 2, and 3, we have the total energy requirement to get to α as follows:

$E_{\text{total}} = \Delta E_1 + \Delta E_2 + \Delta E_{\text{sun}}$

$E_{\text{total}} = 7.2 \times 10^{12} + 3 \times 10^{13}$

$E_{\text{total}} \approx 3.7 \times 10^{13}$ J (to α from the earth)

4   There is only one problem left—that of determining the energy required to escape α from its surface, or from a stable orbit around it.

Now we can make good use of our previous observations. In order to escape α from its surface, we must spend energy

$$E_{escape} = \frac{GM_\alpha m}{R_\alpha}$$

which we can estimate at

$$E_{escape} = \frac{6.7 \times 10^{-11} \times 2.2 \times 10^{16} \times 10^5}{8.6 \times 10^3}$$

$$= 1.7 \times 10^7 \text{ J}$$

This is an insignificant amount compared to the 3.7×10^{13} J required to get to α from earth.

Having arrived at α, we put the ship into a grazing orbit at $R = 9 \times 10^3$ m and observe experimentally that our period of orbit is $T_\alpha = 4.88 \times 10^3$ s. Now the mass of α can be calculated quite accurately as follows:

From previous discussion we know that the orbital period of a satellite is given by

$$T^2 = \frac{4\pi^2 R^3}{GM}$$

Solving for M in the case of α,

$$M_\alpha = \frac{4\pi^2 R^3}{GT^2}$$

$$= \frac{4\pi^2 \times (9 \times 10^3)^3}{6.7 \times 10^{-11} \times (4.88 \times 10^3)^2}$$

$$= 1.8 \times 10^{16} \text{ kg}$$

Remembering the estimated mass of α as 2.2×10^{16} kg, we see that α is not quite as massive as first thought, but that the order of magnitude was estimated correctly.

We now know what to expect from an α research landing. The mean radius of α has been verified at 8.7×10^3 m, and its mass is now known to be 1.8×10 kg. Its density is, therefore, quite close to

$$\delta_\alpha = \frac{M_\alpha}{V_\alpha} = \frac{M_\alpha}{\frac{4}{3}\pi R_\alpha^3}$$

$$= \frac{3 \times 1.8 \times 10^{16}}{4\pi \times (8.7 \times 10^3)^3}$$

$$= 6.526 \times 10^3 \text{ kg/m}^3$$

The mean density of the earth is 5.52×10^3 kg/m³, so α is more dense by a factor of 1.18, very close to the original 1.2 factor assumed.

After landing on α, we must be very careful in our movements outside the ship. The ship, which had a weight mg of 9.8×10^5 N on earth (well over a million pounds), now has a weight mg' of only

$$mg' = \frac{GM_\alpha m}{R_\alpha^2}$$

$$= \frac{6.7 \times 10^{-11} \times 1.8 \times 10^{16} \times 10^5}{(8.7 \times 10^3)^2}$$

$$= 1.6 \times 10^3 \text{ N}$$

or about twice the weight of a man on earth. The acceleration of gravity at α's surface, g', is only

$$g' = \frac{1.6 \times 10^3}{m} = 1.6 \times 10^{-2} \text{ m/s}^2$$

or only about one six-hundredth that of earth. To the ship's crew, the apparent weight of the ship resting on α would be far less than that of a small automobile on earth.

The crew operating outside the ship would find that a tiny effort from their earth muscles would produce startling leaps. Could a man on α put himself into orbit around α by leaping? Could a man stay on α at its rotational equator?

Index